Erie

ERIE

The Lake That Survived

NOEL M. BURNS

ROWMAN & ALLANHELD
PUBLISHERS

ROWMAN & ALLANHELD

Published in the United States of America in 1985
by Rowman & Allanheld, Publishers
(a division of Littlefield, Adams & Company)
81 Adams Drive, Totowa, New Jersey 07512

Library of Congress Cataloging in Publication Data
Burns, Noel M.
  Erie, the lake that survived.
  Bibliography: p.
  Includes index.
  1. Erie, Lake—History. 2. Erie, Lake, Region—History.
3. Natural history—Erie, Lake. I. Title.
4. Erie, Lake—pollution.
F555.B87 1985   977.1′2   84-29822
ISBN 0-8476-7398-7

85 86 87 / 10 9 8 7 6 5 4 3 2 1
Printed in the United States of America

To Lyn
for many, many reasons.

Contents

Tables and Figures

Figures

Preface

I grew up beside the ocean and ever since have needed the sea. Unfortunately, circumstances later took me to live in the Canadian prairies, where for seven long years I had no large vistas of water. A research post eventually brought me to live beside one of the Great Lakes, a large body of water that served as a surrogate ocean and made me feel at home. I have since spent many a month on the lakes doing research and sailing my own boat. Slowly, I have come to realize that I no longer consider the Great Lakes as substitute oceans, but as entities I revere for themselves. I felt this particularly during one summer spent sailing around Lake Erie in a relaxed and reflective mood, in direct contrast to my usual hectically busy time on the lake as project leader on a research ship. My private cruise gave me time to understand many of my feelings and values, and I resolved to write about Lake Erie and share some of the insights I have been privileged to learn with others interested in the lake.

In the mid-sixties, Lake Erie was considered "dead" by many people because of its dreadful state caused by low water levels and massive influx of pollutants. Actually, the only dead area was the deepest part of the Central Basin which, almost every summer, became anoxic and devoid of higher forms of life. Many creatures were alive in other parts of the lake, of course, but the knowledge that a large, once-healthy part of the lake was now lifeless, impelled the people living around the lake to mount an effective environmental protest. Remedial action in the seventies preceded the present (in the eighties) indications of improvement in the lake—hence the title of this book. Part of my purpose in writing this book is to ensure that the remedial program continues and grows so that Lake Erie may not only survive, but one day become a healthy ecosystem.

If I were to attempt to write for everyone, from commercial fishermen to research scientists, I would inevitably frustrate many. So I have chosen to write for the intelligent layman, at the level of undergraduate students taking environmental courses at technical colleges and universities. Since Lake Erie is a richly diverse ecosystem that has been severely stressed by human actions, it provides an excellent case study for persons interested in the environment. For maximum understanding, the cause and effect relationships are drawn in a quantitive manner, which also makes the work useful to government adminitrators and others who must make decisions affecting the lake. Finally, any reader interested in ecology will find himself fascinated by Lake Erie's natural history.

Acknowledgments

I have many persons to thank for the assistance given me in preparing this book. James Barry helped with the text and most generously permitted the use of many of his lovely photographs. Jack Vallentyne and Joe Leach gave me much of their valuable time. Others who generously helped with the text and diagrams are François Mai, Fernando Rosa, Farrell Boyce, Jerome Nriagu, John Coakley, Jerry Farrell, Dave Rathke, Ed Herdendorf, Laura Fay, Rich Thomas, Mike Donnelly, and Bill Finn. In particular, I would like to mention my debt to the Canada Center for Inland Waters and its director, Keith Rodgers, for providing me with the opportunity to learn about Lake Erie. I am truly grateful to all these people.

Frontispiece. Part of the shoreline of the Central Basin. (Photo by J.P. Barry.)

I

HISTORY

1

Changes in the Lake Erie Basin

Lake Erie and its drainage basin cover a total area of 102,000 km² (39,370 square miles), which is considerably larger than Portugal's 91,500 km² (35,320 sq. mi.). The extent of the land drainage area around the lake, 76,800 km² (29,650 sq. mi.), is almost twice the size of Switzerland's 41,300 km² (15,940 sq. mi.), and the lake itself has an area of 25,500 km² (9730 sq. mi.), which is a little more than half the size of Switzerland. Erie provides the world's largest freshwater fishery, while almost all the surrounding land is either arable, grazeable, or suited to forestry. The population of the basin is approximately 13 million people, more than half the population of all of Canada (24 million). If an ecosystem of this magnitude is badly degraded, the causes must be found and understood.

Lake Erie and Lake Ontario are similar in size and are the smallest of the Laurentian Great Lakes, as shown in Figure 1.1. Lake Erie has a general southwest-northeast orientation and a maximum length of more than 390 km (242 mi.); the width averages about 70 km (43 mi.) but reaches a mid-lake maximum of 90 km (56 mi.). Because Lake Erie is relatively shallow (see Figure 1.2), it warms rapidly in the summer to temperatures averaging above 23°C (73°F), while in winter most of the lake freezes over. Most of the land in the drainage basin is either flat or rolling hills, with only the southshore area between the cities of Erie, Pennsylvania, and Buffalo, N.Y., having steep-sided hills. By comparing the few descriptions written about the landscape and lake before settlement by the white man with those of today, we can gain a good idea of the magnitude of the change that has occurred in the Lake Erie Basin.

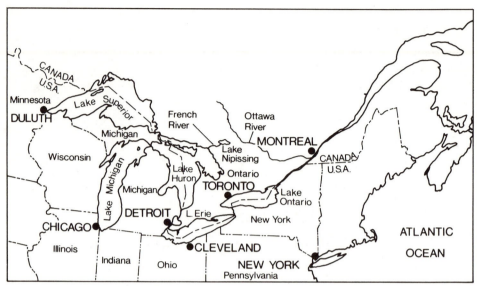

Figure 1.1 The Great Lakes of North America.

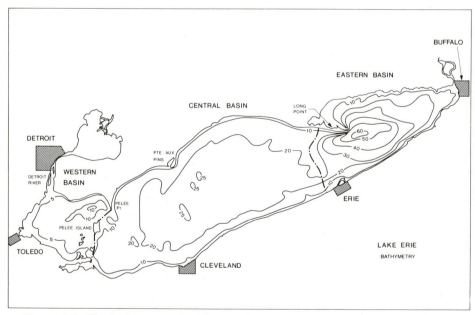

*Figure 1.2 The bathymetry of modern Lake Erie (in meters). The broken lines
(——— . ———.) denote the boundaries between the three basins.*

The Early Landscape

A firsthand description of the animals and vegetation half a mile inland from Port Dover before settlement by the white man is given by Gallinée (Coyne 1903), who wintered there from November 1669 to March 1670. He wrote:

> We hunted meanwhile and killed a considerable number of stags, hinds and roebucks so that we began to have no longer any fear of leaving [suffering] during the winter. We smoked meat of 9 large animals in such a manner, that it could have kept for two or three years and with this provision we awaited the winter with tranquility whilst hunting and making good provision of walnuts and chesnuts which were there in great quantities. We had indeed in our granary 23 or 24 minots of these fruits besides apples, plums and grapes, and alizes [cranberries] of which we had an abundance during the autumn.
>
> I will tell you, by the way, that the vine grows here only in sand, on the banks of lakes and rivers, but although it has no cultivation it does not fail to produce grapes in great quantities as large and as sweet as the finest of France. We even made wine of them with which M. Dollier said Holy Mass all winter, and it was as good as vin de Grave. It is a heavy, dark wine like the latter. Only red grapes are seen here, but in so great quantities, that we found places where one could easily have made 25 or 30 hogsheads of wine.
>
> I leave you to imagine whether we suffered in the midst of this abundance *in the earthly Paradise of Canada,* I call it so, because there is assuredly no more beautiful region in all Canada. The woods are open, interspersed with beautiful meadows, watered by rivers and rivulets filled with fish and beaver, an abundance of fruits, and what is more important so full of game that we saw there at one time more than a hundred roebucks in a single band, herds of fifty or sixty hinds, and bears fatter and of better flavor than the most savory pigs of France.

More recently, Harris and Warkentin (1974) described the precolonial landscape in similar vein as follows:

> As late as 1780 the peninsula bounded by Lakes Huron, Erie and Ontario and by the upper St. Lawrence River was still a densely forested tract broken only here and there by beaver meadows, by Indian campsites or, on some light and excessively drained soils, by prairies dotted with oaks.

One part of the basin, however, was quite different from the rest of the catchment, the Black Swamp (Fig. 1.3) in the Maumee River Plains in the southwest. Many descriptions of the swamp are found in reports and diaries of travelers, missionaries, and military men. Kaatz (1952, 1953) wrote:

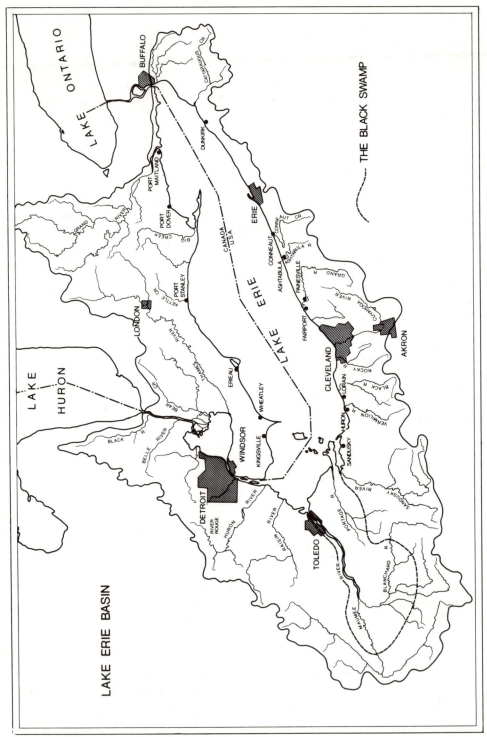

Figure 1.3 The Lake Erie Basin, showing the extent of the original Black Swamp.

The Black Swamp is no more, but until it was drained late in the 19th century, it was a feature to be contended with by all who sought to settle in or travel through northwestern Ohio. Soldiers during the war of 1812, and afterwards immigrants to Michigan and northern Indiana, were unwilling witnesses to its terrors. It was an irregular strip about 30 miles (48 km) wide lying parallel to the east bank of the Maumee River from Lake Erie southwest to New Haven, Indiana, of some 1500 square miles (3900 km²) in extent. Specifically, the Black Swamp is that portion of the lake plain of northwestern Ohio which at the time of settlement was nearly one continuous region of standing water or so wet as to ooze water when walked upon in all seasons except the very driest. In some places in the Black Swamp the trees were about 100 ft. (30m) high and their leaves nearly shut out the sun's rays except during the period of high sun.

Before colonization the majority of the south shore of the West Basin consisted of marshes. These marshes were huge, covering most of the 150 km of shoreline between Detroit and Sandusky, and often extending many kilometers inshore. They teemed with all kinds of birds, fish, and plants. No wild rice grows in the area today, but that was not always the case, as a description by Brown (1815) shows:

Follie avoine [wild rice] grows in about seven feet of water, the stalks near the roots are about an inch in diameter, and grow to a height of 10 feet [3m]. Its yield is very abundant, being half a pint at least from every stalk. This valuable aquatic grain is found at the mouths of all the rivers which fall into the lake west of Sandusky as far as the Detroit River . . . Maumee Bay [contains] several thousand acres of follie avoine.

Fish were also very abundant and apparently easy to catch with the most simple equipment, as innumerable reports describe massive catches in the early days of fishing. Evidently, the water clarity in the West Basin was also very good in those early days. Hopkins (1862) described fishing among the West Basin islands in May 1804:

The small boat was rowed around the islands, whilst we cast our lines, about thirty feet in length, having the hooks baited with the skin of pork and covered in part with a piece of red cloth. In a short time we caught upwards of five dozen black bass—weighing from four to six pounds [1.8 to 2.7 kg]. The lake water is so clear that fish can be seen from twelve to fifteen feet [4 to 5m] below the surface. Many of the fish we saw advancing to our hooks.

Pioneer Attitudes

Even at the start of settlement, when the early farmers regarded the forest as an enemy and ruthlessly cleared as much land around their homes as possible, there was an element of disregard for nature in the Great Lakes

Basin. Harris and Warkentin (1974) commented on these early settlers by saying that:

> Except where they happened on oak openings, Indian campsites, riverine marshes, or beaver meadows, settlers had to establish farms in the forest. For most of them, the forest was unfamiliar and hostile, a barrier between themselves and a farm. Those who acquired land in the oak openings often girdled the trees and planted among them; elsewhere they cut the trees, used oxen or horses to haul them into piles, and burned the piles. Without constant attendance clearings in hardwood forest quickly became patches of fireweed, chokecherry, and hardwood suckers; those in pine lands often sprouted in wild raspberries and poplar. Although some promotional handbooks claimed that a settler could clear, fence, and put under crops ten acres of land a year, far more commonly he was fortunate to clear two to three acres annually. At this rate, clearing and the subsequent struggle against the recolonization of clearings by forest weeds could take most of his productive life. Out of this work developed an ingrained hostility to the forest and, eventually, a severe over-clearing of the land.

Life for a pioneer in the Great Lakes area was dangerous and difficult, a constant struggle against nature, disease, and accidents. Many of the immigrants died from cholera on the trans-Atlantic journey or soon after landing. An epidemic of this disease raged all through the Great Lakes area in 1832. Many men digging the canals died of malaria or blasting accidents. Travel by ship was dangerous, as there were numerous shipwrecks each year on the lakes. Forest fires were frequent and vicious, because of the lumbering methods of the time, and claimed many lives.

In the Great Lakes Basin, man's continual struggle against nature in those times led to the concept of nature as an enemy, to be overcome and controlled. This 19th-century concept, which is really only beginning to disappear in our time, is illustrated somewhat by an incident in 1827, when a large number of people gathered to watch a spectacle. Some sideshow businessmen bought an old schooner, loaded it with animals, and sent it under full sail over the Niagara Falls, carrying a cargo of helpless camel, elk, deer, and dogs to drown in the spray-filled gorge (Hatcher 1944; Rattigan 1960).

The early settlers used their rivers and lakes as garbage dumps, a tradition that has changed little with time. Hatcher (1945) made the following comment about Detroit in 1820:

> Our pioneer forefathers took little thought for the waterfront of their towns on the rivers and lakes; their interests were utilitarian and, in too large a measure, their views have prevailed into our time. The riverbank, which drew from Cadillac a prose poem of admiration for its beauty, was a dumping place for refuse and dead and rotting animals.

Even on the early wooden steamships, where the proximity of fire and wood was dangerous but necessary, occasional carelessness could have been avoided. This is illustrated by an incident in 1868 on the steamer "Seabird," carrying between 75 and 103 people. Evidently a steward cleaned out the hot ashes from a cabin stove in the early morning and threw them overboard. A few coals landed below on the deck cargo of freshly varnished tubs packed with straw, and the fire had already taken hold before it was discovered. In the ensuing panic, the passengers jumped overboard into April waters only recently freed of ice. There was only one survivor (Rattigan 1960). Another example is the "Erie," which left Buffalo in 1841 with 200 passengers, about 140 of whom were immigrants. Six of the passengers were painters, who set their demijohns of turpentine and varnish on the deck directly above the boilers. A few hours after leaving port the demijohns exploded, scattering flaming turpentine and varnish; strong wind soon set the entire ship aflame. A ship that went to the "Erie's" assistance found only 29 survivors (Barry 1973).

The lumber trade in the last half of the 19th century was rapacious. In the lumber baron era in the upper lakes hinterland, only the large logs were taken out of the forests, and huge amounts of drying slash were left behind. Timber fires were commonplace, but no changes in the mode of lumbering were made, even after tragedies like the one that overtook the village of Hinkley. In this little sawmill town, more than 100 people were burned to death when a forest fire overtook the village. Another example of this careless approach to life was the village of Oshkosh, Wisconsin. It was such a tinder box because of its lumber waste that it was swept by fire four times in 15 years: in 1859, 1866, 1874, and 1875 (Hatcher 1944).

The mood of the times was typified by the extinction of the passenger pigeon. In 1850 this species of bird, considered to be one of the most numerous in the world, darkened the skies in the Great Lakes area during migrations. By 1875 their numbers had been greatly reduced (Trautman 1977), but no special measures were taken to preserve them. The last of the species died in a zoo in 1914. Similarly, in Lake Erie the sturgeon was recognized as an important commercial fish in 1880, but was exploited so heavily that by 1900 the species was very scarce. A number of other species have since been extirpated from the lake.

This rough-and-ready or, one might say, survival attitude to growth obviously was the cause of much change to the land around Lake Erie and to the lake itself. These attitudes to nature were widespread in the region and endured for many years.

Present-Day Carelessness

Unfortunately, in the 20th century we seem to have followed the same policies as the pioneers followed in the 19th. Admittedly, we are now more safety conscious, and serious maritime disasters are rare. We do not dump raw garbage into the lakes, but the same disregard for the future, in the name of progress and profit, has continued to be a mark of man's activities in the Lake Erie Basin. This attitude has undergone a change since 1970, but until that decade most of the sewage, even from cities as large as Detroit, was going into the lake virtually untreated. The chemical wastes from the myriad industries and many refineries in the basin were also being freely released to the tributaries and lake as late as the 1960s.

The extent of the careless pollution of Lake Erie and its tributaries can be gathered from information in the U.S. Federal Water Pollution Control Administration's *Lake Erie Report—A Plan for Water Pollution Control* (1968). This report described many instances of pollution. It stated that more than 5,700,000 m^3 day^{-1} (1500 million gallons per day) of wastes from industry and municipalities were added to the Detroit River, changing it from a relatively clean stream at its head to the basin's largest carrier of wastes by the time it entered Lake Erie. The report also described the mid-sixties state of the Black Swamp area of the Maumee River Basin, which was drained and is now heavily cultivated. Few trees remained, nor any remnants of the earlier massive forest. The Maumee River itself (see Fig. 1.3) had copious algae growths, resulting from the loading of phosphorus from agricultural and municipal sources. Yearly about 2,000 metric tons (2204 short tons) of phosphorus, 2,000,000 tons* (2,204,000 short tons) of silt, plus oils, phenols, sewage, refactory chemicals, and oxygen-consuming wastes, passed through the Maumee River into Lake Erie.

Further, the report detailed gross pollution, with bacterial contamination, scum, profuse algae growth, and septic sludge and muck in a number of small tributaries. In the Sandusky, Amherst, and Sheffield-Avon areas this pollution was a potential health hazard: it not only caused oxygen and bacteriological problems in the receiving streams, but served as a source of contaminants to nearby bathing beaches where streams entered the lake.

The lower Cuyahoga River and navigation channel through the Cleveland area was a virtual waste treatment lagoon. At times the river was choked with debris, oils, scums, and floating organic sludges. Foul-smelling gases rose from decomposing materials on the river's bottom. Viewed from the city's observation towers, the river appeared to be chocolate brown or rust-colored. During most of the year this lower section had no visible life, not even low forms such as leeches and sludgeworms, which usually thrive on wastes. Bacteria, debris, suspended solids, oxygen-consuming materials, dead fish, etc., were found along Cleveland's front door—the Lake Erie shoreline. Unlike many cities, which were able to rid themselves of garbage and wastes by discharging them to a nearby river for someone else to worry about, Cleveland's wastes festered in full view of its citizens. Along with inadequately treated wastes from all Cleveland-area treatment plants,

---

*The word "tons" in this book always refers to metric tons.

combined sewer and stormwater overflows poured bacterial contamination onto the shore. Even during dry weather, raw sewage continuously overflowed from Cleveland's overloaded combined sewer system. The sewage and other wastes polluted the local bathing beaches, and Cleveland residents had to travel 100 to 160 km (60 to 100 mi.) to find lakefront beaches suitable for swimming.

Cleveland, Toledo, and Detroit faced severe problems because of their size (see Figure 1.4). Yet even some of the smaller cities, such as Painsville, Ohio, on the Grand River, caused severe problems. At times the river flowing past this town was brightly colored, ranging from bright green to yellow, depending on which chemicals had been discharged. Untreated sewage was also seen there, floating on the surface of the river.

Foam, foul odor, and black-brown discoloration were much in evidence for 15 km (approx. 10 mi.) downshore from a paper company discharge to Lake Erie at Erie, Pennsylvania, under the prevailing westerly winds. When prolonged winds blew from the east, Erie's raw water supply required extensive treatment to prevent severe taste and odor problems in municipal water caused by these wastes. Under these meteorological conditions the color, foam, and objectionable odors made the beaches at Presque Isle State Park esthetically offensive.

Finally, the Lake Erie Report described the Buffalo River as a repulsive holding basin for industrial and municipal wastes under the prevalent sluggish flow conditions. Oil, phenols, color, oxygen-demanding materials, iron, acid, sewage, and exotic organic compounds were present in large amounts. Residents who lived near its backwaters complained vociferously of the odors emanating from the river and of the heavy oil films.

Along the north shore there have been extensive water quality problems for a distance of 15 km (10 mi.) east from the Detroit River, as reported by the International Lake Erie Water Pollution Board (1969). Because of discharges from Windsor, these waters, with coliform bacteria values in excess of 2,000 per 100 ml (½ cup) of water, were often unfit for body contact recreation. At the other end of the lake at Port Colborne, industries discharged wastewaters into an area partially enclosed by jetties. The abundant nutrient supply and protected nature of the area encouraged the accumulation of algae along the beaches east of the town. The large rocky shelf at Cassidy Point provided the substrate for the growth of the nuisance alga *Cladophora*, which was removed from the substrate and deposited on the beaches by wave action, causing an unsightly mess and foul odors.

Many other examples of the degraded condition of the lake and rivers will be cited later. The examples given here are sufficient to demonstrate the tremendous changes that have occurred to the lake, its tributaries, and its surroundings since the arrival of the pioneers.

Figure 1.4 Cleveland and part of its waterfront. (Photo by J.P. Barry.)

Summary

It is easy to understand the carelessness of the pioneers. They were faced with immense virgin lands and huge amounts of unpolluted water. While struggling to build a decent life for themselves and their families, nature conservation would have been far from their minds. In contrast, personal life today is relatively safe; the daily hours of work are reasonable, the standard of living is high, and a large percentage of personal income is spent on recreation. Yet until recently, very little effort or money has been expended on maintaining clear water, clean beaches, and good fishing. It is difficult to understand how the 13 million people living in the Lake Erie Basin in the 1960s could have allowed their rivers and lake to deteriorate to the extent described.

Fortunately, some thoughtful people have always lived in the Great Lakes Basin. As explained by Harris and Warkentin (1974), among the first concerned residents were the farmers in the mid-19th century who were officers retired on half-pay from the British Army and who were acquainted with the writings of the English agricultural experts of their day. Since they had some capital or a regular pension, they were able to pursue a European agricultural ideal in the face of the physical and economic realities of early Ontario. They assumed that a rotation of wheat and fallow exhausted the soil, and they established mixed farms. They developed elaborate crop rotations and purebred stock and experimented with new seeds and crops. With little market for livestock products, most of their farms were unprofitable for years, but they did serve as models for the various forms of mixed farming that gradually replaced wheat-fallow-wheat farming prevalent from about 1840 to 1880.

Another example of a thoughtful individual was Jack Miner of Kingsville, Ontario, a former proficient hunter who changed into an ardent conservationist. Instead of killing ducks when their number declined markedly at the turn of the century, he began to protect them. He gradually turned his farm into a sanctuary and began a serious study of the migratory pattern of the birds flying over the Great Lakes. His example inspired many conservationists, with the result that now there is good duck hunting *and* strong populations of ducks flying over the Lake Erie region. Another example is Dr. Edward Lavitz, who started a reforestry program in Norfolk County in 1920 and brought that area back into productivity after deforestation had caused extensive wind erosion (Barrett 1977).

During the 1960s, many members of the public at large noticed the degraded state of the lower Great Lakes and began to protest about the situation. In response, the Commissioners of the International Joint Commission in 1965 called for a report on the state of the lower lakes. The report titled *The Pollution of Lake Erie, Lake Ontario and International Section of the St. Lawrence River* by the International Lake Erie and Lake Ontario–St. Lawrence River Water Pollution Boards was released in 1969. Ever since that time official action has been undertaken to stop further degradation of Lakes Erie and Ontario and is consuming a considerable amount of money. The restoration of the lakes to a generally acceptable level is going to cost even more, and this money will have to be provided by the inhabitants of the Great Lakes Basin, largely through their rates and taxes. In addition, some industries will have to live with slightly reduced profits, and the inhabitants of the area will have to pay higher prices for some of their goods, to ensure that industry can afford to clean the water it returns to the rivers and lakes.

The time to change our thinking from the old frontier concept of "man against nature" to a more modern idea of "man in harmony with his surroundings" has passed. We must no longer fight nature, but help it. To do this and enjoy the Great Lakes and the land around them, we must learn to understand how this natural system functions. This knowledge is necessary if we are to preserve and restore the many fragile and beautiful parts of the ecosystem. This book explains some of the workings of Lake Erie and its interactions with the surrounding land, and so can help in the restoration of this great body of water to a state fit for the use and enjoyment of all those who live on its borders.

2

The History of Development

Early Indian Occupation of the Lake Erie Basin

The first humans to affect the lake basin in any way were probably the Indians who lived around the lake from A.D. 600 to 1000 (Strothers and Yarnell 1976). These people were apparently changing from a purely nomadic, hunting subsistence to a lifestyle of summer camping in large groups near aquatic lowlands and growing maize in natural clearings. During the fall, the villages broke up and the Indians formed smaller hunting groups for the winter. The disturbance of the land surface and the numbers of spawning fish caught by these people probably did not cause any significant change in the lake.

Around A.D. 1500 the northshore area of Lake Erie was inhabited by the ancestral Neutrals, followed by the Neutral and Tobacco Indians from about 1600 to 1650. These people were totally subdued by the New York Iroquois. Recent evidence leads archeologists to surmise that the Neutrals and the Iroquois lived only in the small area between Lakes Erie and Ontario and used the northshore hinterland of Lake Erie as their traditional hunting ground. Certainly, there were very few Indians living along the north shore when the first Europeans began to move through this area in the late 17th century (Noble 1978).

The area south of the lake also had virtually no aboriginal inhabitants at this time. The Erie nation had occupied this territory previously but were destroyed by the Iroquois in 1656. Farther to the west lived the Miami and Ottawa Indians, but their numbers were never very great because of intertribal wars. Thus, at the time of its discovery by the white man, Lake Erie and the surrounding territory were virtually unaltered by the hand of man.

The White Man's Discovery of Lake Erie

Lake Erie was the last of the Great Lakes to be discovered by the French explorers. For many years after the French first arrived in the New World, the territory around this particular lake was dangerous for travel because of the enmity of the Iroquois. This situation was abetted by Champlain, who had traveled to Georgian Bay in 1615, befriended the Hurons living in that area, and led them on an attack against the Iroquois of New York State. The Huron expedition under Champlain was a complete failure; in fact, it had long-standing consequences because the Iroquois thereafter regarded the French as their implacable enemies. For many years the French had to use the northern route along the Ottawa River to the upper Great Lakes to avoid the Iroquois living south of Lake Ontario.

The Iroquois continued their attacks on the other tribes, slowly expanding their territory westward and northward. In 1649 they attacked the Jesuit mission headquarters at St. Marie-among-the-Hurons near present-day Midland and martyred the priests living there. Middleton and Landon (1927) wrote about the results of these happenings as follows:

The western peninsula [of Ontario] became a wilderness indeed, visited only by wandering Algonquin hunters and by Iroquois hunters or war parties marching westward. . . . For fifteen years following the destruction of the Huron mission (1649), the Iroquois were the virtual masters of Canada. This lasted until 1666 when a number of French soldiers were led in successful expeditions against the Iroquois.

These expeditions resulted in a peace settlement between the French and the Iroquois, and both lower lakes were finally open to travel.

By 1667 explorers and missionaries had traveled all the lakes except Erie, but its existence was known. A map of the entire Great Lakes region evolved in Paris as the missionaries reported information obtained from their travels. In fact, Sanson drew a map of the region in 1650 and another in 1656 (Fig. 2.1) that showed Lake Erie with some accuracy (Coyne 1903).

After the expeditions of the French military, the southern route was safe enough for exploration, and in 1669 La Salle organized an expedition to travel through Lake Erie and down the Ohio River. Two missionaries, Dollier and Gallinée, accompanied him, and they traveled along the southern shore of Lake Ontario. Earlier, however, the governor had dispatched Joliet to find a copper mine reported in the Lake Superior region and to find an easier route than the northern one for transporting the material back to Montreal. On his return Joliet picked up an Indian guide at Sault Ste. Marie, who brought him down Lake Huron and through Lake Erie to Kettle Creek (present Port Stanley). He thus became the first white man to see Lake Erie. From there they traveled overland and met up with

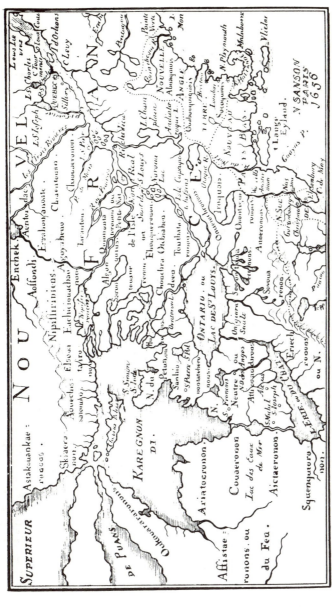

Figure 2.1 Map dated Paris, 1656. "Canada or New France, etc. The Great River of Canada or of St. Laurens, and all neighboring regions are in accordance with the relations of the French. By Sanson d'Abbéville, Geographer-in-Ordinary to the King." (Coyne 1903.)

La Salle's party, who had camped in an Indian village just west of Lake Ontario.

La Salle had to return to Montreal because of illness, but the missionaries proceeded to Lake Erie and wintered at the site of the present Port Dover. At this time Gallinée wrote his description of the "earthly paradise of Canada." The following spring (1670) the missionaries journeyed along the north shore of Lake Erie, and Gallinée, who was a cartographer, mapped it.

The French Period

La Salle did not forget Lake Erie after his return to Montreal in 1669. With much effort, he raised another large party to investigate the southern route, and he sent men with a considerable amount of material across Lake Ontario in three small ships. They offloaded their ships, portaged their materials, and finally encamped above Niagara Falls in late 1678, where they started to build another ship. This vessel, the "Griffon," was about 20 m long and was launched in the summer of 1679 after La Salle joined his party. It was the first ship above Niagara Falls and sailed all the way to Green Bay on Lake Michigan. A large load of furs was taken aboard there, and the ship set sail back to Lake Erie. La Salle did not return with the ship, but journeyed south along the Illinois and Mississippi rivers. Unfortunately, the "Griffon" was lost without a trace during its return journey, and the convenience of the southern route was not immediately realized in Montreal. Later, Cadillac, when stationed at Makinac, realized the possibility of the southern route becoming the main trade route instead of the northern route along the Ottawa River. In 1701, he was commissioned by the Colonial Minister in Paris to build a fort and trading post at Detroit. Soon after this construction, Detroit became a major fur-trading post. For the next 50 years there was considerable fur trading in this area, with many of the furs being collected from the woods in the Lake Erie Basin. There was virtually no settlement of the basin during this time because the French were primarily interested in the fur trade, not in developing the land. Also, the English were continually inciting the Indians against the French, as the English tried to usurp the fur trade from the French. Frontier life became very dangerous because the French retaliated in a similar manner. During the Seven Years War (1756–1763), the French and English began actively to fight each other on Lakes Ontario and Erie. In 1759 the English captured the fort at Niagara, and in 1760 they took over the fort at Detroit. The era of French dominance in the Great Lakes area was ended (Hatcher 1944, 1945).

The Early British Era

The Indians initially accepted the English with some enthusiam, but after the refusal of the governor to distribute the accustomed gifts to the Indians and to provide them with the gun powder they used for hunting, the Indians changed their minds. Pontiac, the most influential chief in the area from Mackinac to Niagara, planned and executed an uprising against the British in 1763. The Indians took the fort at Mackinac and laid seige to the fort at Detroit. This fort was saved only by the action of two British ships, which were able to penetrate through the Indian line of defense on the river. Normally the soldiers traveled in small boats, which were either ambushed by Indians or broken up by storms (Barry 1973). After the seige was broken and the fifteen months of war ended, Pontiac concluded a formal peace agreement with the English, thus leaving them free to expand their fur trade.

During the Revolutionary War (1776–1783) when the American colonists fought for their independence from the British, many of the Indians supported the British and attacked the settlements of the colonials in the Lake Erie–Ohio River region. After the war, the Treaty of Paris (1783) drew the boundary lines between American and British territory. Lake Erie formed part of the northern boundary, with the territorial line drawn down the middle of the lake, as it stands today. When the Americans won their independence, many of the Indians and colonists who had supported the British, the Empire Loyalists, were forced to leave their homes and were settled in Canada by the British. The Indians were granted a large tract of land along the Grand River on the north shore of Lake Erie, and many of the Loyalists were settled in other areas along the north shore of the lake. This marked the beginning of effective settlement in the Lake Erie Basin. Settlement along the south shore was slower because the Indians, afraid of losing their land, continued to attack the American colonists. After General Wayne defeated the Indians in the Battle of Fallen Timbers, a peace agreement was signed in 1795. Detroit had been ceded to the Americans in the Treaty of Paris in 1783; in 1796 they insisted that the British hand it over. The British moved across the Detroit River to Malden, where they established a small fort and settlement.

After the danger of Indian attack was over, settlers began to move into the area south of Lake Erie. In addition to Detroit, fairly large settlements developed at Buffalo and Cleveland, and many other settlements started along the south shore at the mouths of the numerous rivers entering the lake.

After the War of 1812

In 1812, American forces attacked various parts of Upper Canada, and war was declared between the occupants of the two territories. A number of factors contributed to the war, including British harassment of shipping on the high seas, but a major reason was that the Americans wished to add Upper Canada to their territory. They expected an easy victory because the territory was lightly guarded, since Britain was at war with France.

In addition, the Americans thought that many of the Canadian colonists would side with the attackers to rid themselves of British control. This was not the case, and counterattacks were mounted by the Canadian colonists, which were initially effective. But the Americans won a decisive naval battle in Lake Erie in 1813, which gave them control of the lake and some of Upper Canada. In the east the British controlled the St. Lawrence River and parts of Maine, so the result of the war was a stand-off that ended with the Treaty of Ghent in 1814. After the war, the territorial lines were reestablished as they had been before the war, and both sides realized the futility of antagonism. The Rush-Bagot Agreement of 1817 provided the necessary framework for cooperation, and severely limited the numbers and armaments of naval vessels on the Great Lakes.

After 1814, fighting between the British and Americans, and also between the colonists and the Indians, stopped except for some minor skirmishes. Once peace was established, the lower Great Lakes area began to develop rapidly. The 1812 War had emphasized the capabilities of large ships on the lakes, and two large commercial steamers were launched on Lake Ontario in 1817. In 1818, a 135-ft. (41.2m) steamboat, "Walk-in-the-Water," was added to the Lake Erie fleet of sailboats and began a regular, scheduled service between Buffalo and Detroit. By 1830, steamship building began to displace the building of sailing ships; ship transportation increased so rapidly that in 1856 the Lloyds Steamboat Directory listed 1,387 commercial vessels on the Great Lakes (Hatcher 1945).

The businessmen of these early days were not timid. They soon realized the tremendous economic potential of linking the newly developed Great Lakes waterway with the oceans, and so began an era of canal building. In 1817 a ground-breaking ceremony was held for a canal from Buffalo to the Mohawk River, which would thus connect Buffalo with the Hudson River and with New York. When the Erie Canal was opened eight years later in 1825, the cost of moving freight from Lake Erie to New York dropped from $120 to $4 per ton. In the same year the first canal around the St. Lawrence rapids was built, connecting Lake Ontario with Montreal and Quebec. In 1829 the first Welland Canal connecting Lake Erie with Lake Ontario was completed. A canal connecting Cleveland with the Ohio River was completed in 1833, as was another canal in 1845 that connected Toledo via the Maumee and Miami rivers to the Ohio River and thence to the Gulf of Mexico via the Mississippi River. In 1855 the first ship canal at Sault Ste. Marie was built, thus connecting Lake Superior with the other Great Lakes.

The development of rail transport followed the development of water transport, and the decade of the 1850s became the railroad era. Railroads were built to connect all the major centers on the south shore of Lake Erie with each other and also to the important cities to the east, south, and west of the lake. For example, at the end of the 1850s there were eleven railway main lines converging into five passenger terminals in Buffalo.

In Ontario during the same years, major railroads were built through the area to the north of the lake connecting Windsor and Toronto, with spur lines running north and south from the main line, some to ports on Lake Erie.

This system of ship and rail transportation was effective and served the upper and lower lakes areas well. In 1844, for example, it is estimated that 20,000 passengers made the journey from Buffalo to Chicago by boat, the majority of them immigrants. This flood of immigrants to the Great Lakes area and Mid-west continued through most of the 19th century. The transportation system was maintained and expanded by the transport of the produce and goods exported from the immigrant settlements. Because of the transportation system and the prevailing peace, the whole Great Lakes Basin was settled rapidly in the latter half of the 19th century.

Early Development

The 19th century was a tumultuous period in the Great Lakes area. The number of inhabitants grew, and the face of the land changed in spite of deaths caused by cholera, malaria, shipwreck, and forest fires. The immigrants kept coming, largely because life was so difficult in Europe for common people at this time. Hatcher (1944) graphically describes the situation for many:

> The Mediterranean basin was scarred with age and battle; its towns were crowded, its soil thin and long ago preempted. Europe was so old, so cramped, so weary, so hopeless, its forests gone, its land partitioned, its society rigorously classified. But around the Lakes were not just crofters' plots, not mere acres, but whole square miles of lands and forests. It was not buried under the mists of Jutland. The soil was not rocks or sand or swamps, but thick with fertility; not tilted up on end but flat or gently rolling. The summers were long. This Eden was open to all who cared to come, and titles to it were theirs almost for the asking.

The development of the Black Swamp began about 1827, when the first road was put through the area. Opening up this area was difficult because deep drainage ditches, and later, tiled drains, had to be dug to remove the water from the land. The soil was so rich that the pioneers persevered, and finally by about 1900, all the land of the original Black Swamp had been cleared and more than 3000 km (1860 miles) of drainage ditches installed (Kaatz 1952, 1953). Much of the Lake Erie Basin was settled before the big lumber era began in the 1850s. The early settlers in the basin would clear some land on their farm and plant wheat on it. This wheat was their cash crop that gave them money to keep clearing the land and thus slowly expand their farms. The farmers would use or, if possible, sell some of the timber on their fields, but much of it was simply burnt in the clearing process. Thus the clearing of the land was a gradual process with the commercial lumbering being done in pockets.

One of the large areas of commercial lumbering was on the Norfolk Sand Plains north of Long Point from 1840 to 1860. After the natural vegetation had been disturbed, wind erosion became a serious problem in this area of sandy soil (Barrett 1977). Port Maitland on the Grand River was once a major Canadian port, but siltation resulting from this erosion shallowed the river and caused a serious decline in its importance.

A market for agricultural produce other than wheat began to develop in the 1850s. Barley, peas, hogs, cattle, sheep, wool, and butter were exported by rail to the large American cities in the east. Small, localized industries sprang up, and their products were also transported by rail. Toward the end of the century, tobacco production became commercially important in Ontario. Grapes, wine, and fruit became cash produce in the eastern area along the southern shore and on the islands in the West Basin of the lake.

As mentioned, after the War of 1812, the settlers first moved to areas around the harbors in Lake Erie. Along the American shore fourteen or so settlements grew up around harbors, but only about five such sites were settled along the Canadian shore. (There are far more rivers flowing into the lake along the American shore.) In general, the American harbors were also bigger and better than the Canadian ones, because most of the Canadian streams are small.

This situation might have changed if wheat had remained the prime agricultural crop, because the bulkiness of wheat would have caused the Canadians to develop their harbors to handle this product. Meat and dairy products, however, became marketable at about the time the railway was built from Toronto to Windsor and were easily sent east via the railroads. Small industries such as shoemaking started and produced light goods, which were also transported by rail. As a result, the northshore ports declined in importance. It is strange that this situation has remained almost to the present day. The northshore hinterland is still agricultural, and produce is primarily moved by rail; except for Windsor and Port Colborne at the head of the Welland Canal, the Canadian ports on Lake Erie are still small fishing villages.

The earlier hurried development began to slow down and consolidate in Ontario in the latter half of the 19th century, but this was not the case along the American shore. If anything, the rate of development there became more hectic.

Coal, Iron, and Steel

Two accidents of nature and one of history caused the development of the American part of the Lake Erie Basin to be dramatically different from the Canadian. The first is the location of the tremendous deposits of coal in the hills of Pennsylvania, West Virginia, Kentucky, and southeastern Ohio, which contrasts with the almost complete absence of coal in Ontario. The other is that most of the huge deposits of iron ore first discovered in the Lake Superior region happened to be in American territory. Mining of the Marquette deposits started in 1844. In 1855 the Sault canal was completed, and by 1856 11,000 tons (12,100 short tons) of ore passed annually through the canal to Detroit and eastward.

The accident of history affecting Lake Erie was the start of the American Civil War in 1861. This created an immediate need of iron for the war machine of the North, which, combined with the existing geographic factors, led to the rapid development of one of the largest iron and steel manufacturing complexes in the world. The iron ore was transported south to the coal because, in the mid-19th century, to produce iron required four tons of coal to one of iron ore. Besides, the coal fields were close to developed areas, whereas the iron fields were in the northern wilderness. Hatcher (1945) described it as follows:

> These two primary ingredients for making iron and steel [iron ore and coal] were separated by a thousand miles, but they were joined by the free waterway of the Great Lakes system. That is one of the stupendous facts in American history, for it has given this country its supreme industrial advantage over other nations. It is the key to the development of Lake Erie.

The advent of the railways in the 1850s had decreased the importance of the Canadian ports on Lake Erie. At the same time, the discovery of iron increased the importance of the American ports because of the proximity of the coal to the southshore harbors and the convenience of the transport of iron ore by water. The Vermillion and Minnesota range deposits were discovered in the 1860s, and the huge Mesabi deposits began production in the 1890s. In 1902, 27.5 million tons (30.25 million short tons) of ore passed through the Sault Ste. Marie locks. Transport by ship was the only economical way to move the iron ore, and many of the ships returning north would carry a cargo of coal for use there. Thus, while the railways decreased the importance of shipping in Ontario, the American railways added to the importance of the southshore ports by bringing coal to them and taking ore, iron, and manufactured goods from them. Cleveland is one of these ports, and Figure 2.2 shows that this activity has continued to the present day.

Detroit was an established center before the advent of iron, but grew considerably when it began making iron, steel, and many goods manufactured from these materials. A host of other nonferrous goods were also produced, with the result that the population increased from 31,000 in 1850 to 290,000 at the turn of the century. Further, when the inventions of Henry Ford made Detroit into the prime automobile-producing city in America, the population increased rapidly to 1,670,000 in 1960. Toledo, on the Maumee

Figure 2.2 Industrial traffic on the Cuyahoga River at Cleveland. (Photo by J.P. Barry.)

River, became an important town because of its natural situation. The river gave Toledo a good, accessible harbor that was developed to provide 29 km (18 miles) of dock space. Many railroads now converge on this city, and with these facilities Toledo has become a major transhipment center for coal and other bulk materials. Many manufacturing industries have also developed in this city, glass-making in particular.

The ports of Lake Erie continue to be active. Large quantities of bulk materials are still shipped into and out of Detroit, Toledo, Huron, Sandusky, Lorain, Cleveland, Ashtabula, Conneaut, and Buffalo. Since the opening of the St. Lawrence Seaway, both bulk freight and general-cargo ocean vessels have carried freight to and from ports on the lakes, including those of Lake Erie. Also, Lake Erie shipyards have launched many ships, including a large number of vessels for ocean service during two world wars. Lorain and Toledo are the main shipbuilding centers. A large shipyard at Erie, Pennsylvania, has been inactive in recent years. Figures 2.2 and 2.3 give some idea of the shipping activity in Lake Erie today.

The Great Lakes Basin Commission (GLBC App. C9 1975) estimated that nearly 28 percent of the present Lake Erie Basin population is supported by work and income from bulk and general-cargo waterborne commerce. The bulk cargoes are iron ore, coal, limestone, fuel oil, and grain. Major deposits of iron ore have been found in Quebec and Labrador in recent years, and many Canadian ships now follow the practice of "back-hauling," which has considerably reduced shipping costs. Lakers transport grain down to the lower St. Lawrence ports, where they offload and take on a cargo of iron ore, which they haul back to the two lower lakes. Most American ships entering Lake Erie ports bring iron ore from the upper lakes and return empty.

As the latest installment in the saga of iron and steel on Lake Erie, in 1980 the Canadians began to make steel at Nanticoke on the north shore at the eastern end of the lake, more than a century after the first iron works were established on the American side. Steel production has always led to the establishment of secondary industry and large-scale urbanization of the nearby areas. This, in turn, has led to the development of intense agriculture in surrounding areas, if the soil conditions are suitable. This is the case in the Nanticoke region, where a new urban area surrounded by intense agriculture will develop. Much more knowledge now exists on how to control urban and industrial pollution, and it is being used at Nanticoke. Nevertheless, the question remains whether present-day attitudes to industrial growth and environmental preservation will insist on the use of modern knowledge and technology to ensure the future good quality of the lake water in this area.

Summary

Lake Erie has changed drastically from the time of its sighting by Joliet in 1669. The north shore has been transformed from its original wild state

Figure 2.3 Two freighters. **Top:** *A Canadian freighter carrying grain from the Upper Lakes to the Gulf of St. Lawrence passes the steel mills of Detroit.* **Bottom:** *A West German freighter on Lake Erie. (Photos by J.P. Barry.)*

to one of extensive agriculture, with a few fishing villages located at the mouths of streams. The southshore and western areas have undergone more extreme change, with many once-agricultural parts now industrialized; the small southshore harbors were transformed by their proximity to nearby coalfields and the cheap transport for American iron ore from the Lake Superior deposits. Some of these small ports developed into massive cities containing large industrial complexes, so that the degree of development along the southern lakeshore is now far greater than that along the northern shore.

3

Geological Development
of Lake Erie

Geological Development of the Lake Erie Basin

Since geological time scales are so much longer than human ones, the reader may question whether the geological history of the lake basin is pertinent to an understanding of changes that have happened only in the last 200 years. The history of geological change is of interest because it leads to an understanding of the present features of the Lake Erie Basin, many of which have determined the pattern of settlement of the area. The modern configuration of the five Laurentian Great Lakes of North America is shown in Figure 1.1. The lakes have existed with their present shapes for only about 10,000 years, a very short period in geological time. Yet the history of their development goes back about 1,000 million years, when the Precambrian rocks of the Canadian Shield were formed. These rock types still dominate in the northern part of the Great Lakes Basin as the Laurentian and Superior Uplands (see Figure 3.1).

Geologists still argue about the details of the development of the Great Lakes, but are in agreement about the major processes that led to their formation. The brief summary in the next four paragraphs is taken from the writings of Hough (1958) and Allen (1970).

About 450 million years ago in the Ordovician period, while waters of a vast inland sea lapped the Precambrian rocks of the Canadian Shield, thick deposits of material eroding from the surrounding land were laid down on these seafloors. These deposits now form the base sedimentary rock shown as Queenston shales in Figure 3.2. The Silurian period followed the Ordovician and continued for about 50 million years. During this time

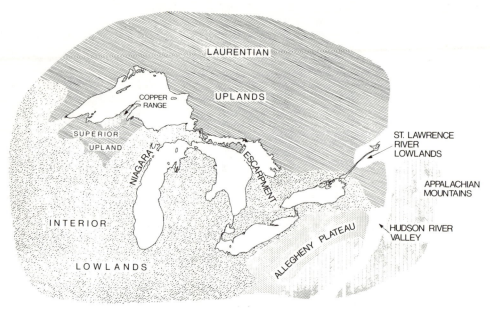

Figure 3.1 Physiographic map showing the major land forms of the Great Lakes Basin.

many communities of coral builders existed in the seas in the present Great Lakes area. Their reefs eventually led to the formation of stratified deposits of limestone and dolomite, two similar carbonate rocks that are fairly hard and resistant to wear. Also during this period many isolated lagoons came into existence as a result of the reef-building activity, particularly in the area now located between Lakes Huron and Erie. Evaporation from these lagoons eventually formed large salt deposits, or salinas. Simultaneously, organic debris from the marine organisms settled to the floor, leading to the formation of the oil and natural gas deposits that are presently found in the Lake Erie area.

The Devonian period followed the Silurian, and further sequences of sedimentary rocks were laid down. These were followed by localized deposits in the Mississippian and Pennsylvanian ages. This process of building up layers of sedimentary rock interspersed with carbonate rock formations would have continued indefinitely, but at the start of the Permian period, about 280 million years ago, the uplift of the continental land mass and the retreat of the seas put an end to sediment deposition in this area.

During the almost 280 million years between the retreat of the inland seas and the onset of the glacial epoch 2 million years ago, the Great Lakes area was subject to normal weathering processess. Mature stream systems cut valleys into the less-resistant rocks, forming a drainage pattern that reflected the nature of the local geology.

The Pleistocene epoch was the time of the great ice ages, which ended about 10,000 years ago. During this epoch there were four ice ages, periods

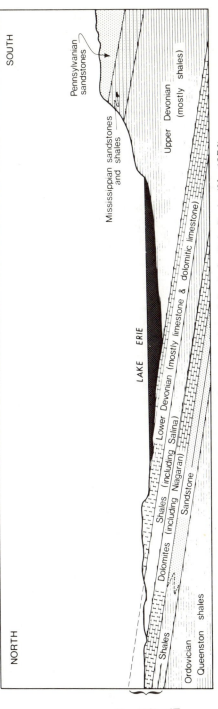

Figure 3.2 A bedrock stratigraphy cross-section of the Lake Erie Basin (Sly 1976).

when massive glaciers advanced southward over the North American continent. They were interspersed with four interglacial periods, including the present, when the glaciers retreated back to the Arctic. Within each ice age were many short periods of minor retreats and advances. This was a very important period in the development of the Great Lakes Basin, because the glaciers drastically modified the land over which they moved. In particular, they caused the excavation of the basins of all the Great Lakes—except Superior, which is almost completely surrounded by resistant Precambrian rock.

Newberry (1874a,b) claimed that the scouring action of the glaciers followed the creation of a channel by the erosive action of an ancient river. This river probably flowed from Lake Superior, through the sites of the present Lakes Huron, Erie, and Ontario, and then down the Mohawk Valley into the trough of the Hudson River. The river valley probably controlled the flow of glaciers so that their scouring action resulted in the formation of the basins of the present lakes. The outcrops of the harder limestone and dolomite of the Niagara Escarpment (see Fig. 3.1) resisted the action of the glaciers, while the softer shales were excavated. The location of this rock formation and the softer shales were probably factors in determining the present shapes of Lakes Ontario, Erie, Huron, and Michigan. A domelike geological structure, the Findlay Arch shown in Figure 3.3, probably caused the separation of Lakes Erie and Huron. The hard-rock types of the Findlay Arch also resulted in the formation of the Lake Erie Islands of the West Basin. One of these, Kelley's Island, has striated rocks that dramatically demonstrate the scouring action of the glaciers (Fig. 3.4).

Since the Great Lakes area is located close to the southern terminus of the Pleistocene glaciers, their numerous advances and retreats have left a complex of land forms in the basin. These include many different moraines (ridgelike deposits left at the foot of a melting glacier) of sand and gravel. Some are small, while others are long and wide, such as the Port Huron moraine, which can be traced from the western shores of Lake Michigan to New York State (Hough 1958). This moraine divides the Central Basin from the East Basin of Lake Erie (Fig. 3.5), where it is named the Norfolk moraine.

Large lakes were often ponded at the feet of the melting glaciers. These early lakes had very different shapes from the modern lakes and left relict beaches high above present lake levels. Large raised deltas of the rivers that flowed into the early lakes are also found. Perhaps the most important remnants of the glacial lakes are the deposits of sediment laid down when the lakes existed for long periods of time. Many of these glaciolacustrine deposits are not only found within the boundaries of the modern lakes, but also form part of their drainage basin. These ancient lake sediments are flat and usually provide rich agricultural soils. The other major soil type in the Great Lakes area is glacial till, the unsorted debris deposited

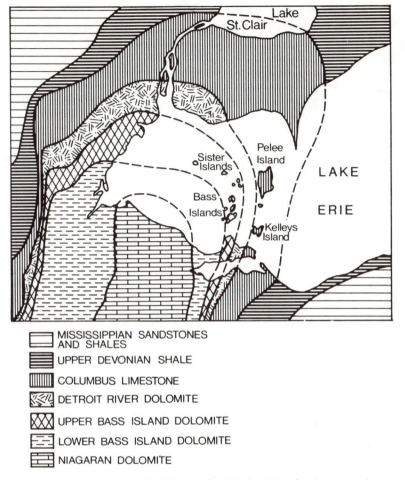

Figure 3.3 Geology of the West Basin of Lake Erie, showing a portion of the Findlay Arch consisting of limestones and dolomites. The islands occur in zones of these more resistant rocks (Hough 1958).

by glaciers when they retreated by melting. There are many slightly different types of till, but this class of soil is usually fine-grained, containing sand, gravel, and rocks in different proportions.

The glaciers depressed the land over which they moved. Since some glaciers were more than a thousand meters thick, their weight caused considerable lowering of the underlying crust, especially in the northern part of the Great Lakes Basin. The isostatic rebound, or uplifting, of the land following the disappearance of the glaciers is still occurring in the basins of all the lakes, particularly in the Georgian Bay area of Lake Huron. This rebound process has affected the depths of the lakes by changing the altitude of the outlets of the various lakes.

Figure 3.4 Rocks in Kelley's Island State Park, showing the striations left by the glaciers passing over the island. (Photo by CLEAR.)

A detailed description of the recent physiographic evolution of Lake Erie has been given by Sly (1976), who emphasized the effects of successive high and low lake levels.

The sequence of known lake stages in the Erie basin began with the retreat of the Erie ice lobe from the Fort Wayne moraine in Michigan, Indiana, and Ohio about 14,000 yr. ago. Meltwater, ponded between the ice and this moraine, formed Lake Maumee I at 244m [800 ft] above sea level (a.s.l.) which discharged westward to the Mississippi system. General retreat with minor re-advance during the next 500–1000 yr. gradually enlarged the area inundated by lake waters, until the whole basin was probably submerged. It is likely that the Pelee and Erieau moraines [Fig. 3.5] and possibly the Port Maitland moraine were constructed at this time. Subsequently, lake levels

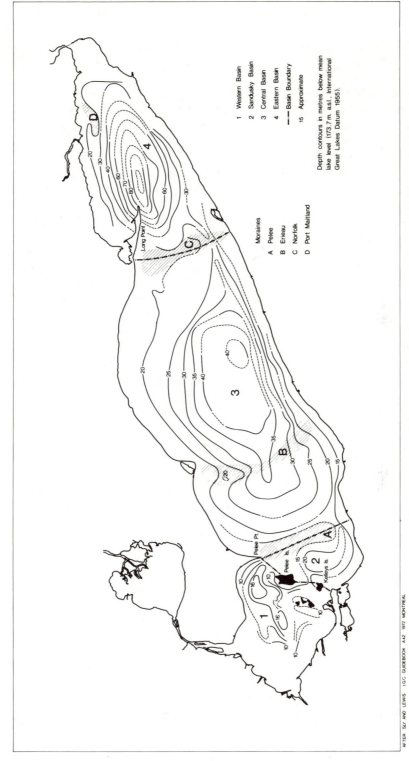

Figure 3.5 Inferred bathymetry of early Lake Erie showing moraines that caused ridges or elevated areas on the bottom of the lake. Contours are drawn relative to present lake level. (After Sly and Lewis 1972.)

dropped and fluctuated as new outlets were opened and old outlets were deepened.

About 13,000 years ago, ice readvanced into the Erie depression. This ice excavated the East Basin to a greater depth, constructed the Norfolk (Port Huron) moraine, and raised the water level in the remainder of the basin to 225m (738 ft) above sea level, compared to the present 174m (571 ft) above sea level. Thereafter, ice gradually evacuated the Erie basin and parts of the adjacent Michigan, Huron, and Ontario basins. New outlets through the Huron and Michigan basins, opened by this retreat, allowed lake levels to fall.

By 12,600 years before the present, ice had retreated sufficiently to free the Mohawk–Hudson Valley route and allow Lake Iroquois, the precursor of Lake Ontario, to come into existence in the Ontario basin. Simultaneously, Erie water levels fell as they drained over the Niagara Escarpment into Lake Iroquois via the modern Niagara River. This event marked the end of glacial influence in the Erie Basin and brought into being Early Lake Erie, a lake whose altitude was, and is, controlled by the elevation of the sill at Buffalo.

At this time, part of the East Basin around Buffalo was still depressed by 35m (115 ft) or more relative to the Central and West Basins, because the western end of the lake recovered from the ice loading more rapidly than the eastern end when Early Lake Erie came into existence. The water level in this lake stood at about 135m (443 ft) above sea level, and the West and Central Basins were effectively drained. Water ponded in the deepest parts of the Central Basin, between the Pelee and Norfolk moraines, discharged over them toward the east, incising channels across their southern termini. The outlet at Buffalo then began to rise rapidly, and by about 11,000 years ago the water level in the lake had risen by about 20m (66 ft) to approximately 18m (59 ft) below the present lake level. Water levels subsequently rose more slowly, except for a rapid, 8m (26 ft) jump about 4000 years ago, to present levels after the Upper Great Lakes discharge south from Lake Michigan ceased. Figure 3.5 shows an estimate of the lake bathymetry soon after it reached its modern configuration about 4,000 years ago, but before extensive shoreline erosion and inputs from the watershed had begun to fill in the lake. The shoreline shown is the modern one, because geologists are not yet sure about the earlier configurations, other than that the area of the lake in the recent past was smaller than that of today.

Relief and Soil Types

Some parts of the shoreline along the northern shore of the East Basin are rocky and resistant to erosion because they consist of limestone out-croppings, but the majority of the shoreline of the modern lake consists of erodable glacial till. In many areas this till shoreline consists of steep bluffs as high as 38m (125 ft) which the lake waters continually erode. Sly (1976) has estimated that the lake has shallowed by 30 to 35 percent, while surface area has increased by as much as 15 to 20 percent over the past 2000 years. Figure 1.2 shows the present bathymetry of Lake Erie, and a comparison with Figure 3.5 gives an idea of the depth of recent sedimentation.

The Canadian part of the Lake Erie catchment shows much less relief than the American part, except in the northeast section, as shown in Figure 3.6. In the west of the American section, much of the area consists of the lake bed of ancient Lake Whittlesey and as a result is very flat.

The major soil types around the lake are shown in Figure 3.7. There are two clay plains (A) on the north shore. The Haldimand clay plain, on the east, extends over some 3,400 km² (1300 sq. mi.), and most of the soil is composed of a mixture of thin lacustrine clay overlying clay till. Slight local relief is provided by swells in the till plain. In the west are the St. Clair clay plains, which cover an area about 5800 km² (2240 sq. mi.). The region is generally flat, although the Blenheim and Charing Cross moraines develop 15 to 30m (50 to 100 ft) of relief. Most soils are derived from shallow deposits of lacustrine silty clay, which overlie a leveled surface of glacial till. This soil type is very similar to that of the Maumee River Basin (Type 5, Fig. 3.7), because both these soils were once part of the lake floor of the ancient Lakes Whittlesey and Maumee (Sly 1976).

East of this area, the Bothwell sand plain (B–west) occurs in the form of thinly layered sands that overlie a region of some 1800 km² (695 sq. mi.). In patches, where the sand cover is very thin, standing water and swamps overlie the clay. The till plain (C) is made up of materials deposited when the glaciers melted: a mix of stones, pebbles, and sand in a silt and clay matrix. This material is not sorted into layers, as are sediments deposited in running and standing water, and since it resembles tilled soil, it is called glacial till. The Mount Elgin ridges (E) form the watershed divide between the upper Thames River (near London) and the Norfolk sand plain, covering an area of some 1400 km² (540 sq. mi.). Locally, relief exceeds 30m (100 ft), and the land rises generally to the northeast to reach an elevation of more than 230m (754 ft) above lake level. Drainage is often incomplete, and in lowlands, swamp, marsh, and peat areas exist.

The Norfolk sand plain (B–east) covers an area of about 3100 km² (1200 sq. mi.) and forms much of the land adjacent to Long Point. The sands and silts of this area were deposited as a delta in glacial Lakes Whittlesey and Warren and reach a maximum thickness of about 25m (80 ft) over till and morainic materials; the average thickness is about 10m (30 ft). Most of the drainage to Lake Erie is by short creeks whose valleys may be incised as much as 30m (100 ft) into the surrounding plain. To the north, drainage runs into the Grand River (see Fig. 1.3) from an area of some 6600 km² (2550 sq. mi.) on the dip slope of the Niagara Escarpment

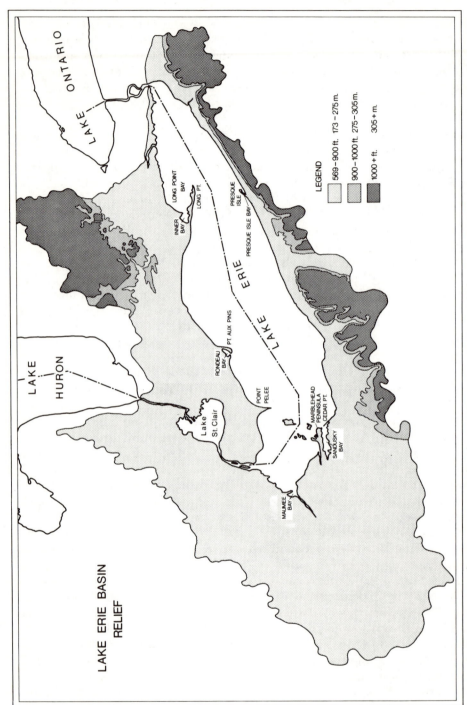

Figure 3.6 Lake Erie Basin relief, showing the major points and bays in the lake.

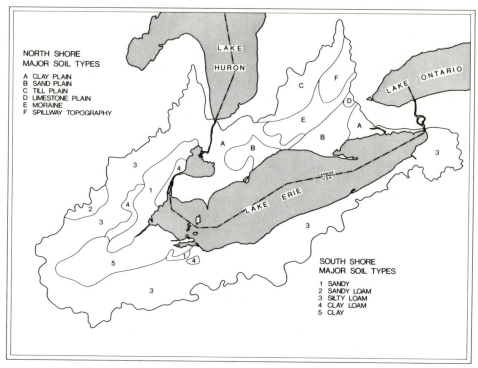

Figure 3.7 The major soil types (simplified) in the Lake Erie and Lake St. Clair Basins. The transit time of the water from Lake Huron through Lake St. Clair to Lake Erie is in the order of a week, so the waters draining into Lake St. Clair effectively form part of the Lake Erie drainage basin.

and intersects both the Haldimand and Norfolk plains. The river has a length of about 290 km (180 miles), and the upper reaches (F) drain a complex of glacial spillways formed in the till plains of central, southern Ontario (Sly 1976).

The landforms in the eastern segment of the southern part of the lake basin are quite different from those north of the lake. From Buffalo to Cleveland, the Portage Escarpment of the Allegheny Plateau approaches very close to the lake shore (see Fig. 3.6). The escarpment rises to a height of 60 to 100m (200 to 330 ft) above the lake plain, which is only about 8 km (5 miles) wide. The Allegheny Plateau does not extend past Cleveland, and the land from this point to the west is lower and flatter (Figures 3.6, 1.3). South of Buffalo are many sandy ridges formed at the shoreline beaches of the different stages of the glacial lakes. To the west of this area, there is only a narrow band of lake-deposited sands. In the remainder of the eastern half of the basin, soils are formed of glacial till and outwash and are generally silty loams and clay loams. The Maumee basin is located at the extreme west of the basin. This flat area, with slopes often less than

0.2 percent, was one of the drainage areas for the early lakes before the Niagara outlet was established. The central portion of this basin contains most of the clay and silty-clay textured soils found in the southern part of the basin. Even so, the Defiance moraine in the northwest part of the Maumee basin has steep slopes of clay loam and silty-loam soils (U.S. Army Corp. of Eng. 1979).

Figure 1.3 shows the streams and rivers entering Lake Erie and, since most of the towns and cities are situated on the harbors formed by these rivers, they are also shown. The streams entering Lake Erie originate either within or just outside the boundaries of the plain surrounding the lake. In the parts where the land is high relative to the lake, the river valleys are generally narrow and winding, with steep to vertical walls. These slopes indicate that most of the valleys are in a youthful state of maturity, having been cut rapidly since the last ice age. The Maumee River flowing through flat land is not incised and is the second-largest river flowing into the lake. The largest river, the Detroit, is almost 6 km (3.7 miles) wide as it enters Lake Erie and flows with an average discharge of about 5,300m^3 sec^{-1} (1,400,000 gals per sec) and a speed of almost 2 knots (1m sec^{-1} or 3.3 ft per sec). The Grand River (Ont.) is the third largest. The remainder of the rivers are important but have significantly smaller flows than the three major rivers. The Thames River is large but flows into Lake St. Clair and thence into Lake Erie.

The present shoreline of the lake consists of three main types. The major part of the shoreline in the Central Basin consists of clay bluffs that are continually being eroded away. It is unlikely that the nature of this feature has changed appreciably in the last five centuries. The second type of shoreline is comprised of rock or low-lying plain adjacent to the lake. These forms give rise to a shoreline of promontories and bays. At present, these shorelines have cottages or lakeside homes along them, but earlier would have been wooded up to the beach line. The other type of shoreline consists of marshes such as presently exist in Inner Bay, near Long Point and Point Pelee. The largest marshes are found along the southwest shore of the West Basin, where the low-lying lake plain forms the shoreline.

Summary

The geological history of the Lake Erie Basin has determined many of its present characteristics. The lake itself was excavated from the softer shales by advancing glaciers, but its islands remain because they consist of the harder rocks of the Silurian period. The seas of this ancient period caused the creation of the hydrocarbon and salt deposits now found in the basin. The marshes and rich agricultural land surrounding the West Basin result from the existence of more-recent glacial lakes. The eroding banks of the

Central Basin are a legacy of the thick deposits of glacial till, while the peninsulas of the lake, which add so much to its character, are remnants of the earlier moraines. The rich world of nature that developed after the glaciers disappeared partly results from the diverse landforms that now make up the lake and its drainage basin.

II

PROCESSES IN
LAKE ERIE

In the natural world all parts of each system interact, but some parts and some processes in each system are more fundamental than others. These are usually the physical and chemical processes, and we can gain a better understanding of the natural world by studying these fundamental parts first and the more-dependent parts later. Then, when we have some idea of the nature of the individual parts, we can synthesize all aspects into a living whole. This final synthesis is the most difficult task in gaining knowledge and, regrettably, is often not done. The processes described in this section are basic, and are only part of the larger picture which is completed later.

Units of Conversion

The metric system has been used in this book because virtually all the material has been extracted from scientific publications, where values are given in metric units. For those more familiar with the imperial system, a table of conversion factors is presented below, together with a note on the scientific sign convention.

Mass	1 g	= 1 gram	= 0.0353 ounce
	1 kg	= 1 kilogram	= 2.20 pounds
	1 ton	= 1 metric ton	= 0.984 long ton = 1.102 short tons
Length	1 cm	= 1 centimeter	= 0.394 inch
	1 m	= 1 meter	= 3.28 feet
			= 1.09 yards
	1 km	= 1 kilometer	= 0.621 mile
Area	1 m^2	= 1 square meter	= 1.20 square yards
	1 ha	= 1 hectare	= 2.47 acres
	1 km^2	= 1 square kilometer	= 0.386 square mile
Volume	1 m^3	= 1 cubic meter	= 1.31 cubic yd. = 264.2 U.S. gals.
	1 l	= 1 liter	= 1.76 imp. pts. = 2.11 U.S. pts.
	1 km^3	= 1 cubic kilometer	= 0.239 cubic mile
Temperature	1°C	= 1 degree Celsius	= ($\frac{9}{5}$°C + 32) degrees Fahrenheit
Scientific Sign Convention	1 cm sec^{-1}	= 1 cm/sec	= 1 centimeter per second
	1 kg cm^{-2}	= 1 kg/cm^2	= 1 kilogram per square cm
	1 gm cm^{-3}	= 1 gm/cm^3	= 1gm per cubic cm
Velocity	1 m sec^{-1}	= 1 meter per sec.	= 3.28 feet per second
	1 km hr^{-1}	= 1 kilometer per hr.	= .621 mph
Pressure	1 kg cm^{-2}	= 1 kilogram per square cm = 0.968 atmospheres	
Density	1 g cm^{-3}	= 1 gram per cubic cm = 0.0361 lb per cubic inch	
Interconversion	1 kg	= 10^3 g = 10^6 mg	
	1 m^3	= 10^3 l = 10^6 ml (milliliters)	
	1 p.p.m.	= 1 part per million = 1 g m^{-3}	
	1 p.p.b.	= 1 part per billion = 1 mg m^{-3}	

4

Climate, Weather, and Erosion

Climate: Wind and Weather

The nature of a lake is as dependent on the prevailing climate and weather as it is on its geology, bathymetry, and nutrient supply. The climate of the Great Lakes Basin is extreme in terms of temperature and wind variability, although the lakes, with their combined surface area of approximately 250,000 km², do moderate their own climate somewhat. The range between mean summer and winter air temperature in the Lake Erie Basin is about 24°C (75°F). The summer mean air temperature is about 23°C (73°F) in the southwestern part, and 21°C (70°F) in northeastern areas; in the winter the mean daily temperature is about −2°C (28°F) in the southwestern part and −4°C (25°F) in the northeastern areas. About 70 percent of the lake is frozen during most winters, and it is completely frozen over during colder winters. In contrast, the summer water temperatures often reach 25°C (77°F).

The warm summer waters of the lake make it very popular for recreation. During July and August almost clear skies (less than 20 percent sky cover) prevail for 40 percent of the time, and each day averages more than 10 hours of sunshine. In winter, heavy cloud cover prevails 70 percent of the time, with an average of less than three hours of sunshine per day. There are about 200 days free from frost along the south shore, and about 180 along the north shore. The frost-free days decrease noticeably away from the shoreline, being as few as 140 in some places within 50 km of the lake (Philips and McCulloch 1972).

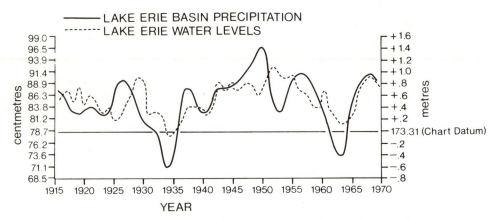

Figure 4.1 Precipitation in the Lake Erie Basin and water levels in the lake, showing the nature of the variability in both. (After Philips and McCulloch 1972.)

Lake Erie is large enough to induce lake and land breezes. During the day in summer, the lake often is cooler than the surrounding land, and the breeze blows onshore and gives welcome relief from heat to the people living within 30 to 40 km of the lake. At night the lake is warmer than the land, and the direction of the breeze changes and blows from the land. These effects cause downdrafts of air over the lake during the day, which tend to disperse the clouds and give the lake about an hour more of sunlight each day than the surrounding land. At night, however, the updrafts over the lake can lead to severe thunderstorms, a real danger to pleasure boaters late at night or in the early hours of the morning (Philips and McCullogh 1972). In winter, the lake is the cause of lake-effect snowfalls, usually caused by northwest winds blowing across the lake. The temperature of these winds is much colder than that of the lake, and the water that evaporates from the lake's surface is soon condensed into snow. This snowfall on the southshore areas, especially between Cleveland and Buffalo, can be from 50 to 150 cm greater than on the north shore.

The average long-term combined precipitation of rain and snow in the drainage basin of the lake is 86 cm per annum and falls more or less evenly throughout the year. The variability in precipitation between years, however, is very high, as shown in Figure 4.1. Evaporation is also variable from year to year, with low evaporation rates occurring during the wetter years, and high evaporation during drier years. Thus the effect of evaporation is to accentuate rather than moderate the extreme effects of variation in precipitation. Since wet and dry years do not alternate but occur in a grouped pattern, large periodic variations in the annual average lake level result. In 1963–1964 the average lake level was about 0.8m lower than in 1967 (see Fig. 4.1). Water levels also vary during the year, with winter levels usually being 0.4 to 0.5m lower than summer. Thus, the mean lake level can vary by 1.5m from low water during a dry period to high water during a wet period. This variation in lake level increases the erosion of the lakeshore.

An examination of tributary flows (Burns, Rosa, and Chan 1976; U.S. FWPCA 1968) shows that about 88 percent of the water inflow to the lake comes from the Detroit River, which brings in the water from Lake Huron via Lake St. Clair. This flow is fairly steady at an average of 5,800 m³ sec⁻¹, but does vary within a year by a factor of 1.4 of the minimum flow. The smaller rivers draining the lake basin show much greater variation in flow, because their combined flow can vary from 230 m³ sec⁻¹ (cubic meters per second) in August to more than 1600 m³ sec⁻¹ in March. The Maumee River, for instance, had a flow of 32 m³ sec⁻¹ in September 1970, compared with 969 m³ sec⁻¹ in April 1970, a 30-fold difference. The large spring river flows are mostly caused by the melting of the snowpack on the land in March.

During spring there is very little evaporation; in fact, in April and May when the lake water is often cooler than the air, water is added to the lake by condensation. In October when the lake water is often warmer than the air, evaporation can reach 15 cm month⁻¹. Over the year, however, the precipitation directly on the lake surface and the evaporation from the lake are usually about equal. The net result of low spring evaporation, high spring tributary flow, and high midsummer flow from the Detroit River causes the highest lake water levels to occur in June. The inflow from the Detroit River is lowest in February, coinciding with the lowest lake levels.

The climate of the Great Lakes is characterized by the rapid passage of different weather systems through the area. The settled weather associated with high-pressure systems is usually interrupted every few days by passage of low-pressure storm systems that are characterized by overcast skies, precipitation, and changes of wind direction.

Three different air masses dominate the Great Lakes area. The first is the maritime Tropical from the Gulf of Mexico and is present in the Lake Erie area about 40 percent of the time in the summer and less than 1 percent of the time in January. In summer this air mass is characterized by oppressively high temperatures and humidites together with haze and frequent thunderstorms. In winter this warm air tends to override the colder air from the north, but on the rare occasion when it does reach ground level, it causes the "January thaw."

The second set of air masses originates over the Pacific. One of the two is called the Maritime Polar air mass, since it comes from the northern Pacific Ocean. This Maritime Polar or cool Pacific air flows over the Canadian Northwest and arrives cool and dry in the Great Lakes area, bringing bright skies and summer relief from the haze and pollution associated with the tropical air. It is the prevailing air mass for somewhat more than 10 percent of the time in the summer. If the Pacific air mass originates farther south, it is termed mild Pacific air and is warmer and more humid than air from the Northwest. It is the dominant air mass in the Lake Erie area during the summer. During winter one or other of these Pacific air masses covers the Great Lakes area for more than 75 percent of the time. If the air is from the north it brings raw weather, and if from the American Rocky Mountains it brings cool, cloudy, moist weather.

The third distinct air mass of interest is the Continental Artic air mass, which originates in the Polar regions. It is very cold and dry and covers the Lake Erie area about 20 percent of the time in winter. This air mass is not felt at all in summer, when it remains in the north (Philips and McCulloch 1972).

From June through October, hurricane remnants can pass close to the lake and produce heavy rain and wind. In general, the structure of the air masses over North America is more complex in winter than in summer. The average position of the lines of contact of the different air masses for the two different seasons are shown in Figure 4.2. These lines of air mass contact are continually moving about their average positions, causing a fixed spot on the earth to experience changeable weather. If the temperature difference between the air masses is large enough, a cyclonic storm will develop. The passage of one of the these storms brings precipitation and wind of changing direction and strength.

Lake Erie is close to the average position of contact for different air masses for the eight months from October to May, as shown in Figure 4.2 and the diagrams of Bryson (1966). As a result, Lake Erie experiences many cyclonic storms during this period: about one every four days, in contrast to one about every eight days in summer. The most violent cyclonic storms usually occur in the fall and spring, when winds of over 100 km hr^{-1} have frequently been measured. If these winds are associated with a cyclonic storm they can blow for a day or two, but if associated with a thunderstorm they will seldom last for more than half an hour. The lake, however, is not always windy and does enjoy long periods of calm or light winds, particularly in the summer. In July the mean wind speed varies from 14 to 22 km hr^{-1}. There are also many thunderstorms during summer, usually between 40 and 45 a year. During the other three seasons the wind speeds are higher, with the mean speeds for the eight major directions varying between 18 and 26 km hr^{-1}.

The majority of the strong winds come from the southwest, and the lake is particularly vulnerable to these winds since its long axis (388 km) lies in this direction. Strong southwest winds, or the occasional northeast wind blowing from the opposite direction, can cause large waves at the downwind end of the lake; these waves can reach heights in excess of 5m at the eastern end in deep water. The strong winds also blow large masses of water ahead of them and can raise the level of the lake at the downwind end by more than 2.5m (Sly 1976). If this happens during one of the high-

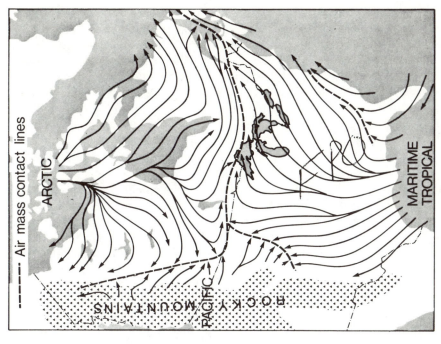

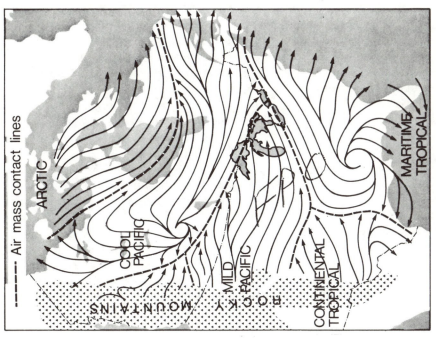

Figure 4.2 Streamlines of the surface resultant wind. Left: In December, air mass contact links pass over Lake Erie. Right: In June, the air mass contact lines are north of the Great Lakes. (After Bryson 1966.)

water periods in the lake, the lake water can rise three or more meters above normal level. Should this increase be coupled with the effect of large waves, the lake water can reach shoreline that has never been affected by wave action and cause havoc, usually in the form of extensive shoreline erosion or severe flooding of low-lying areas. In 1972–73, for example, extensive flooding and shoreline erosion occurred when water levels reached a record high of 175.0m above sea level, 1.7m above datum. This is illustrated in Figure 4.3.

Sheet Erosion

Another weather-induced erosive process is the sheet erosion of arable land which, in the drainage basin of Lake Erie, carries 6.5 million tons, or about $3 \times 10^6 m^3$, of suspended solids into the lake each year (PLUARG 1978). This is a tremendous input of material to Lake Erie, the smallest of the Great Lakes. The erosional load to Lake Superior, the largest of the Great Lakes, is only 1.4 million tons yr^{-1}, while Lake Ontario, which is similar in size to Lake Erie, has a load of 1.6 million tons per year. This huge load of solids to Lake Erie comes primarily from the intensely cultivated lands surrounding the western half of the lake.

When the early glacial lakes retreated they left an extensive area of fine-grained glaciolacustrine clays in the western part of the lake basin (see Fig. 3.7). These materials form prime agricultural soils but, unfortunately, fine-grained clays are easily suspended by rainfall and can be transported large distances as they do not settle readily (PLUARG 1978). Heavy rainstorms occurring in the spring before the earth has completely thawed contribute to excessive erosion. Meltwater in the surface soil freezes and thaws during the changeable spring weather, making the soil friable and erodible. If it rains heavily at this time, maximum sheet erosion occurs because many of the raindrops strike the soft, bare earth and suspend the clay in the rainwater. This combines with the meltwater, causing huge quantities of muddy runoff water to flow into the lake.

The largest source of riverborne clay material is the Maumee River, carrying 1.8 million tons of clay-sized material into the lake per year (Kemp, McInnes, and Harper 1977). This fairly recent phenomenon occurs in the cleared area around the western end of the lake. Before settlement, the Maumee and the other rivers draining the 4000 km^2 Black Swamp ran clear with a fairly steady flow all year. At that time, before cleared ground and manmade drainage ditches, the vegetation and natural contours of the land held back the floodwaters. The bare earth and the drainage ditches now cause much erosion, as explained by Langlois (1954):

> Nowadays, farm lands are left bare and exposed to erosion by winter winds and spring rains. Fields are tiled to hasten rainwater away, while ditches are dug deep and left with bare, steep slopes which wash away with every rainfall.

Figure 4.3 Cottages at Locust Point on the southwestern shore after a northeasterly storm. (Photo by J.P. Barry.)

The melting snows and heavy rains of spring nowadays are not held for later use, and streams rise quickly to flood stages. Topsoil is eroded from lands which may be quite flat, and the streams carry vast loads of silt down into the lake. The fine materials gathered by sheet erosion in northwestern Ohio, carried by the Maumee River, Portage River, and the Sandusky River, remain long in suspension in Lake Erie.

The land in Ontario along the north shore is some of the prime land in the province, and it also is extensively drained. The drainage water from these lands first flows into Lake St. Clair, and then into Lake Erie via the Detroit River. The present load resulting from this process is 1.4 million tons of sediment per year, almost as much as that carried by the Maumee. Although small, the Sandusky River brings down another 0.1 million tons per year. In addition, the many short streams running into the lake, particularly on the American side, can carry substantial amounts of sediment during the summer. Brief, intense summer storms often cause brief, high-flow events that may carry much material to the lake but are seldom monitored (Ongley 1976). The resulting silt loads are not precisely known.

In addition to causing the loss of much valuable soil, sheet erosion loads much sediment into an already shallow Lake Erie. But its worst effect has been to cause a tremendous loss of fish-spawning areas and aquatic vegetation from the rivers and bays in the lake. This topic will be dealt with later.

Eroded soil also leads to the silting of many harbors. Toledo Harbor requires frequent dredging because of the silt brought down by the Maumee River. A 27 km shipping channel extending from Toledo out into the lake must be dredged frequently, largely because of the riverborne sediment. The river is dredged for 10 km upstream, including 8 km in Maumee Bay, and these dredgings are put behind special disposal structures because of their toxic nature. The dredgings from the outer 17 km of the channel are disposed of in the open lake and amount to about 764,000m³ per year (Herdendorf et al. 1977).

Shoreline Erosion and Flooding

Lake Erie is the shallowest of the Great Lakes for two reasons: first, the lake basin remaining after the retreat of the glaciers was probably shallower than that of the other lakes (see Fig. 3.5). Second, the lake is almost completely surrounded by an easily erodible shoreline of glacial till, whose by-products have filled in the lake considerably since its formation. A typical example of this type of shoreline is shown in Figure 4.4 and the Frontispiece. The north shore of the lake consists approximately of 45 percent unconsolidated materials, such as glacial till bluffs, 38 percent sandy shorelines, 13 percent wetlands and marshes, and 4 percent erosion-resistant materials, such as bedrock and artificial shore protection (Boulden 1975). The south

Figure 4.4 A not-infrequent sight around Lake Erie—a house built without adequate knowledge of the bluff recession rate. (Photo by CLEAR.)

shore consists of 64 percent erodible bluffs, 17 percent wetlands and low plain, 13 percent artificial protection and resultant beaches, 3 percent sand dunes, and 3 percent nonerodable bedrock (Upchurch 1975). The distribution of these shore types are shown in Figure 4.5. The erodable parts of the north shore have a distance-weighted average historical recession rate of 0.7m yr^{-1}. Values range from an accretion rate of 1.2m yr^{-1} on the east side of Rondeau peninsula to a recession rate of 5.1m yr^{-1} along a piece of shoreline 9 km east of Point Burwell (Boulden 1975). Along the south shore, the shoreline in Maumee Bay has been receding at 3m yr^{-1}; from Sandusky to Cleveland the recession rate has been approximately 1m yr^{-1}, and from Cleveland to Erie the bluffs have been receding at about

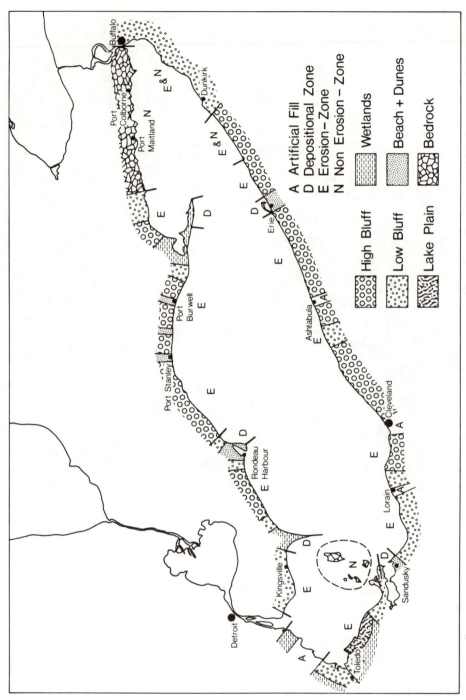

Figure 4.5 Physiography and erodability of the Lake Erie shoreline. (After Herdendorf 1975.)

1.5m yr⁻¹ (Herdendorf 1975). The 1950–1972 interval used for estimating the south shore rates spans two high-water periods and one low-water period, so the south shore recession rates are biased toward high values.

One reason for the high recession rate of the bluffs is that virtually all shorelines face a wind fetch (distance of open water) of 50 km or more. Although the predominant winds blow from the southwest, storm-force winds do blow from any direction at least some time during the year. This means that all shorelines will face large storm-generated waves on occasion, and if this happens during a high-water period, massive changes will result to undeveloped and developed land. Storms during low-lake-level periods cause far less erosion because a wave-absorbing beach is usually present at the base of the erodible bluffs. During high-water periods, however, the lake water often laps the foot of the bluffs. One large windstorm during a high-water period can erode more material from a shore than would be eroded during years of more-normal conditions. This point is illustrated by an incident documented by Coakley, Haras, and Freeman (1973).

During the very high water period of November 1972, a storm with northeast winds having a maximum velocity of more than 100 km hr⁻¹ and averaging 55 km hr⁻¹ blew for more than 24 hours. The beach on the east side of Point Pelee faced waves generated over a 240 km fetch. The resulting large waves ran up the beach to about 1m above the prevailing lake level. At the time of the storm the mean lake level was 174.4m above sea level (a.s.l.), and this was increased by 0.6m at Point Pelee by the wind. Thus the waves reached shorelines to a level of about 176.0m a.s.l., a height of 2.0m above mean level. Beach profiles had been measured before the storm on 26 June, 26 October, and 20 December 1972. During the summer, from 26 June to 26 October, there had actually been a gain of 0.9m³ of sand per meter of beach. The measurements after the November storm revealed a loss of 5.6m³ of material per meter, with the waterline eroded back by 13.8m at one point on the beach. At observation station E-1-30 on this beach, the long-term erosion rate is 0.6m yr⁻¹ (Boulden 1975), but 5.4m was eroded from this place by the storm in two days. This example also illustrates that many of the physical changes in the lake occur quickly during violent storms, rather than gradually over long periods of time.

A fairly common sight in the bluff areas of the lake is a house that is beginning to fall into the lake. The builder, unaware of the rapid rate of erosion, had built too close to the shore. During the 1970–1980 high-water period there was a great deal of shoreline damage, and as a result the Canadian and American governments carried out extensive studies of the Great Lakes shorelines. Nowadays, anyone building on a shoreline property can consult the government publications that define both the 100-yr erosion limit and the land that has a 1 percent chance of flooding during any one year.

The nature of the eroding bluff material basically controls the type of shorelines found on Lake Erie. The bluff material consists mostly of silt—particles with diameters from 4 microns (μm) to 60 μm mixed with clay (less than 4 μm)—with some sand (60 to 1000 μm) and gravel (Boulden 1975). If the bluff material were largely made up of sand there would be many sandy beaches around the lake, because the amount of sand removed by littoral drift would be replenished by fresh supplies from eroded bluffs. Instead, the majority of the beaches along the shoreline consist of recently slumped silty-clay bluff material in the process of being sorted by waves. Since the clays and silts do not settle easily, they are moved out to the mid-basin areas and settle there permanently. Some of the sandy material moves into the deeper nearshore areas, while the balance remains in the nearshore zone. This material moves along the shoreline by means of littoral drift, with sand beaches being formed in scattered areas of accretion. As there is not much sand in the bluff material, there are realtively few sandy beaches.

Littoral Drift of Eroded Material

Littoral drift is the process of transporting sand-sized particles along beaches in the shallow-water zone. This material is moved in the nearshore area by currents resulting from wave action. When waves break on a beach they loose their kinetic energy and, in so doing, redistribute the beach materials. If the waves approach at right angles to the beach, these materials are moved either inshore or offshore. If waves approach a beach at an angle of less than 90°, some of the kinetic energy will not be lost through friction, and net transport of water will result. This is caused by the shore-parallel component of the kinetic energy of the water, which forces the water to move along the beach in a direction similar to that of the wave approach. These longshore currents transport shoreline materials along the shoreline with most of the littoral drift occurring in water less than 2m deep.

Littoral drift is thus dependent on the height, direction, and frequency of the waves striking the shore. The amount of material transported over an extended period is thus dependent not only on the dominant wind, but also on the fetch, which controls the height of the waves and hence the strength of the littoral current. An occasional wind blowing over a large fetch can cause the movement of more material than a wind blowing frequently over a small fetch. An interesting example is Point Pelee where the dominant westerly winds cause material to drift from the bluffs in the west to the point and even possibly around the point to the east shore. On the other hand, the less-frequent easterly winds blow over a much longer fetch and move material from the east to the south and west of the point. In this case, a study by Coakley (1976) has shown that the net overall long-term transport is from east to west and that Point Pelee has migrated slowly to the west.

The pattern of littoral drift currents around Lake Erie is not simple, because the shorelines are complicated by the land forms of Point Pelee, Point aux Pins, Long Point, and Marblehead Peninsula. The net effect of the resultant littorial drift can be determined relatively easily by using a well-knowm rule governing shoreline phenomena: if a large solid obstruction (for instance, groyne or breakwall) is built out at right angles to a shoreline where there is littoral drift, material will collect on the upstream side of the construction, and the shoreline will tend to erode away on the downstream side of the obstruction. This process is dramatically demonstrated in the photograph of Port Bruce harbor shown in Figure 4.6.

When the factors producing littoral currents are balanced for two opposing directions, a neutral or nodal zone occurs. These zones may be classified as areas of either divergence or convergence. Those of divergence are areas where littoral currents flow away from each other and erosion generally occurs; those of convergence are areas where drifts of opposing direction meet, producing accretion or sedimentation. Areas of convergence and divergence are generally marked by distinct configurations of the shoreline: elongated spits and sand deposits are usually found in areas of convergence, and broad, gently rounded headlands in areas of divergence.

Herdendorf (1975) has examined the process of littoral drift around Lake Erie and has found that the area between Avon Point and Cedar Point has a known predominant westward drift (Fig. 4.7). Near Avon Point the diverging opposing littoral forces nearly balance, but to the west the forces become more and more unbalanced, and a maximum westward movement occurs at Cedar Point. This movement then loses its energy rapidly upon meeting the opposing force coming southward from Marblehead, and deposition takes place in this convergence zone. The most-pronounced areas of convergence in Lake Erie are on the north shore at Pelee Point, Point aux Pins (Rondeau), and Long Point, Ontario. As mentioned, Point Pelee is eroding away on the east side and building on the west. Rondeau Peninsula is building along its eastern edge with rates of more than a meter per year, while Long Point has been building along parts of its southern shore and eroding in others since the turn of the century. There are no comparable convergence areas on the south shore, but areas of divergence are better marked on the south shore than on the north shore. These are found at Locust Point, Scott Point, Marblehead, and Avon Point. Scott Point and Marblehead appear to be bedrock-controlled and not dependent on littoral drift.

The westerly drift from Avon Point to Cedar Point is of interest in that this current is in the opposite direction to the prevailing offshore current, which is to the east. This westerly littoral drift causes a collection of sand against the east side of a number of harbor entrance breakwalls between Cedar Point and Avon Point. The westerly drift occurs where the shoreline is open to east winds with long fetches (for example, Cedar Point), or

Figure 4.6 Port Bruce harbor on the north shore of the Central Basin. The predominant current is from west to east (left to right in the photograph) and demonstrates the sediment accumulation on the upstream side. (Photo by N. Rukavina.)

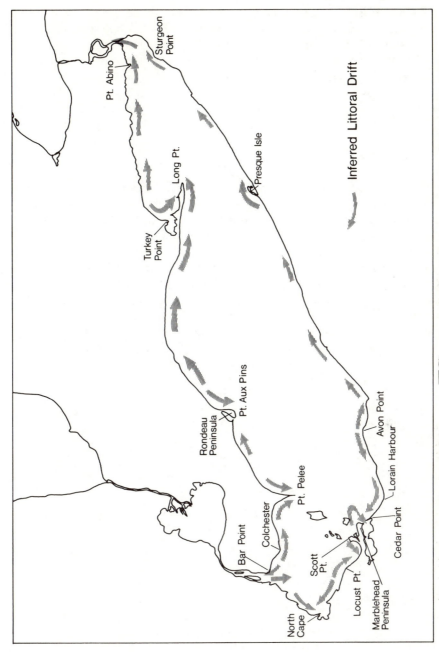

Figure 4.7 Generalized map of littoral drift associated with nearshore currents. (After Herdendorf 1975.)

where the shoreline orientation protects the shore from the prevailing west winds, for example, at Turkey Point behind Long Point (Fig. 4.7). Otherwise there is a easterly littoral drift along most of the shoreline of the lake. Presque Isle, for example, is migrating steadily toward the east (Jennings 1930). The result of these processes is that good beaches are found on the west side of shoreline obstructions and points of land where there is deposition, while erosion occurs on the east side of the constructions or points, exposing rock or leaving the bluffs without a protective beach.

Summary

Lake Erie lies in an area frequently covered by the contact zones of different air masses from October to May. Very changeable weather occurs during these months, but the summer months are calmer. Much soil is eroded when spring rains melt the snow and cause floods. The high banks of the lake are also eroded at this time and at any other time when the water levels in the lake are high. Bank and shoreline erosion is caused by large waves, which occur whenever winds blow over lengthy fetches of open water, a frequent occurrence because the prevailing wind direction lies in a similar direction to the long axis of the lake. The resulting large waves also cause the transport of sandy material in a complex pattern along the shorelines. The winds can cause temporary increases in water level, which often result in extensive flooding of low-lying areas.

5

Water Movement and Sediment Transport

Temperature and Stratification

An isothermal (constant temperature) column of water in contact with the sediments of a lake will, in general, have a different chemistry and support a different biological community than will a thermally stratified water mass having colder water beneath warmer water. For this reason a knowledge of the thermal structure of Lake Erie water is essential to an understanding of the lake. In early March the winter ice starts to melt off the West Basin (see Figure 5.1), the first part of the lake to show evidence of warming (Stewart 1973). By late April the West Basin waters have usually warmed to about 5°C, the Central Basin waters are cooler, and the East Basin is usually still partially covered with ice, much of which has been blown to this end of the lake from the other basins. The differential warming rate is not primarily a result of ice movement, but results from the different depths of the basins. The shallower West Basin (mean depth 7.6m) warms more quickly than the Central Basin (17.8m), which in turn is shallower and warms more quickly than the relatively deep East Basin (27.0m). The heat absorbed through the surface of a lake is distributed through the upper mixed layer. If the layer is thin or the lake shallow, the water warms rapidly. A thicker water column would require more heat and thus take longer to warm up. Similarly, since the major pathway of heat leaving a lake is through its surface, shallow waters cool more quickly than deep waters. During the autumn cooling period, the East Basin cools more slowly than the West Basin.

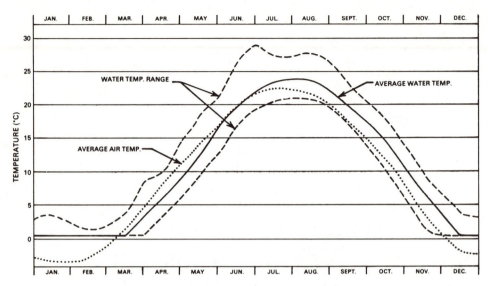

Figure 5.1 Long-term averages of water temperatures of the West Basin at Put-in-Bay, South Bass Island, together with air temperatures at Toledo, from 1919 to 1965.

The West Basin never stratifies thermally for any length of time, because the surface stress developed by winds of over 20 knots blowing for a few hours is sufficient to cause complete vertical mixing in such shallow water. During calm periods in this basin, however, the lower water in contact with the sediments will become 1° to 2°C cooler than the overlying water and form a thin layer of temporarily stratified water. In the Central Basin, stable stratification with a thermocline, a layer of water between the upper and lower masses where temperature decreases rapidly with depth, is usually present from early June to early September. The duration of this condition can vary by a month depending on the prevailing weather conditions. Strong winds terminate the stratified period by turbulent entrainment of the cool underlying water into the wind-mixed upper layer.

The main features of the thermocline in the Central Basin are that it is relatively deep—18 to 20m below the surface—and very sharp (as shown in Figure 5.2), often having a gradient as steep as 10°C per meter. The main reason is that the large fetch across the basin permits the wind to generate strong currents in both the surface and bottom waters, resulting in strong shear forces across the thermocline, which cause the thermocline to be sharp. In the deeper part of the basin (depths greater than 24m), the average thickness of the epilimnion (upper mixed layer) is about 17 meters, with a 2 to 3m thick thermocline and a 3 to 5m thick hypolimnion (lower mixed layer). It is surprising to find permanent summer stratification in such a large, shallow body of water as the Central Basin, but this situation has been observed every year that measurements have been taken.

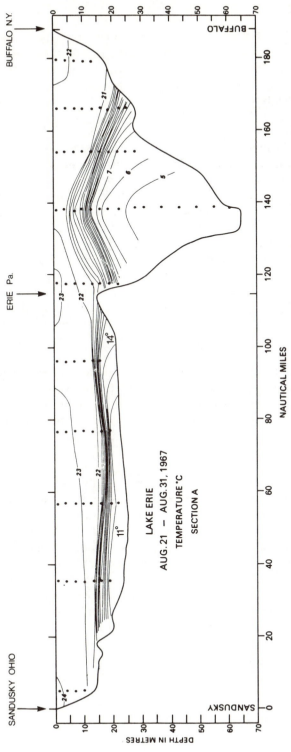

Figure 5.2 A cross-section of the Central and East Basins, showing a typical mid-summer temperature structure. The epilimnion, or upper mixed layer, extends to the 22°C isotherm in the Central Basin and 21°C in the East Basin. The thermocline, or zone of rapidly changing temperature, lies between the 22°C and 11°C isotherms in the Central and 21°C and 6°C in the East Basin. Separate hypolimnia, or lower mixed layers, underlie the thermocline in each basin.

The last ice melts off the East Basin in April, and the stratification begins in late May or early June, soon after all the water in the basin has become isothermal at 4°C. Thereafter, a 20m thick epilimnion forms with a 5 to 10m thick thermocline. The top of the hypolimnion is usually found at a depth of approximately 28 m. This thick thermocline has a gradient of about 1.5°C per meter. The epilimnion starts to deepen in September, and the last remains of stratification usually disappear in late October.

By late October all the water in the lake is vertically isothermal, although the water at the east end of the lake is warmer than that at the west. These conditions prevail until December, when the shallow West Basin cools to 0.1°C (Burns 1976c) and the surface water begins to freeze. In a normal year this basin will be completely frozen over by January. By this time the Central Basin is uniformly at 0.1°C and also beings to freeze, but it never completely freezes over except during unusually cold winters (Stewart 1973; Burns, Rosa, and Gedeon 1978). Since the East Basin is deep, one would expect its water to cool to 4°C, the temperature of greatest density for water, and inverse stratification to set up, with dense 4°C water forming the lower layer and colder, less-dense water forming the upper layer. This is not the case; the fall and winter turbulence is so great that the waters of the East Basin are mixed right to the bottom until they, too, reach 0.1°C, and then the surface waters begin to freeze. The East Basin is usually covered by ice, but it is not the smooth ice typical of the West Basin. It is very rough, with huge ridges formed by ice floes overriding each other under the pressure generated by the westerly winds. These conditions prevail until the ice begins to melt in the spring and the annual heat cycle recommences.

Water Movement

The science of water movements in large lakes and oceans is extremely complex, but an understanding of these phenomena is vital to an understanding of the Great Lakes. Any parcel of water in a lake usually has more than one force acting on it at a time, so its actual motion will be determined by the resultant of all the forces. The characteristics of these processes in the Great Lakes have been well explained by Boyce (1974). Perhaps the simplest way to describe the water movements in Lake Erie is to list the various types of water movements and then describe their general characteristics and behavior.

I.   Horizontal Currents
    A. Riverine flow
    B. Wind-driven currents
    C. Alongshore littoral currents
    D. Nearshore currents
    E. Seiche currents

F. Hypolimnion currents

G. Inertial currents

II. Horizontal and Vertical Circulation

A. Density currents

B. Downwelling and upwelling currents

C. Langmuir circulations

D. Turbulence

III. Waves

A. Surface waves

B. Internal waves

(After Herdendorf 1975.)

I. HORIZONTAL CURRENTS

A. Riverine Flow

1. Results from river input of water.

2. Has net eastward movement in Lake Erie.

3. Has low velocity.

4. Has no compensating return flow.

5. Has other, larger and variable currents superimposed that often mask the steady flow.

6. Is important in distribution of dissolved substances.

7. Is unimportant in transport of suspended material except in restricted channels.

The two largest rivers entering the lake are the Detroit and Maumee, which flow into the west end of the lake at the combined rate of 15.6 km³ per month, constituting about 95 percent of the flow through the lake. Since the volume of the West Basin is about 28 km³ and the water has a residence time of 1.8 months, it must flow through the basin at a minimum average speed of 1.7 cm sec⁻¹. The Central Basin has a volume of 274 km³ and an average residence time of 28 months, so there the minimum average hydraulic flow is 0.45 cm sec⁻¹. The East Basin, with a volume of 166 km³ and a water residence time of 11 months, has a minimum hydraulic flow of 0.4 cm sec⁻¹. Due to variable bottom topography, friction, thermal stratification, and the earth's rotation, the actual distribution of hydraulic flow may not be uniform, with some currents being substantially faster than the average in places (Hamblin 1971).

B. Wind-driven Currents

1. Are caused by wind stress on water surface.

2. Vary in direction according to wind direction.

3. Move faster on the surface at speeds up to 2 to 3 percent of the speed of the wind.

4. Decrease in velocity with increasing depth.

5. Move large volumes of water in a short period of time.

6. Often have subsurface return flow associated with them.
7. Are modified by Coriolis Force, remnant currents, basin topography, air and water temperatures, and characteristics of the wind.

The principal source of mechanical energy to lakes is the wind. In addition to causing waves, the frictional drag of the wind on the water surface actually drives the surface lake water in the general direction of the wind at a speed that is characteristically about 2 percent of the wind speed (Wetzel 1975). Since large volumes of water are moved downwind, there has to be a return flow to keep the lake surface more or less level. These return flows usually occur in the center of the lake at an intermediate depth and in an opposite direction to the surface wind-driven currents. In Lake Erie the wind-driven currents are modified by the Coriolis Force, a consequence of the earth's rotation causing the currents to flow in a direction to the right of the wind direction. Wind-driven currents flowing toward the east are deflected toward the south shore for example, and the resultant accummulation of water in that area causes an alongshore current to flow parallel to the shore in an easterly direction.

    C. Littoral Currents
       1. Are generated by breaking waves in the nearshore zone.
       2. Have movement generally parallel to shoreline (controlled by nearshore topography).
       3. Have direction at an angle to prevailing wind or waves.
       4. Have rapid velocity (up to 125 cm/sec).
       5. Are capable of transporting sand and gravel-sized particles (littoral drift).
       6. Operate usually within 500m of the shoreline.
       7. Dissipate rapidly when storms subside.

The nature of littoral drift currents in Lake Erie has already been described in Chapter 4.

    D. Nearshore Currents
       1. Occur between 1 and 10 km offshore.
       2. Are strong (15–20 cm sec^{-1}), parallel to shore, and persist in one direction for days.
       3. Direction can reverse following major changes in wind systems.
       4. Characterized by complex mechanisms, but main cause is the existence of boundaries in a lake; offshore flows encountering shorelines are the common cause of nearshore currents.

The nearshore current regime in Lake Erie has not been investigated in depth. Most recent data suggests that the coastal boundary layer in which the nearshore currents flow is thinner in the Central Basin than in

Lake Ontario, being between 1 to 6 km offshore (F.M. Boyce personal communication). These coastal currents are usually persistent and are able to flow against the wind for a brief period after a major change in the wind direction. Thereafter, the flow usually ceases and commences again in the opposite direction so that it is shore-parallel and approximately aligned with the new wind direction. Because the summer winds in Lake Erie prevail from the west, the nearshore currents are usually easterly. The direction of nearshore currents is more variable in the other three seasons, because the major winds are more variable. Mixing characteristics in the nearshore zone are significantly different from those offshore, in that lateral mixing in the coastal currents is generally very feeble during periods of persistent flow. As a result, obvious plumes of discharged material can often be seen. During the periods of reversal of current direction, however, very rapid mixing between nearshore and offshore waters can occur.

    E. Seiche Currents
         1. Flow when standing waves are suddenly created by changing wind conditions.
         2. Are degenerated by bottom and interfacial friction.
         3. Have minimum velocity at areas of maximum vertical displacement of lake surface.
         4. Have maximum velocity at zone of minimum displacement of lake surface.
         5. Accomplish no net transport of water (balanced by to-and-fro motion).
         6. Occur in different flow patterns in stratified and unstratified lakes.

Closed basins of water act as mechanical oscillators. The sloshing motion in a large, shallow pan of water after it has been moved is an example of such a natural oscillation. This type of motion occurs frequently in lakes and is called a seiche. Seiches are caused most readily by sudden changes in the wind blowing over the lake either at the onset or after the passage of a storm. Seiche motions appear at both the surface and at the thermocline, since this acts as a free surface between the warm and cold waters.

When a strong wind begins to blow down a lake, the wind-driven currents moving down the lake pile up at the shoreline and increase the water level in that area dramatically. The water level at the other end of the lake drops by a corresponding amount. This starts the seiche process in motion (the sequence of events is illustrated in Figure 5.3). The lake level increases initially and then drops as the free surface wave oscillates back and forth across the basin, until the new equilibrium water level, caused by the wind, is attained at the downwind end of the lake. When the wind stops blowing, the seiche oscillations repeat themselves as the lake levels equilibrate to

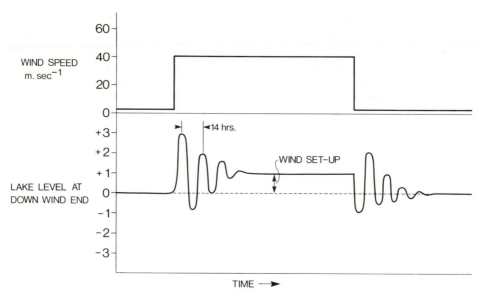

Figure 5.3 Free surface seiches at one end of the lake, showing half the total set-up that develops when the wind conditions become steady. The other half of the set-up is at the upwind end of the lake, where the lake level has dropped below normal. Lake level is shown in meters.

normal. These oscillations can pass through a number of cycles that, in Lake Erie, have periods of almost 14 hours. The difference between the level of the high water at the downwind end and the low water at the upwind end is called the lake set-up. The Buffalo minus Toledo set-up has been as great as 4.0m (Platzman 1963).

F. Hypolimnion Currents
    1. Are generated by thermocline depression or elevation as a result of
        a. wind set-up and internal seiche,
        b. sinking water masses,
        c. upwelling water masses, and
        d. counterflow due to surface currents.
    2. Normally have low velocity, but can have high velocities capable of resuspending bottom sediments.
    3. Occur only in summer when lake is stratified (restricted to hypolimnion by thermocline).

Lake set-ups affect hypolimnion (i.e., bottom) waters considerably. When epilimnion (i.e., surface) waters pile up at the downwind end of the lake, they depress the thermocline, causing the hypolimnion waters to move to the upwind end. When the wind stops, the surface waters oscillate back and forth while the hypolimnion waters tend to move back to their equilibrium position.

When strong wind-driven currents flow steadily in one direction, a return flow occurs at depth in the opposite direction to compensate for the volume of water moved. In the Central Basin this return flow occurs in the lower epilimnion and in the hypolimnion.

G. Inertial Currents
    1. Caused by the rotation of the earth (Coriolis Force).
    2. Water particles tend to move horizontally in clockwise circular orbit, initially to the right of suddenly applied forces in the Northern Hemisphere, with a period that depends on latitude. Actual flow patterns are very nearly circular offshore, but become increasingly elliptical nearer the shore because the onshore/offshore components are reduced.
    3. Occur at depths and in all seasons as well as under ice cover.

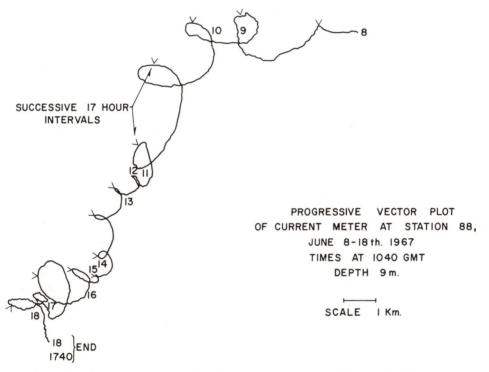

Figure 5.4 A progressive vector plot of a current meter sited 40 km north of Cleveland near the center of the Central Basin. The inertial current rotates through 360° approximately every 17 hours (Hamblin 1971). GMT means Greenwich Mean Time; the record ends at 1740 GMT on 18th June.

If a mass of water is given a strong push by a wind that stops suddenly, its inertia will cause the water to continue to move in a straight line. Because the earth is rotating, a particle attempting to move in a straight line in space actually describes a curved path on the earth's surface. The path followed by the water will seem to have veered to the right in the Northern Hemisphere, apparently deflected by the Coriolis Force (see B on page 66). The effects of the earth's rotation are pronnounced in large lakes and are strongly apparent in Lake Erie. Mid-lake surface currents responding to a sudden wind have a strong rotary component; water particles return close to their point of origin in an inertial period, approximately 18 hours in Lake Erie. (This should not be confused with the primary seiche period of 14 hours.) Hamblin (1971) shows a dramatic example of inertial currents recorded by a current meter in the middle of the Central Basin (Figure 5.4).

II. HORIZONTAL AND VERTICAL CIRCULATION

    A. Density Currents
        1. Are the result of density differences between water masses.
        2. Have density differences caused by temperature, by dissolved solid content, and by suspended material content.
        3. Density differences affect distribution of tributary inputs, which can
            a. underrun lake water when incoming water is more dense than lake water (turbidity current), or
            b. override lake water when incoming water is less dense than lake water.
        4. Cause lakeward progression of thermal bar in the later stages of its existence.

These phenomena are largely self-explanatory, except for the thermal bar. This feature occurs in the spring parallel to the shoreline, where warm inshore surface waters mix with colder offshore waters. The region where the cooler and warmer waters meet to create a mix at 4°C is called the thermal bar. Since water at 4°C has a greater density than either warmer or colder water, this dense water sinks to join the hypolimnion and the thermal bar progresses toward the center of the lake. The duration of the thermal bar depends on the mass of cold water in the center of the lake. It lasts only for a few days in the East Basin of Lake Erie, but for months in Lake Superior because of the lake's large size.

    B. Downwelling and Upwelling Currents
        1. Sinking currents are caused by the convergence of horizontal currents on the downwind shore of a lake forcing a downward movement of water to create a level surface.

2. Upwelling currents are caused by divergences of horizontal currents resulting in an upward movement to level the surface at the upwind end of the lake.
3. Local convective downwelling may be caused by rapid surface cooling, particularly in the fall. Downwelling can also occur in early spring during the warming period before a water temperature of 4°C is reached.

In summer the windward (upwind) side of the lake usually has colder water, because water has welled up from below to replace the warmer surface water blown before the wind. The downwind shore then enjoys the warmest water. On occasion, the interaction of the force and direction of wind with the configuration of the lake can cause upwellings of such magnitude that hypolimnion waters come to the surface. This has been recorded in the Central Basin between Long Point and Rondeau (Blanton and Winklhofer 1972). During the spring, downwelling convection cells keep lake waters isothermal until the lake has warmed to 4°C. Summer thermal stratification usually starts when this temperature has been reached. Convection cells in September and October also cause the rapid cooling of the lake at that time of year.

C. Langmuir Circulations
    1. Are wind-and-wave–induced vertical circulation cells.
    2. Commence with wind speeds of 2 to 3m sec^{-1} (7 to 10 km hr^{-1}), and convection cells increase in diameter with wind speed.
    3. Consist of horizontal vortices of circulating water aligned to the wind.
    4. Are visible due to lines of convergence at zones of downwelling (streaks), with upwelling between the streaks.

Langmuir vortices consist of alternately rotating horizontal vortices of water with the axes of the vortices lying parallel to the wind. Streaks of foam and floating material form on the surface where the downwelling waters meet (Wetzel 1975). These complex circulations are a common phenomenon, and the characteristic streaks are seen on all water bodies, from ponds to oceans, if wind is blowing. There has been no published research on these circulations in Lake Erie, but they are probably involved in creating the isothermal epilimnia common in Lake Erie during the summer. In this regard, Boyce (1974) writes that "the time scale of complete vertical mixing in a Great Lake's summer epilimnion under moderate winds, is only a few hours."

D. Turbulence
    1. Has random motion with horizontal and vertical components.

2. Is associated with other types of currents (particularly with wind-driven and wave-generated currents).
3. Is effective in mixing and dispersing water masses.

Almost all water movements in lakes and rivers are turbulent, consisting of an organized motion upon which is superimposed a random component. The distinction between random and organized motion depends often on the point of view and in particular on the time or length scales used to average out the fluctuations. Over any brief period of time, a wind or a current moves in a definite direction, and one can calculate the advective transport in the specific direction associated with the wind or current. Over a longer period of time, however, the wind and thus the current directions will change and cover many points of the compass. In this case, the water will have moved in all directions and mixed, so that the water movement could be described as diffusive transport if the overall advective transport in one direction has been minimal. Boyce and Hamblin (1975) have examined in some detail the idea that diffusive transport is a function of time. They concluded that over periods of a year or so, transport in the Central Basin can be considered as a diffusional process superimposed on the basic hydraulic flow, and that the horizontal diffusion coefficient in this case has a value of approximately 1.5×10^6 cm^2 sec^{-1}. They suggest that the diffusion pattern of material released from the shore of the Central Basin would be in an equilibrium state about two months after a continuous release had commenced.

III. WAVES

A. Surface Waves
1. Increase in height with water depth, fetch, and duration of wind, reaching a steady-state value.
2. Move horizontally at relatively high speeds (depending on wave length and water depth) of up to tens of m sec^{-1}. Net displacement of the water particles is small, consisting of a slow drift of surface water in the direction of wave propagation. Once a wave has broken, the white water then moves at the speed of the wave.
3. Will break in shallow water when water depth is less than half the wave length, moving water in the direction of the wave.

"Wave heights in excess of 5m are not uncommonly generated within the East Basin of the lake and maximum wave heights may possibly exceed 7m under severe conditions" (Sly 1976). This statement may be checked to some degree with a commonly applied empirical formula for maximum steady-state wave height,

$$H = 0.105 \sqrt{x}$$

where x is the distance of the fetch in centimeters (Wetzel 1975). The length of Lake Erie (fetch) is 388 km, and the equation gives a value of 6.5m for H, indicating that the wave heights generated are normal. Figure 5.5 illustrates the size of waves in Lake Erie by showing a photograph taken from the after-structure of a large lake steamer in heavy weather.

When there is no surface current, water undergoing wave motion does not move forward, but in circles as shown in Figure 5.6. The cycloid (diameter), h, halves for every increase in depth equal to $1 \div 9$ (l = wave length). Waves in deep water experience no interaction with the bottom, but when the water shallows to about half the wave length, the wave motions are affected by the bottom and the cycloidal motions are transformed into back-and-forth movements along the bottom. Waves have h:l ratios varying between 1:100 and 1:10; when they reach a steepness of 1:10 they do not become steeper, but start to form whitecaps and will break if the water becomes shallow enough. This means, for example, that a wave with a height of 1m and a steepness of 1:50 could begin to experience bottom effects in 25m of water, which is the maximum depth of the Central Basin. Winds of 25 knots (45 km hr^{-1}) are common on Lake Erie and, after blowing for only a few hours, generate waves of a meter or more in height with large whitecaps. These waves would be large enough to "feel" the bottom over much of the basin and steepen up. If the winds continue, this tendency will spread to deeper areas as the waves become higher and the wave lengths longer. Indeed, Lake Erie has the reputation among sailors and commercial fishermen of being able to develop rough, steep seas in a short time.

B. Internal Waves
    1. Propagate along the thermocline.
    2. Have wave lengths from tens to hundreds of meters and periods of minutes to hours.
    3. Are caused by epilimnion and hypolimnion seiche currents moving in opposing directions; also by changes in bottom topography.

Internal waves are known to exist in the Central Basin, because the thermocline has been seen to oscillate vertically up or down by over a meter or two in a few minutes; but this research has not yet been published. The research findings on internal waves in Lake Ontario cannot be extrapolated to Lake Erie because of the difference in depth of the two lakes.

Possibly the most important aspect of internal waves is that they can break (Mortimer 1961) and mix epilimnion and thermocline water, on the one hand, and thermocline and hypolimnion water, on the other. This

Figure 5.5 A view from the afterstructure of the freighter "W. H. Truesdale" on Lake Erie in the 1930s. The ship is of a similar size to that shown in Figure 2.2, and since the deck is under water this picture illustrates the size of the waves that can occur. (Centre for Archival Collections—BGSU.)

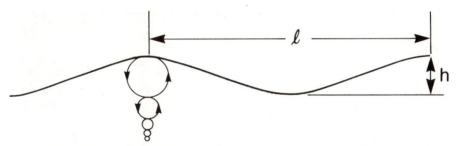

Figure 5.6 The pattern of movement of water particles during the passage of a wave (l is the wave length and h is the wave height). The decrease in the cycloid diameter of water movement with depth is also shown.

breaking of internal waves beneath the surface of a lake can occur when the epilimnion and hypolimnion currents are strong and cause excessive shear forces across the thermocline, which leads to internal waves of large amplitude. These waves become unstable and break and thus cause mixing of water from adjacent layers.

General Flow Patterns

With all the different forces described above causing different water movements, it is obvious that there is no single pattern of flow in Lake Erie, although there may be a dominant average one. By examining the results of studies on surface drift cards, bottom drifters, and current meters, Hamblin (1971) has been able to infer the general circulation patterns in Lake Erie. The Detroit River flow has considerable momentum and sweeps far south, but is unable to proceed eastward because of the many reefs and islands blocking this flow. Pelee Passage, north of Pelee Island, is relatively open and deep, and most of the Detroit flow veers north and passes into the Central Basin through this opening, as shown in Figure 5.7 (*top*). The open-water surface flow moves south-easterly toward the southern shore, creating the southshore easterly drift. At a number of places one should note that the offshore currents flow in the opposite direction to the littoral drift, as can be seen just west of Cleveland. This is because the forces driving littoral currents are quite different from those driving the nearshore and offshore currents.

Since the surface easterly flow is much greater than the hydraulic flow, there has to be a return of water to the west. This occurs offshore at intermediate depths. Since the surface drift has a southerly component, a compensatory, northerly return flow is required and occurs close to the bottom, as shown in Figure 5.7 (*bottom*), and has been confirmed by Hartley (1968).

While drift cards give the overall pattern of surface movement, they do not give any detail of surface flow under different wind conditions. Current

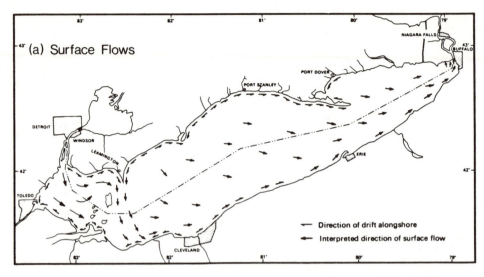

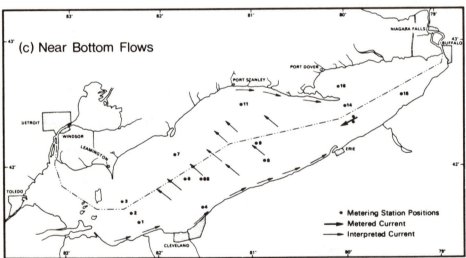

Figure 5.7 General circulation patterns at the surface and near the bottom in Lake Erie. (International Lake Erie Water Pollution Board 1969.) Not shown: flow at intermediate depths.

meters cannot give information on surface flow or flow in shallow water because of the interferring effects of wave motion on the current meters. They do give data on flow at greater depths, but many hundreds of these expensive meters would have to be deployed if detailed patterns of flow were required. Luckily, the science of hydrodynamic modeling is now sufficiently advanced to enable the estimation of flows at different depths and numerous positions in the lake. These estimated flows can be checked by setting current meters at appropriate sites in the lake and comparing computed flows with observed flows. The computation of water movements is considered in the Appendix.

MERCURY AS AN INDICATOR OF FLOW PATTERNS

Persistent current patterns can often be ascertained more easily from a study of the sediments than from a study of instantaneous currents, which are normally very variable. The distribution of sediment in a lake can be used as an indicator of prevailing currents, since the distribution depends on the currents as well as on the source and nature of the sediment materials.

Thomas and Jaquet (1976) have made a study of the levels of mercury contaminating the sediments of Lake Erie. They found that the mercury was strongly associated with the organic carbon in the sediments and was probably deposited in association with organic carbon. The pattern of mercury concentration clearly marks the Detroit River as the main source of mercury (see [1] in Figure 5.8). The long west-to-east trail of 1000 to 2000 p.p.b. concentrations from near Pt. Pellee to Presque Isle (2) indicates the main flow path from the West Basin through Pelee passage to the south shore of the Central Basin. Two areas of high concentration (labeled 3) indicate areas of backflow to the west from Erie, Pennsylvania, and Buffalo, New York. The other high concentration area (4) probably indicates the depositional zone for waste materials from Cleveland. The low concentration south of Point Pelee (5) is the Pelee moraine, an area of sand bottom that is kept clear of sedimented materials by strong currents.

SEDIMENT SOURCES, SORTING, AND DEPOSITION

Shoreline erosion is the main source of sediment to Lake Erie. Kemp et al. (1976) estimated erosion of shoreline during the high-water years of 1970 to 1974 to be approximately 25.7 million tons per year. In a later study, Kemp, McInnes, and Harper (1977) determined that the long-term average rate of shoreline erosion was approximately 7.9 million tons per year, as shown in Table 5.1. These materials consist mainly of silt (particle diameters between 4 and 60 microns (μm) and fine clays (less than 4μm), with some sand (60 to 1000 μm) and gravel. A considerable load of fine-grained material comes into the lake from rivers, as well. The West Basin gets most of its sediment load from rivers, while the Central and East Basins derive their load largely from the shorelines. The Detroit River carries a large load that originates in the Ontario farmlands, flows via the Thames River to Lake St. Clair, and thence via the Detroit into Lake Erie (Thomas, Jaquet, and Mudroch 1975).

Once the shoreline has been eroded and rivers have brought sediment into the lake, the primary sorting action on the sediment is done by wave action. Large surface waves cause the water near the bottom to oscillate back and forth, with the magnitude of the oscillation increasing with shallowness and wave height. This action resuspends the smaller particles

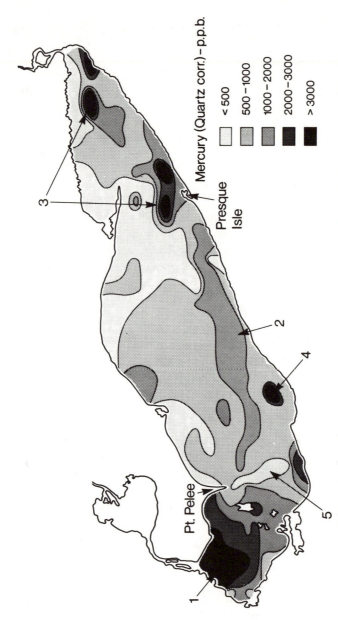

Figure 5.8 Distribution of quartz-corrected mercury in the surficial 3 cm of sediment in Lake Erie. The specially numbered features are explained in the text (p.p.m. = parts per billion or µg of mercury per kg sediment). (Thomas and Jaquet 1976.)

Table 5.1 Estimated Quantity of Clay and Silt-Sized Sediment Inputs from Various Sources

Source	Zone	Yield of fine-grained material per annum (million metric tons)
Shoreline erosion	Detroit River to Point Pelee	0.1
	Point Pelee to Rondeau	0.2
	Rondeau to Long Point	5.2
	Long Point to Niagara River	0.2
	Michigan shoreline	0.1
	Ohio shoreline	1.6
	Pennsylvania shoreline	0.4
	New York shoreline	0.1
	Total	7.9
River inputs	Detroit River	1.4
	Maumee River	1.8
	Other rivers	0.9
	Total	4.1
Airborne particles		0.5
Autochthonous organic matter		1.0
Dredged spoils		1.4

Source: Kemp, McInnes, and Harper 1977.

and leaves the larger ones on the bottom. Currents then move the resuspended fine particles to areas of lower turbulence where they settle out, either temporarily or permanently.

The pattern of sediment and bottom types in Lake Erie is complex, as shown in Figure 5.9. Nearly all post-glacial sedimentation has occurred in the soft mud (M) and mud mixed with silt and sand (SM) areas of the Central and East Basins. In the West Basin the effect of the loading of the two rivers is large enough to cause permanent sedimentation over all areas except the reefs that show bedrock. The area close to the eroded Central Basin northshore bluffs, GL (glacial sediments), is devoid of modern sediments because of the high wave energy and strong currents in that area. The modern material eroded from the bluffs first settles there initially but is later resuspended, transported, and finally deposited in the main part of the Central Basin or the East Basin.

Sedimentation Rates

Two different methods can be used to date Great Lakes sediments. One uses the pollen of different plant species that have been preserved in the sediment, and the other uses the distribution of radionuclides in sediments. Pollen can be preserved in sediments for long periods and can act as

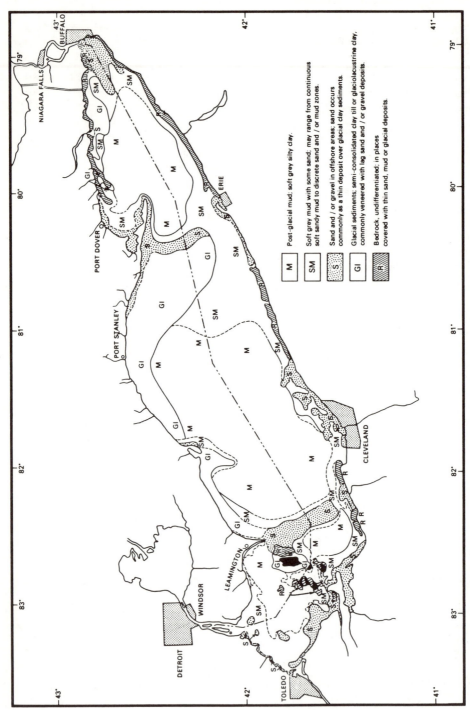

Figure 5.9 Distribution of surficial sediment types in Lake Erie. (International Lake Erie Water Pollution Board 1969.)

reference points in time. If a sudden appearance or disappearance of a plant species in the basin of the lake was recorded, then the position of appearance or disappearance of that species of pollen in the lake sediments sets a date for that horizon in the sediment record. While colonists began to settle in the Lake Erie Basin in the early 1800s, extensive areas of land were not cleared until about 1850. This clearing removed much of the pine and led to a large increase in the amount of ragweed (*Ambrosia*), which is reflected by a decrease in the amount of pine (*Pinus*) pollen found in lake sediments along with an increase in the amount of *Ambrosia* pollen (Kemp, McInnes, and Harper 1977; McAndrews 1976). The layered sediments of Crawford Lake, northwest of Lake Ontario, enabled Boyko (1973) to date the *Ambrosia* horizon at about 1850.

In the same way, the distribution pattern of certain radionuclides permits dates to be associated with certain levels in the sediments. The radioactive isotope ^{137}Cs began to settle out of the atmosphere in the 1950s as a result of nuclear tests carried out at that time. Its appearance in the sediment marks the horizon of A.D. 1952 ± 2, and its half-life of 30.2 yr means that it will be present in relative abundance for some time to come. The other isotope yielding much information is ^{210}Pb, and its use has been described by Robbins, Edgington, and Kemp (1978):

> Geochronology with ^{210}Pb is based on a different principle. This naturally occurring member of the ^{238}U series is a decay product of radon present in the atmosphere and is added to sediments of the Great Lakes at a practically constant rate. The determination of a sedimentation rate in this case does not involve the identification of a horizon, but is based on the continuing decay of the isotope (which has a half-life of 22.3 yr) after burial (Robbins, 1978). This method is in principle able to reveal much more detail about the sedimentation process than methods involving discrete time markers.

The sedimentation rates for Lake Erie determined by ^{210}Pb (Robbins, Edgington, and Kemp 1978) are more accurate than those based on pollen dating (Kemp, McInness, and Harper 1977) because the assignment of the *Ambrosia* pollen horizon in a core can be uncertain. Also, in some cases, the decline of *Pinus* pollen in the sample cores is not coincident with the rise of *Ambrosia* pollen. Nevertheless, there is basic agreement in the sedimentation rates calculated by the two methods, with the ^{210}Pb rates being 10 to 20 percent greater than those based on pollen horizons.

Linear sedimentation rates are very variable since they are dependent on the water content of the sediment, which is not constant; thus the weight deposited per unit area is a more constant measure of sedimentation rate. Some of the results of Kemp, McInnes, and Harper (1977) study are shown in Figure 5.9 and are extensive enough to permit estimation of average sedimentation rates for the depositional parts of the basins. These rates are:

West Basin	2100 g m^{-2} yr, or approximately 3.1 mm yr^{-1}
Central Basin	580 g m^{-2} yr, or approximately 1.5 mm yr^{-1}
East Basin	1340 g m^{-2} yr, or approximately 3.0 mm yr^{-1}

Robbins, Edgington, and Kemp (1978) estimate the sedimentation rate in the deep area of the East Basin (Stn M32, Fig. 5.10) to be 14 mm yr^{-1}. In addition, Kemp, McInness, and Harper (1977) estimate the sedimentation rate to be greater than 7 mm yr^{-1} near the mouths of the Detroit and Maumee Rivers (Fig. 5.10). These are probably the highest sedimentation rates in offshore areas in any of the Great Lakes.

Perhaps the most significant aspect of ^{210}Pb geochronology is that it enables missing parts of the sediment record to be identified and dated. Robbins, Edgington, and Kemp (1978) found parts missing from the sediment record for the three cores they studied taken at M32, G16 and U42 (see Fig. 5.10). The data from M32 showed a break in the core at 15 cm depth, representing a loss of sediment in A.D. 1960 ± 2. At G16, perturbations in the sediment profile were observed at depths corresponding to A.D. 1956 ± 3, 1943 ± 3, and 1903 ± 4; and at U42, at depths corresponding to A.D. 1964 ± 3, 1918 ± 3, and 1862 ± 7. Except for 1964, these dates correspond to storms recorded in the Great Lakes area in 1958, 1940, 1918, 1916, 1905 and 1860 (U.S. Weather Service, Murty and Palovarapu, 1975). On this basis Robbins, Edgington and Kemp interpret the anomalies in the cores they examined to be due to sediment lost or disturbed during one or the other of these storm events.

It is difficult to believe that a storm would remove a large amount of sediment from the sediment surface at a depth of 58 m at M32, but this evidence is basically in accordance with the information on bottom effects of waves presented earlier in this chapter. Large storm waves in the East Basin *can* cause orbital velocities capable of resuspending the sediment in the deeper parts of the East Basin. Using nomograms developed by Donelan (1980), one can estimate that a westerly wind of 40 knots (20m sec^{-1}) blowing down the axis of the lake for 10 hrs would generate maximum wave heights of 7.2m in the East Basin. These waves could generate orbital velocities of approximately 8.0 cm sec^{-1} at 58m depth. These velocities are considerably greater than the 2 to 3 cm sec^{-1} suggested by Lam and Jaquet (1976) as being the orbital velocities capable of resuspending sediments. Further, a storm of this magnitude would generate strong horizontal currents, which would assist the orbital currents in disturbing the sediments.

Summary

Surface waters in Lake Erie change in temperature from 0°C to more than 25°C between winter and summer. The range for bottom waters is from 0°C to about 15°C, except for the West Basin where the waters are usually isothermal. These temperature differences, together with the many

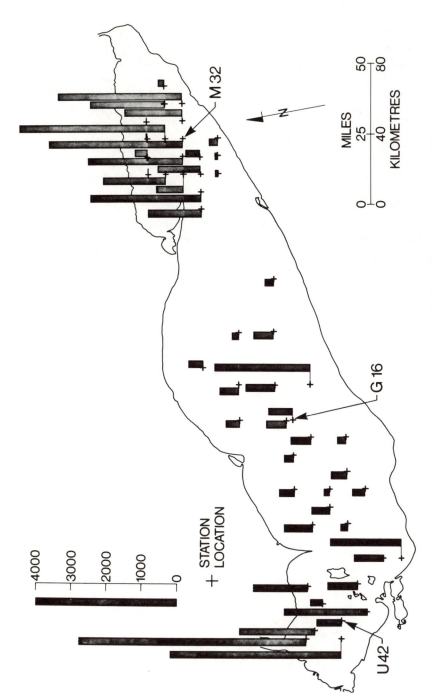

Figure 5.10 Distribution of present-day sedimentation rates in Lake Erie, showing the location of three important sampling stations (Kemp, McInnes, and Harper 1977). Sedimentation rates are in grams meter^{-2} year^{-1}.

other factors that affect water movements, result in about thirteen different types of currents occurring in the lake. The study of water movements is thus a complex matter, with the actual currents flowing usually resulting from the combination of a number of individual forces. The determination of dominant current patterns is simplified somewhat by the study of sediment distribution patterns in the lake. Chemical tracers absorbed on sediment outline some of the major pathways. Some cores have parts of the sediment record missing, but dating techniques have permitted the period of sediment disappearance to be determined. In nearly all cores, these dates cover a period when a major storm occurred, whose waves, sometimes acting to surprising depths, are considered to have dispersed the missing sediment. Water movement and sediment studies augment each other and are important in lake ecology because these physical phenomena to a large extent control the nature of biological communities. The location of plant and animal types depends on current velocities, temperature, sediment texture, and water turbidity. The supply and distribution of plant nutrients to parts of the lake also control the nature of the attached and floating plants.

6

Loading of Nutrient and Non-toxic Materials to the Lake

Sediment is not the only material to have accumulated in Lake Erie in excess quantities through the actions of man. Salts, phosphorus and nitrogen compounds, pathogenic bacteria, and toxic chemicals have all entered the lake in increasing quantities since development in the drainage basin of the lake began. This chapter discusses the problems associated with the increased loading of bacteria, salts, and plant nutrients into the lake.

Nearshore Pollution

During the last century, wells and other sources of water in or near the big cities in the Great Lakes area became contaminated with human and animal wastes. Severe cholera outbreaks in the middle of the last century convinced municipal officials to build sewers to drain wastes away from the populated areas. These wastes went untreated into the nearest river or bay; in fact, it is likely that the rivers were more contaminated with bacteria before the turn of the century, when there were no primary treatment plants, than they are today.

The first intensive investigations of the harbors and nearshore areas in Lake Erie were undertaken in 1929 and 1930 by Fish and Associates (1960) and Wright (1955). They found evidence of pollution in most of the harbors and rivers running into the lake, but found almost nothing detectable in the lake except at two stations: one about 5 km from the Grand River at

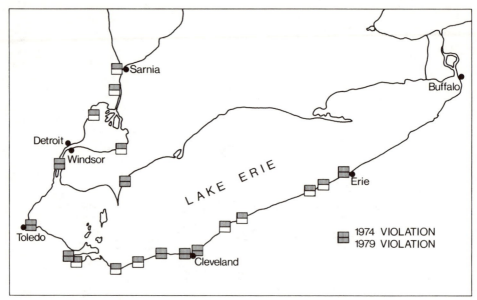

Figure 6.1 Sites where unacceptable concentrations of bacteria have been observed. (Great Lakes Water Quality Board 1976, 1980.)

Fairport, the other about 8 km from the Maumee River at Toledo (C.J. Munter in Fish and Associates 1960). At that time the cities were much smaller than today, so contaminant loads were small. By 1960, however, the problem was far more widespread, with "approximately one third of the United States–Lake Erie shoreline either continuously or intermittently fouled by bacterial contamination" (U.S. FWPCA 1968).

The situation improved considerably after 1972 following the increase in wastewater treatment plant construction. But in 1979 there were still eight areas around Lake Erie with major violations of the Great Lakes Water Quality Agreement standard of 1000 coliform or 200 fecal coliform bacteria per 100 ml of water (Fig. 6.1, Great Lakes Water Quality Board 1980). The main cause was the rain and melted snow drained from city streets by storm sewers. Often untreated before being emptied into the lake, these waters could be badly contaminated by the wastes of pets and birds. While in some cities the storm and sanitary sewers are combined, and therefore treated for much of the year, in times of heavy storms this type of system becomes badly overloaded. Treatment plant operators are then forced to let out large quantities of incompletely treated sewage (PLUARG 1978). This situation obviously requires correction, even though its solution is expensive.

Major Ions

Salts leached out of the soil flow down rivers into lakes and oceans. Rough estimates of the early chloride concentrations indicate only a slight increase

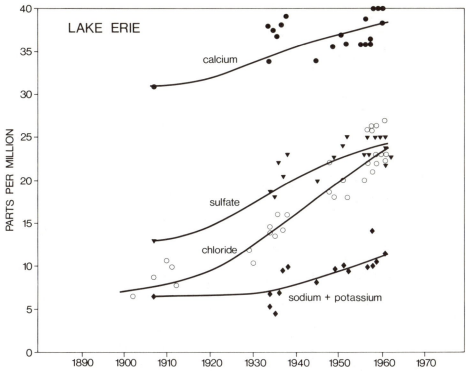

Figure 6.2 Increases in concentrations of different ions in Lake Erie since the turn of the century. (Beeton 1965.)

from Lake Superior to Lake Erie of from 3 g m^{-3} to 8 g m^{-3}, as the waters moved down the Great Lakes chain at the turn of the century. Since then all the lakes except Superior have undergone concentration increases. Lake Erie has shown the most dramatic increase, with Lake Ontario's increase largely being a result of the concentration increase in Lake Erie. A number of the other ions from salts released by industry have also increased in concentration with time, as shown in Figure 6.2.

The patterns in the distribution maps for chloride, sulfate, and calcium (Fig. 6.3 a,b,c) show the sites at which the different ions enter the lake. Chloride is primarily brought into Lake Erie in the water flowing along the eastern bank of the Detroit River, as a by-product of the table-salt refining industries there. (The ancient oceans that once occupied the area left deep deposits of salt and petroleum.) Chloride is continually added to the water as it moves along the south shore, with the Grand River at Fairport, Ohio, constituting a major source. An industry on this river has released such large amounts of salts that concentrations of greater than 1000 g m^{-3} have been observed. Official action has caused the industry to clean up, so that chloride concentrations have been slightly reduced to 300 ± 225 g m^{-3} in 1980 (U.S. Geological Survey 1980).

Sulfate appears to be more concentrated in the west side of the Detroit

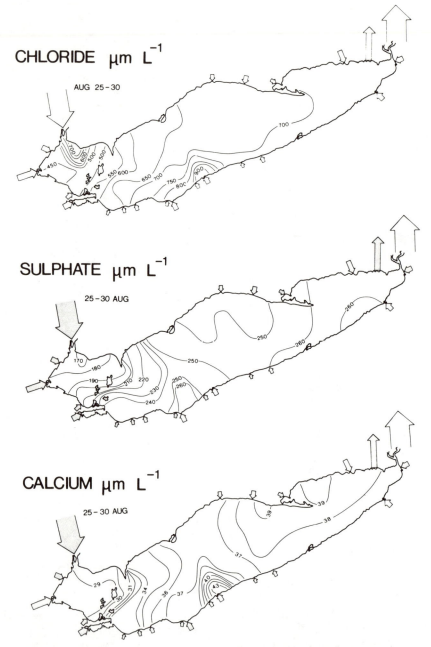

Figure 6.3 Distribution patterns of chloride, sulphate, and clacium ions observed in Lake Erie during 1970. (Burns, Rosa, and Chan 1976.) Units are micromoles of ion per liter.

River and off Cleveland. These concentrations probably reflect the release of sulphuric acid from the steel-making industries in the two cities. Calcium increases gradually from west to east along the lake, except for a concentration increase at the Grand River, Ohio, because of the release of calcium chloride at that point.

The observed concentration of salts in Lake Erie is also dependent on the quantity of water flowing through the lake, since the larger flows cause a greater dilution of the inputs. Thus in 1967, when the average Detroit River flow was 5.39×10^3 m^3 sec^{-1}, the lake average chloride concentration was estimated at 25.2 g m^{-3}. In 1973, when the average flow was higher at approximately 6.73×10^3 m^3 sec^{-1}, the corresponding Cl concentration was lower at 22.7 g m^{-3} (Bennett 1976). These changes in water flow have to be kept in mind when comparing concentrations of conservative substances loaded into the lake.

Problems from Nutrient Overloading

Plant nutrients are essential to all the living things in a lake, since they provide the base of the food web. Nevertheless, too great a loading of nutrients into a natural water system can cause large shifts in the nature of the plant community, which in turn affects all the biota in the system, often to their detriment. This has happened to an alarming degree in Lake Erie, because there has been a massive increase in the amount of nutrients loaded into the system. The process of increasing the fertility of the waters of a lake is called eutrophication and is a widespread problem in the Great Lakes and elsewhere in the world.

Most of the water sampling and research on eutrophication in the Great Lakes is done from large ships. Thus studies have concentrated on the offshore areas that are accessible to the larger research vessels, while the nearshore zone has been neglected. This policy is now being reversed, and much more attention is being paid to the nearshore zone, the area to which the majority of people living around a large lake have access. As explained by Beeton and Edmondson (1972), these zones are the most affected by excessive loading and must be studied because

> In very large lakes, the inshore areas are affected first by increased nutrient loading, and gradually offshore waters are altered. Inshore areas of Lake Erie, Michigan, and Ontario are more eutrophic than offshore waters. Sufficient data were collected in the early and recent surveys of Lake Erie to demonstrate that the inshore waters were first affected by pollution. As the pollution loading continually increased, eutrophication progressed from inshore to offshore.

By the same reasoning, when nutrient loadings are decreased, the larger improvements will be first noticed in inshore regions, particularly those closest to the source of loading.

The results of nutrient oversupply depend on the nature of the area involved. Exposed shorelines of clean rocks become covered with increasingly thicker growths of the attached alga, *Cladophora*, with offshore rocky ledges and boulders supporting growths to depths of four meters in Lake Erie (Neil and Owen 1964). As these plants mature, they break off from their points of attachment during storms and sink to the bottom or wash ashore. In particular, *Cladophora* accumulates on the rocks and nearby beaches, with the results graphically described by Fetteroff (1975):

> I wish I could inundate you with pictures: pictures of deserted bathing beaches covered with layers of rotting *Cladophora* instead of bathers; pictures of bulldozers pushing *Cladophora* into mountains; pictures of front-end loaders scooping *Cladophora* and loading trucks for disposal elsewhere or burial on the beach, and the yellow-brown dried crust of rotting *Cladophora* stretching along the beaches in front of otherwise-desirable lake front cottages. The only stimulus needed to complete your abhorrence of the situation would be the accompanying flies and pig-pen odor which go hand in hand with rotting protein.

Nearshore nutrient levels are high enough to support extensive growths of *Cladophora* along much of Lake Erie's shoreline. Fortunately, many of the nearshore areas do not suffer from *Cladophora* problems, because the eroding banks do not provide suitable rocky substrates for growth of the alga. The West and East Basins do have rocky areas, however, and do suffer from the problem. In the East Basin, accumulations 16m wide and 0.75m deep have been observed on some beaches (Neil and Owen 1964). Sandy spawning areas often exist close to the rocky areas, and the algae, detached from the rocks, settle in these areas and suffocate fish eggs that have been laid there.

The smell and ugliness of rotting piles of *Cladophora* are real, but *Cladophora* has its place. It is an important part of the ecosystem and existed in the West Basin during the last century when conditions were still pristine (Taft and Kishler 1973). The filaments of the plants shelter many small invertebrates, such as gammerids, cladocerans, rotifers, molluscs, and young crayfish. These constitute an important assemblage of food for organisms such as young fish, that feed close to shore. Mallards and black ducks also feed extensively on *Cladophora* beds (Taft 1975). The desired objective should be to reduce the excess growth of *Cladophora* to levels where it is a beneficial component of the ecosystem. Small washups of *Cladophora* will always occur on beach areas where there are light growths of the alga, but this situation is no worse than finding leaves on one's lawn from trees in the garden.

Cladophora is a problem only in rocky areas, because it draws its nutrients from the water and needs the rocky substratum as an anchoring point; it cannot grow in soft sediment. In protected shoreline areas with muddy bottoms, increases in nutrient concentration usually result in increased growth of macrophytes and weeds, which obtain their nutritional requirements from both water and sediment. Sparse beds of these aquatic plants can be beneficial to fish populations, but as the growths in the shallower waters thicken to solid mats, they become undesirable. In waters of three or more meters depth, the plants first increase with increased nutrient supply, but eventually disappear as the nutrient level is increased further. At these depths the higher nutrient levels permit phytoplankton growths in the overlying water to be heavy enough to shade the rooted macrophytes growing from the sediments, causing them to die. The nutrients released by the decomposing macrophytes promote even denser phytoplankton growths, further shading the macrophytes and diminishing their population. In addition, once the macrophytes die they no longer bind the sediments, so the turbidity from resuspended mud increases the total turbidity. This makes it even more difficult for the macrophytes to reestablish. This sequence of events causes a fairly rapid replacement of rooted plants by floating phytoplankton as nutrient concentrations increase. Plant growth is not induced by high nutrient concentrations in most shoreline zones with mud bottoms, because there is no substratum for *Cladophora* attachment and the waters in Lake Erie are too turbulent for the survival of macrophytes. In this case, increased nutrient concentration causes a shift in the phytoplankton population from diatom species to blue-greens. Diatoms form a part of the food web, but blue-greens are usually not grazed by zooplankton. When increased nutrients cause heavy concentrations of blue-greens, the blue-greens affect water supplies by clogging filters and imparting a taste to the water.

If the supply of nutrients continues to increase to a level that nearshore growth processes cannot absorb, then offshore concentrations of nutrients begin to increase and changes follow in the offshore ecology. Initially there is an increase in algal biomass, often in the form of algal blooms and floating scums, together with a species shift to undesirable blue-green phytoplankton. The increased production of organic matter causes an increase in the amount of material settling to the lower waters, which then utilizes more oxygen for decomposition. In shallower lakes such as Lake Erie, this means that higher nutrient loading can cause oxygen concentrations in the colder hypolimnion waters to decrease to the point where cold-water fish species are eliminated. Also, predominant populations of benthic organisms may change from mayfly nymphs to species of sludge worms which can tolerate the lower oxygen conditions.

Nitrogen Loading

Nitrogen loadings to Lake Erie are increasing steadily. In 1976 they were estimated to be 292,000 tons, up about 45 percent from 1970 loadings (Fraser and Wilson 1981). The main cause of the higher nitrogen loading

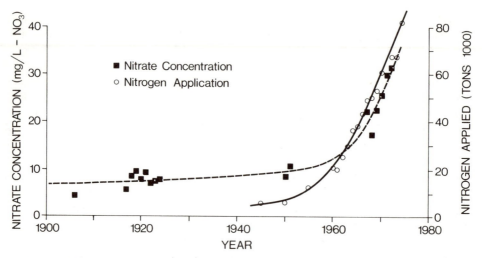

Figure 6.4 Nitrate concentrations in the Maumee River compared with the application of nitrogen fertilizers in the West Basin catchment. (Appman 1975.)

is the increased use of nitrogen fertilizers on the lands surrounding the lake. The nitrate ion is extremely soluble and is not absorbed by clay, so much of the excess nitrate drains away from the land. Ammonia is also applied, and part of the excess ammonia is oxidized by soil bacteria into nitrate. While nitrate is usually held in the ground water, it is mobilized by soaking rains, rather than by heavy rains and flash floods (Baker 1980), and then drains from the land and eventually into the lake.

Figure 6.4 shows the close relationship betwen increased use of nitrogen fertilizer in the West Basin drainage area and the increasing concentrations of nitrate in the Maumee River. The mean concentration of nitrate in the Maumee River in 1967 was 4,900 mg NO_3-N m^{-3}, almost five times the optimum nitrate drinking-water level of 1000 mg NO_3-N m^{-3} (Federal-Provincial Working Group on Drinking Water 1978). On occasion the river water concentration of nitrate plus nitrite exceeds the drinking-water standard maximum acceptable concentration of 10,000 mg of NO_3 plus NO_2 per m^3.

The ammonia concentrations of the rivers now sometimes exceed the 1000 mg NH_3-N m^{-3} level, which is well above the acute toxicity level of total ammonia for fish. Ammonia, however, can exist in two forms in water, with the un-ionized ammonia (NH_3) form present in greater abundance in alkaline waters than the ionized NH_4^+ form. Concentrations of the un-ionized form of approximately 10 mg NH_3-N m^{-3} support the growth of fungi on the gills of fish, which quickly prove fatal to the fish (Giussani, Borroni, and Grimaldi 1976). These levels of un-ionized NH_3 occur in water where the total ammonia levels are 100 to 200 mg NH_3-N m^{-3}, which are frequently exceeded in the Detroit River and Ohio tributaries to Lake Erie. Thus, concentrations of these materials in the rivers are approaching dangerous levels.

The direct loading of nitrogen nutrients to the lake from the atmosphere is also significant. This loading has been estimated at 38,000 tons N yr^{-1}, representing about 13 percent of the total nitrogen load. A large part of this load is probably due to agricultural fertilizer previously lost to the atmosphere.

Silica

The three elements for which aquatic plants have the highest requirements relative to supply are N-Si-P; nitrogen, silica, and phosphorus. Soluble silica, SiO_2, is used in large quantities to form the cell walls of the diatom species of algae (Fig. 6.5a). These phytoplankton are frequently present in greatest abundance in the Great Lakes and are one of the most important elements of the food web. Since silica is not a nutrient element vital to other species of algae, a significant decrease in silica availability can cause a swing away from populations dominated by diatoms to assemblages dominated by green, blue-green, or flagellate (Fig. 6.5b,c) species of algae. Sometimes if phosphorus levels are high, diatoms may not be capable of competing with other algae, and silica may not be depleted from the water column.

Dissolved silica is usually present in the Great Lakes in concentrations much greater than those required by diatoms. Lake Superior, for example, has mean concentrations of about 2300 mg m^{-3} of SiO_2, partly from high silica concentrations of inflowing streams. Most of the silica is returned to the water column by resuspension and redissolution of siliceous frustules of diatoms that had settled to the bottom (Nriagu 1978). Many fragmented frustules are also redissolved right in the water column at depths close to those at which the diatoms are grazed by zooplankton. Low concentrations of silica in Great Lakes waters are achieved by excessive loading of bioavailable phosphorus and nitrogen (Schelske and Stoermer 1972), such as happens in Lake Erie in the spring. This permits extensive growth of diatoms that absorb all three nutrients and then settle to the bottom, removing the nutrients from the water in the process. In summer, with the disappearance of many of the diatoms, the silica concentrations increase substantially as frustules redissolve.

The lowest relative abundance of diatoms in the lake occurs in early June, because in late May the Central and East Basins stratify. This factor causes diatom populations to decrease because their high silica content tends to make them settle faster than other algal genera (Burns and Rosa 1980). As a result, diatoms are easily lost from the relatively thin layer of warm water at the surface of a stratified lake. They survive relatively better in deep, isothermal water masses that are being circulated from top to bottom by physical processes, as they tend to keep the diatoms in suspension.

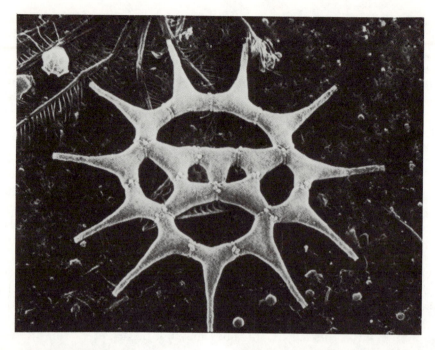

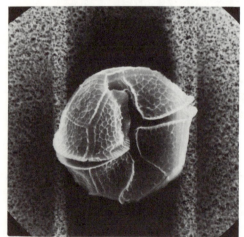 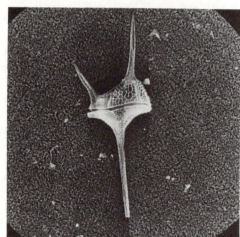

Figure 6.5 Electron microscope photographs of plankton. Top: *A diatom skeleton.* Left: *A* Peridinium *species of phytoplankton.* Right: *A* Ceratium Hirundella. (*Photo by K. Etheredge.*)

Thus in June, the combined stresses of low silica concentrations and thermal stratification severely deplete the diatom population. The data of Munawar and Munawar (1976) show that the diatoms really become dominant only after the summer, from September on, when the waters of the lake are vertically well mixed by strong winds. The non-diatom species are normally dominant during the summer, because they are less dependent on physical mixing processes to keep them in suspension.

Which Nutrient Controls Summer Growth?

Which of the remaining two nutrients, nitrogen or phosphorus, is the growth-controlling factor of the non-diatom species of phytoplankton during the summer? The answer of the International Lake Erie Water Pollution Board in 1969 was that phosphorus was responsible and that phosphorus loading to Lake Erie should be reduced immediately. This conclusion was challenged by Legge and Dingeldein (1970), who maintained that carbon, required for the formation of organic matter, and not phosphorus, was the limiting nutrient. A vigorous scientific debate resulted, with the "carbon-limiting" point of view being supported by the detergent industry. The debate is well described by Vallentyne (1974) in the *Algal Bowl*. The final outcome was that carbon availability does not limit growth, because the atmosphere provides an inexhaustible supply of carbon in the form of carbon dioxide. The conclusion that phosphorus was the nutrient limiting to growth was then accepted without further question.

Ten lakewide surveys of Lake Erie were carried out in 1970. Soluble reactive phosphorus concentrations were found to be very low over large areas of the lake during six of these surveys, from 6 May to 27 September. Nitrate and ammonia concentrations were found to be very low during only two of the surveys (Burns 1976c). The maps from the 6–10 May survey, Figure 6.6, show the distributions found and the areas of phosphate shortage, while adequate nitrate was generally present. The much higher incidence of low phosphorus concentration indicates phosphorus to have been more limiting to growth during 1970 than nitrogen.

Other data pertinent to this discussion are the relative loadings of phosphorus and nitrogen to the lake. In 1970, the phosphorus and nitrogen loadings were 23,500 and 196,700 tons yr^{-1}, at a ratio of P to N of 1:8.4 (Fraser and Wilson 1981). The P:N loading in 1978 was 1:22, and at this ratio there would be more surplus NO_3 than in 1970. The combined effect of the increase in unused nitrate and the increased loading of nitrogen to the lake is shown by the data in Figure 6.7. One can conclude from this information that phosphorus is the limiting nutrient in Lake Erie when availability of nutrients, and not physical factors such as light or temperature, control growth. Further, the tendency for phosphorus to be the growth-limiting nutrient has increased in recent years.

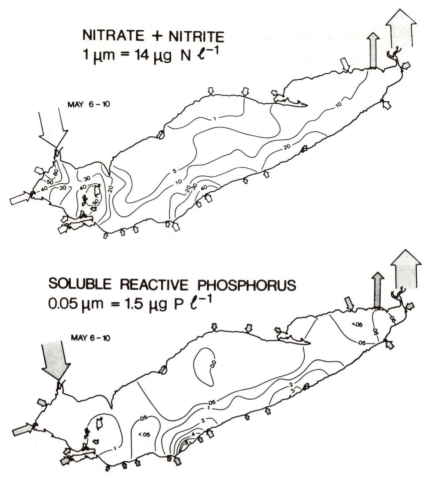

Figure 6.6 Concentrations of soluble reactive phosphorus (SRP) and nitrate + nitrite (NO₃ + NO₂) in Lake Erie during May 1970, showing the relative abundance of NO₃ + NO₂ with corresponding low concentrations of SRP, particularly in the West Basin (Burns 1976c). Contour values are in μm.

The conclusion that phosphorus is the nutrient controlling growth in Lake Erie has been confirmed by the measurements on phosphorus limitation made by Lean et al. (1983). They used a method devised by Lean and Pick (1981) to test for phosphorus limitation. The absorption ratios of carbon to phosphorus by algae can be quite variable, the C:P ratio being as low as 3 μg C to 1 μg P when algae, which are starved for phosphorus, suddenly have it made available to them and indulge in luxury uptake of the element. Alternatively, absorption ratios of 300 μg C:1 μg P can occur with algae that contain much excess phosphorus and only need to absorb carbon for growth. Using the knowledge of this process, Lean et al.

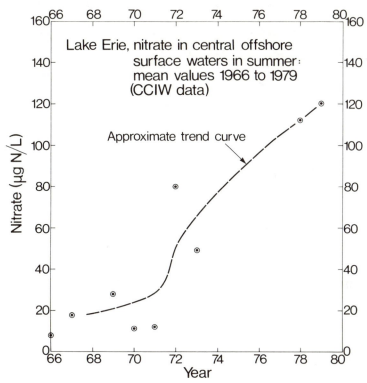

Figure 6.7 Changes in nitrate concentrations with time in the Central Basin during summer, showing an increase in concentration of NO₃. (Dobson, personal communication.)

measured phosphorus deficiency, the results of which are shown for the stratification period of 1979 in Figure 6.8. The measurements for the East Basin indicate that phosphorus was limiting to growth from July to September in that basin. The phosphorus limitation started sooner in the Central Basin but diminished in September, when the enriched hypolimnetic waters in this basin were mixed up into the photic zone. Since phosphorus is limiting to growth during the summer, the conclusion is that control of phytoplankton population density during summer will eventually be achieved by phosphorus control.

In the first major surveys of Lake Erie in 1929 and 1930, nitrogen variables were measured, but no phosphorus parameters were measured. At that time, the fundamental importance of phosphorus to all bioligical systems was not realized. Phosphorus is used in organisms as part of their genetic systems, but its major role is in forming part of the ADP (adenosine diphosphate) and ATP (adenosine triphosphate) interconversion system, by which organisms store energy until they require it.

In 1968 Vollenweider concluded that eutrophication of water bodies was caused by the simultaneous loading of large quantities of nitrogen and

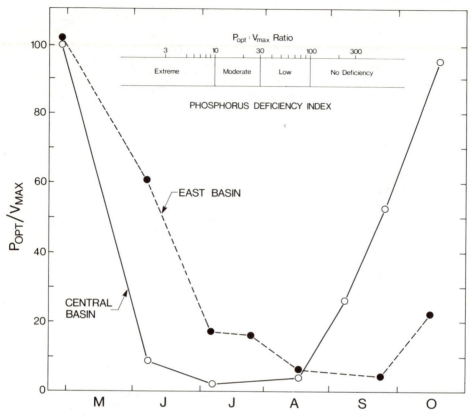

Figure 6.8 Values of phosphorus deficiency index measured in the Central and East Basins during the stratified period in 1979, showing extreme deficiency of phosphorus (values less than 10) in both basins toward the end of the stratified periods. (Lean et al. 1983.)

phosphorus to them. In addition, we also know that they will *not* eutrophy if only high levels of nitrogen are available. One only need look at Lake Superior, one of the cleanest lakes in the world. It has average nitrate concentrations of 260 mg N m^{-3} in the surface waters at the end of the growing season (Weiler 1978), showing that nitrogen alone cannot cause eutrophication. Neither does silica alone cause eutrophication, because the concentration of this material remaining in the waters of Lake Superior at the end of the growth season is about 2,200 mg SiO_2 m^{-3}. At this time of year, however, the total phosphorus levels are down to 5 mg P m^{-3} in this lake. The low biomass levels in Lake Superior are caused by a shortage of phosphorus alone.

Can high phosphorus loadings without correspondingly high loadings of nitrogen and silica cause eutrophic conditions? Fee (1979,1980) and Schindler (1980) have debated this point. The evidence they present and that of

Murphy, Hall, and Yasaki (1983) suggest that high loadings of only phosphorus to lakes can cause heavy blooms of blue-green algae. These algae can fix the nitrogen they require from atmospheric nitrogen and do not require silica. In the non-bloom periods, however, these lakes can be quite clear, certainly much clearer than lakes with a similar phosphorus loading that is accompanied by a significant nitrogen loading.

The evidence indicates that the fertility of lakes definitely depends on phosphorus availability and, to a lesser extent, on nitrogen, while the dependence on the availability of silica is very weak. It is fortunate that phosphorus is the essential element, because it is the most controllable of the three basic nutrients. Silica is dissolved slowly whenever water is in contact with clay, quartz, sand, or rock, a process making silica loading to lakes uncontrollable by man. Nitrogen compounds are very difficult to control, partly because of widespread use in fertilizers and its production in the atmosphere during electric storms. And nitrate and ammonium are very soluble ions which are difficult to remove from wastewaters cheaply. The phosphate ion, on the other hand, is present in only limited concentration in most natural systems, either aqueous or atmospheric. Since it is strongly surface active, it chelates easily with hydroxides and other materials, such as clay. It can be adsorbed on particulates and removed from water. The two characteristics of biological necessity and chemical controllability make the elimination of phosphorus the most manageable means of controlling the eutrophication of water bodies. As a result, it is important to have a detailed knowledge of the chemical behavior of phosphorus and its loading into Lake Erie.

Phosphorus Loading

The Detroit River has always been the largest source of phosphorus to Lake Erie. It carries the phosphorus in the water leaving Lake Huron, the agricultural load from southwest Ontario and the sewage and industrial loads of Detroit and Windsor. The next-largest combined source of phosphorus to the lake is the American tributaries, followed by American cities, and then the Canadian tributaries. The atmospheric load of phosphorus is small in contrast to that of nitrogen, and the Canadian municipal load is almost negligible. The amount of phosphorus eroded into the lake from the bluffs is large (Burns et al. 1976b). Yet it does not affect growth processes in the lake because it is in an insoluble form, and for this reason is not usually included in phosphorus-loading estimates. Much of the soil-adsorbed phosphorus that is loaded into the lake via the tributaries is similarly unavailable for growth, but this phosphorus is included in the annual loading estimates. This leads to an illogical method of estimating loadings.

The erosional loadings to the lake highlight an issue that has been avoided for some time but is now being faced: the bioavailability of the phosphorus from the different sources. Samples from the eroding northshore bluffs were taken to determine the bioavailability of the phosphorus they contained. The phosphorus in the bluffs was found to be present in three quite different forms by Williams, Murphy, and Mayer (1976). The primary form of phosphorus was the mineral apatite (AP) at 545 µg P g^{-1} of soil, the second form was non-apatite inorganic (NAIP) at 18 µg P g^{-1}, while the third form was organic (OP) at 12 µg P g^{-1}. Bioavailability experiments on this material (Williams, Shear, and Thomas, 1980) showed that virtually all the apatite phosphorus in the bluff samples was unavailable, presumably because the solubility of apatite in lake water is extremely low. These experiments also showed that the phosphorus extracted from the samples with 0.1 N NaOH (NaOH-P) solution provided a good measure of the bioavailable phosphorus in the material. The final result of the investigation was that the bluff samples probably contained about 13 µg P g^{-1}, or 2.3 percent of the phosphorus in available form.

Much work has been done recently on measuring the bioavailability of phosphorus in the rivers flowing into Lake Erie (DePinto, Young, and Martin 1981; Dorich, Nelson, and Sommers 1980; Logan, Aloya, and Yaksich 1979), and the results were summarized by Sonzogni et al. (1981). They consider that approximately 50 percent of the phosphorus load of these rivers is bioavailable. Some exceptions are the New York State tributaries, which have about 15 percent lower bioavailable phosphorus than the Ohio rivers. On the other hand, the Grand River, Ontario, had about 80 percent bioavailability in 1970 (Ongley 1976) because of the discharges from a phosphorus reduction factory located close to the mouth of the river. This source is now under control and the bioavailability of phosphorus in this river is changing. Since bioavailability is a relatively new area of research, initial estimates may later be revised somewhat.

Sewage treatment plants, even those with tertiary treatment, do not seem to have a marked effect on the bioavailability of the phosphorus passing through them; they only reduce the total quantity of phosphorus released. The bioavailable phosphorus in treatment plant effluents is in the order of 80 percent (DePinto et al. 1980). Also, the phosphorus loaded to Lake Erie from the atmosphere probably has a greater than 50 percent bioavailability for growth (Murphy and Doskey 1976). The bioavailability of phosphorus is an important topic and is considered again in Chapter 12, where maximum possible loads of phosphorus for Lake Erie are discussed.

The correct estimation of phosphorus loads into Lake Erie from rivers is difficult because the flow vs. concentration relationships for this material is not inverse, but direct. Chloride, as shown in Figure 6.9 (top), has an inverse relationship with flow, and the calculated total flux does not vary tremendously with time or flow. This is not the case for either total phosphorus, Figure 6.9 (middle) or soluble phosphorus concentrations, Figure 6.9 (bottom), which increase with flow. A direct relationship such as this means that most of the phosphorus is transported into the lake during high flow or storm events, when the river waters have the highest

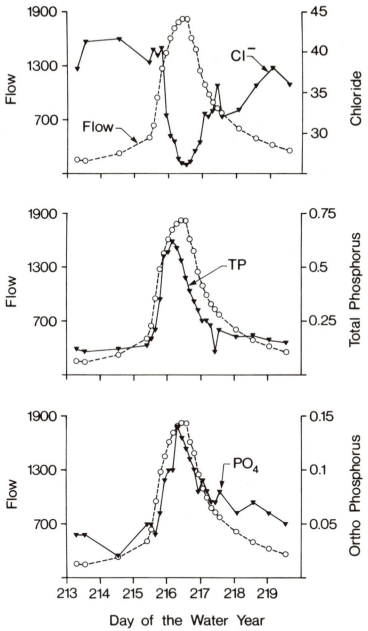

Figure 6.9 The inverse relationship of chloride with flow (top) *and the direct relationship of total phosphorus and orthophosphate with the flow of Wolf Creek, a tributary of the Sandusky River. Concentration units are grams* m^{-3}. *(Baker 1980.)*

phosphorus concentrations. If these high-flow events are not sampled, the underestimate can range from between 10 percent and 30 percent of the tributary load (Phosphorus Management Strategies Task Force 1980). To diminish this error, the U.S. Army Corps of Engineers, Buffalo, N.Y., supported work on river loadings to Lake Erie, and a generalized model, the Phosphorus Loading Model, has been developed (Verhoff, Yasich, and Melfi 1980). This model accurately calculates the loading of phosphorus by streams where the basic phosphorus concentration vs. flow data has been obtained and flows are continuously monitored.

Until recently, the load of phosphorus has always increased with time (see Fig. 6.10) because the population in the basin has grown continuously, causing an increase in the waste phosphorus from cities and from the use of fertilizers. The largest increase of phosphorus released to the lake occurred after World War II, following the rapid replacement of soap by phosphorus-based detergents. Because detergent phosphorus is completely bioavailable, the wastewaters released to the lakes have very high concentrations of bioavailable phosphorus. These massive loads of bioavailable phosphorus cause large areas around the outfalls of treatment plants and the mouths of rivers to suffer from the unpleasant conditions associated with severe eutrophication. The area near Cleveland is an example of high phosphorus concentrations and quite unsatisfactory nearshore conditions (see Fig. 6.6).

Estimates of recent loads of phosphorus to Lake Erie are shown in Figure 6.10 and the resulting concentrations in the lake in Figure 6.11. The loads are fairly variable because their calculation is difficult and is a somewhat contentious issue. The loading estimates, however, do show a decline starting in the late sixties. In 1970, legislation controlling the maximum amount of phosphorus in detergents was introduced in many areas around Lake Erie and resulted in a considerable reduction in the load of bioavailable phosphorus. After 1972, a program of building and upgrading wastewater treatment plants began. This also caused a considerable reduction in phosphorus loading. The data in Figure 6.10 (bottom) show, however, that nearly all the decrease has occurred in the Detroit River load, so the greatest drop in phosphorus concentration has occcured in the West Basin. The average total phosphorus concentration from April to November in 1970 was 43.4 ± 9.8 mg P m^{-3}. During the same period in 1980, it was 23.5 ± 8.6 mg Pm^{-3}, a decrease of approximately 45 percent. The concentrations from May to November in the Central Basin changed from an average of 19.1 ± 6.2 in 1970 to 12.0 ± 7.1 mg P m^{-3} in 1980. In the East Basin during the same periods the mean concentration dropped from 14.4 ± 4.6 to 11.0 ± 1.6 mg P m^{-3}. These are among the first definite signs that conditions in the lake are improving or, one might say, that the program to save the lake is working.

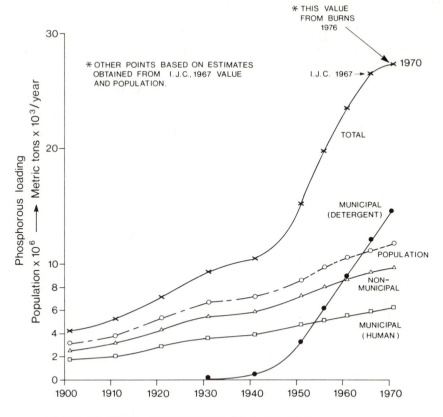

LOADS OF TOTAL PHOSPHORUS TO LAKE ERIE

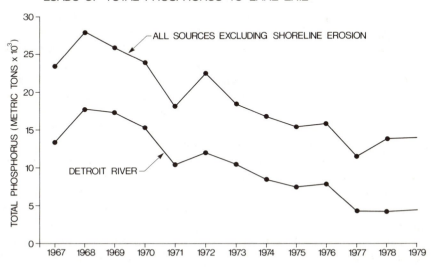

Figure 6.10. **Top:** *Estimates of the different forms of phosphorus loading and the total loading of phosphorus to Lake Erie (Sly 1976).* **Bottom:** *Loads of total phosphorus to Lake Erie (Fraser and Wilson 1981).*

1970 ANNUAL MEAN EPILIMNION VALUES

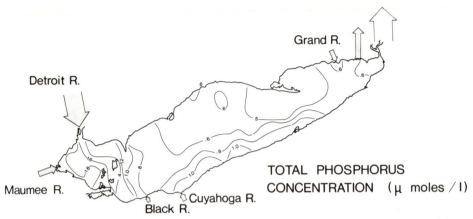

Figure 6.11 The average distribution of total phosphorus in Lake Erie in 1970, showing the general west-to-east decline in concentration and the effect of some of the major point sources (l $\mu ml^{-1}=31$ mg P m^{-3}). (Burns et al. 1976a.)

Phosphorus Processes

Since phosphorus management is usually the best method of controlling the tropic status of a lake, the processes controlling the cycling of phosphorus in the Lake Erie ecosystem are important and should be understood. We have seen that the loadings of phosphorus to Lake Erie have increased with time and that recent sediments show higher phosphorus levels than older ones, but historical phosphorus loadings cannot be deduced from phosphorus concentrations in the sediments. Phosphorus, unlike lead, is vertically mobile in the sediments (Carignan and Flett 1981), and its distribution in the sediment column does not entirely reflect its time of loading, as does ^{210}Pb. Particulate organic carbon, although it decays with time, does not migrate vertically except by physical mixing of the sediment, and it can give an idea of changes in production of a lake. Since organic production in Lake Erie is strongly related to phosphorus availability, organic carbon profiles do indicate historic changes in phosphorus availability. Kemp, Gray, and Mudrochova (1972) found that the data for Lakes Erie and Ontario show a trend toward increasing productivity around the turn of the century, which has continued to the present day. This is in contrast to the information from South Bay in Lake Huron (Fig. 6.12). South Bay provides a baseline of an unaffected locality because even today the area around the bay is very lightly inhabited and the bay has little exchange of water with the open lake. On examining Beeton's (1965) curves for increasing salt concentrations (Fig. 6.2), one finds that they also show a marked increase beginning around 1900. From this information, one can

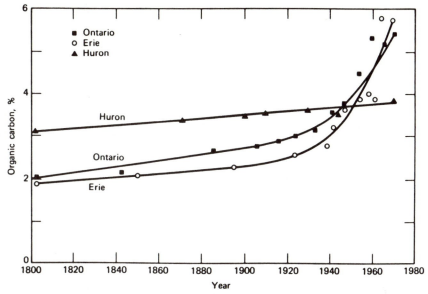

Figure 6.12 Changes in organic carbon concentrations in sediments by the approximate time of deposition in Lakes Ontario, Erie, and the South Bay of Huron. (Kemp, Gray, and Mudrochova 1972.)

consider that the trophic state of Lake Erie began to change markedly at the turn of this century.

The return of phosphorus from the sediments to the overlying water governs the response of a lake to nutrient abatement programs. This makes a knowledge of sediment phosphorus chemistry vital. Williams, Mayer, and Nriagu (1980a) and Nriagu and Dell (1974) have studied this topic and found that similar concentrations of non-apatite inorganic phosphorus (NAIP) at different depths can consist of many of the different minerals shown in Figure 6.13. This happens because NAIP is a classification determined by use of chemical extractants, not by the identification and quantification of specific minerals. Since these extractants can dissolve a number of different minerals, separate tests must be used to determine which minerals actually comprise the NAIP in a paricular sample. The determination of the actual mineral phases present can be very difficult (and often impossible) if the mineral gains are very small. This is unfortunate because phosphorus release from sediments is dependent on the mineral phases present.

One of the variables controlling the sediment processes is redox potential, which is usually about 400 to 500 millivolts in an environment with oxygen present (oxidized state). It can be close to zero or be negative when oxygen is absent (anoxic) and the materials in the sediment are in a reduced state. Possible geochemical transformations in the sediment which are affected

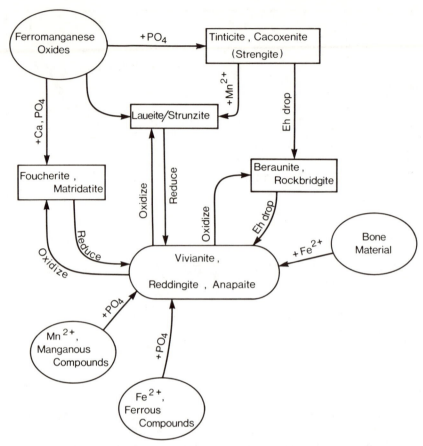

Figure 6.13 The source material and associated phosphate minerals likely to be encountered in recent lake and river sediments. (Nriagu and Dell 1974.)

by redox potential are summarized in Figure 6.13. Iron and phosphorus coprecipitate in oxidized environments as the ferrosoferric hydroxyphosphates, tinticite and cacoxenite, and can change easily into beraunite and rockbridgite. These minerals are very insoluble and can be in equilibrium with very low concentrations of phosphate in the surrounding water. As these minerals are buried by fresh sediment, they move into an environment where the organic carbon in the sediment uses up the oxygen faster than it can diffuse down, so that the redox potential drops considerably. In these reduced conditions, the above minerals change into ferrous phosphate $Fe_3(PO_4)_2.8H_2O$, known as vivianite, and are found in the deeper Lake Erie sediments. Vivianite is fairly soluble, being in equilibrium with phosphate concentrations in the interstitial water of between 1 and 4 μm (30 to 120 mg P m^{-3}).

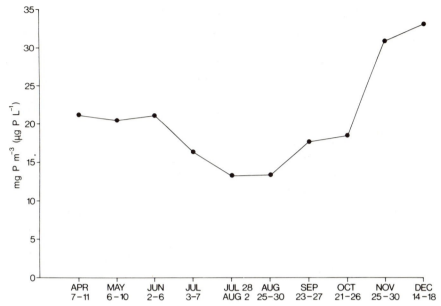

Figure 6.14 Changes in the volume-weighted total phosphorus average concentrations in Lake Erie for 1970, showing the decrease in content of phosphorus in the lake waters during the summer and dramatic increase during the stormy months of November and December. (Burns, Rosa, and Chan 1976.)

Normally, the vivianite system does not exist at the sediment-water interface, and little of this phosphate-rich interstitial water exchanges with the water above the sediments. The lakewater phosphate concentration can also be increased by decomposition of the fresh organic material lying on the sediment surface. These two processes acting in the Central and East Basins seldom cause concentration increases in oxic waters (oxygen present) of more than 0.2 µm P or 7 mg P m^{-3} of soluble reactive phosphorus. But if the waters above the sediment become anoxic, the vivianite system becomes the controlling one even at the sediment interface. The phosphate-containing materials, together with the available ferosoferric hydroxyphosphate, dissolve until concentrations of 4 µm P (125 mg P m^{-3}) of orthophosphate (soluble reactive phosphorus) are achieved. This is an extremely high concentration of phosphorus for Lake Erie waters, but concentrations of this magnitude have been observed in the bottom waters of the Central Basin (Burns and Ross 1972a).

Other processes affect the concentration of phosphorus in the Lake quite markedly. The uptake of soluble phosphorus by algae decreases the amount of phosphorus in the lake. Much of the phosphorus ends up settling out of the water to the sediments in the form of organic particles during the stratified summer season. The result of this process can be seen in the data of Figure 6.14. The opposite process happens in the fall when the thermal stratification in the lake breaks down, permitting wind-induced turbulence to reach the lake bottom and resuspend the settled material. The turbulence can also cause much soluble phosphorus to be extracted from the sediments. This occurred significantly in November 1970 (see Figure 6.14). Most of the soluble phosphorus reentered the phosphorus cycle of the lake when the total phosphorus concentration of the lake increased from 18.6 to 31 mg P m^{-3}, with about 40 percent of the increase being soluble phosphorus.

Much of the particulate phosphorus resuspended by wave action is in the form of fine grains of apatite or is strongly bound to the clays. This phosphorus is not bioavailable and merely settles out when the turbulence subsides. Thus the observed mean phosphorus concentration in the water can be increased temporarily by resuspended phosphorus. This is particularly apparent in the West Basin, which is shallow and subject to bottom resuspension. Using background information, the total P content of this water can be increased by about 7 mg P m^{-3} with heavy storms, with an average increase of 2 mg P m^{-3} due to resuspension of biologically inert phosphorus alone.

Remedial Action

On deciding to restore Lake Erie to an acceptable trophic state, the prime necessity is to reduce the loads of bioavailable phosphorus to the lake, but the processes described above must be kept in mind if reductions are to achieve maximum effect. The relatively large loads of apatite phosphorus do not seem to have much effect on the system. The reduction of phosphorus loads is not only a matter of quantity; the concentration of the input is also a factor that must be taken into account.

The importance of concentration is illustrated in the following example. In 1970 the bioavailable phosphorus entering the lake from the atmosphere was about 387 tons at a mean concentration of about 25 mg P m^{-3} in the precipitation, a concentration similar to that of the lake. The load from the Cuyahoga River was about 186 tons at approximately 202 mg P m^{-3}. The atmospheric phosphorus fell fairly evenly over the whole lake surface. It probably did more good than harm by helping to maintain algal productivity at a steady but not excessive level during the summer, when surface biomass concentrations can be quite low. In contrast, the Cuyahoga River load entered the lake at a high concentration. This led to excessive blue-green populations in the water in a zone around the river mouth, together with large *Cladophora* growths where there was suitable substratum. This caused diminished acceptability of the lake water as a municipal water source, together with many fouled beaches. Obviously, the phosphorus from the atmosphere is not a problem, while that from the Cuyahoga River is.

The factor controlling the trophic state of a nearshore zone close to a river or outfall is the concentration of phosphorus in the water of the nearshore zone. This will depend on the concentration of phosphorus in the source and its rate of dilution. The dilution factor at a point is dependent primarily on its distance from the source and prevailing current speed. The data in a study by Lam and Murthy (1978), developed for the Great Lakes, indicate that, in a plume moving at 25 cm sec^{-1}, a 5 to 1 dilution would occur 1.2 km from the source, and a 10 to 1 dilution would occur at about 3 km. This velocity is reasonably common in the vicinity of the shoreline where the nearshore currents flow. Estimation of the distance of travel from the source required for a 100 to 1 dilution is difficult but intuitively it could be between 20 and 30 km from the source. This means that it is easy to effect a small dilution, but much space is required to effect a large dilution. If the area of relatively high concentration is to be kept small, then the required concentration of river water must be kept low. It would seem that a reasonable guideline for dilution of river plumes would be about 5 to 1, because this dilution is significant and the corresponding nearshore area of elevated concentrations would not be too large. This assumption can be used to estimate desired river concentrations.

Concentration objectives for the total phosphorus concentrations in the basins of Lake Erie have been recommended by the Phosphorus Management Strategies Task Force (1980) as follows: West Basin at 15 mg P m^{-3} and the Central and East Basin at 10 mg P m^{-3}. Using the 5 to 1 dilution factor, this means that the streams flowing into the West Basin, excluding the Detroit River, should not exceed bioavailable P concentrations of 75 mg P m^{-3} or total P concentrations of 150 mg P m^{-3} since approximately 50 percent of the phosphorus is bioavailable. For the Central Basin streams, which also have almost 50 percent of the phosphorus in bioavailable form, this would mean a concentration maximum of bioavailable P of 50 mg m^{-3} or total P of 100 mg m^{-3}. For the East Basin streams in which only about 30 percent of the phosphorus is bioavailable, concentrations should not exceed 50 mg m^{-3} bioavailable P or 160 mg m^{-3} of total P. The Detroit River has such an enormous flow, constituting about 90 percent of the total tributary flow, that the normal rules of dilution do not apply. It must be treated as a special case and contain no more than the West Basin objective of 15 mg bioavailable or 30 mg total P m^{-3}, since about half of the phosphorus in this river is unavailable and settles out.

Although appropriate phosphorus concentrations in the tributaries and lake waters have been listed above, the determination of required phosphorus loads is far more complex, because all the processes described in this section have to be considered in the estimate. Since the task has to be carried out in a quantitative manner, the actual dependence of phosphorus concentrations on the total load to the lake is considered later in Chapter 12 and the Appendix. Here, it is sufficient to state that the proper phosphorus loads to the lake to ensure an acceptable trophic state can be achieved reasonably easily by the inhabitants of the lake basin.

Summary

Manifestations of pollution are usually first observed in nearshore regions, but they are also the first ones to improve when remedial action is taken. Increased amount of salts, plant nutrients, and bacteria have been loaded into Lake Erie for almost a century by the actions of man. The effects of the nutrients are the most obvious, for they cause extensive growths of *Cladophora* in shallow exposed areas, aquatic weeds in protected zones, and massive blooms in offshore areas.

Nitrogen, silica, and phosphorus are the three most-important elements affecting growth, with phosphorus being essential for all types of aquatic plants. Since control of phosphorus availability can lead to control of plant growth in the lake, some factors controlling the bioavailability of phosphorus were described. Knowledge of these processes has enabled the formulation of a strategy to maintain phosphorus concentrations at an optimum level. The most-important part of the plan is the reduction of phosphorus loads to the lake. Another important requirement is to keep total phosphorus concentrations below 150 g P m^{-3} in the tributary rivers or 30 g P m^{-3} in the Detroit River.

7

Toxic Materials in the Lake

The loading of toxic materials into the lake is related to both the total population of the basin and behavior of the individuals forming the population. The concept that the effect of man on an ecosystem is the product of both man's population density and his behavior has been explored by Vallentyne (1978) and Vollenweider (1982). The increase in this effect, named demophoric growth, can be very great in developed countries with growing populations, as each individual uses large amounts of material goods and energy.

At the time of its discovery by European man in 1669, the basin was virtually uninhabited, even by Indians. It remained this way until about 1800, when the settlers began to move into the basin in significant numbers. After 1850, growth in both population and industrialization were dramatic, causing a great increase in the rate of demophoric growth that has continued to recent times. The expansion in the population has been rapid (Inland Waters Directorate 1973),

Date	Population
1890	2,674,048
1900	3,134,021
1910	3,711,533
1920	5,153,159
1930	6,669,249
1940	7,069,655
1950	8,546,819
1960	10,517,738

1970   11,616,130
1980   13,000,000 (approx.)

but the recent load of anthropogenic (man-derived) materials into the lake
has increased at an even greater rate than the population. For example,
the pioneers used about 23 liters (l) of water per person per day, but
modern man has a domestic use of about 225 l daily. This does not include
the tremendous quantity of water used by present-day industry; for example,
about 250×10^3 l of water is needed to produce a ton of steel. Most of
the water used to produce steel in the Lake Erie Basin returns to the lake.
The effects of modern industrialism have been felt more in Lake Erie than
in the other Great Lakes, since Erie has the smallest volume of any of the
lakes with which to absorb the output from a large population.

Harbor Contamination

The most obvious contamination around the lake occurs in the harbors.
Harbors the world over are seldom clean, and those of Lake Erie are no
exception. In addition to the usual flotsam, there are wastes from the
nearby industries and from the inflowing rivers, since most of the harbors
are sited on river mouths. Fairport harbor is an example of this situation
(Figure 7.1).

Cleveland and Toledo are the two most-polluted harbors on the lake.
Concentrations of contaminants are greatest in Cleveland because the small
flow of the Cuyahoga River through Cleveland does not dilute the wastes
very much. The heavy sediment load of the Maumee River, through Toledo,
both dilutes contaminant concentrations in the deposited mud sediments
and causes frequent dredging, which removes these materials from the
harbor. Detroit Harbor also is not as polluted as it might be, because the
speed of flow of the Detroit River resuspends sediments and moves them
away.

The method of disposing of dredged material depends on the degree
of contamination of the material. Until recently, nearly all harbor dredgings
were disposed of by the cheapest method: dumping in assigned areas in
the lake. Now, diked disposal areas, such as Toledo Island, keep the most-
contaminated sediments from interacting directly with the lake waters.
Unfortunately, some of the contaminants in the diked areas leach out into
the lake, but these amounts are much smaller than would leach if the
sediments were simply dumped into open water.

The U.S. Environmental Protection Agency proposed stringent guidelines
for dumping in the open lake. Information developed later, however, showed
that the open-water sediments of the lake often had concentrations of
metals and phosphorus higher than those specified in these guidelines for
contaminated sediments. As a result, Thomas and Mudroch (1979) evaluated
the concentrations of phosphorus and metals in sediments deposited before

Figure 7.1 Fairport harbor at the mouth of the Grand River, Ohio. Note debris on beach and in shallow water. (Photo by J.P. Barry.)

Table 7.1   Recommended Guidelines for Open Lake Dredged Spoil Disposal for the Lower Great Lakes

Parameter	Concentration (ppm)[a]	Cleveland[b] STN 11-1977
Volatile solids		
(loss on ignition 600°C)	60,000	74,000
COD	50,000	110,000
Total N	2,000	2,000
Total P	1004/1000	2,200
Hg	0.3	0.6
Pb	50	444
Zn	105	1,900
Fe	45,500	100,000
Cr	120	260
Cu	45	240
As	8	67
Cd	1.5	24
Cyanide	0.1	—
Ammonia	100	300
Ni	90	150
Mn	1,625	1,200
Ba	—	—
PCB	0.05	2.8
Oils and greases	1,500	8,500

[a]Guidelines are from Thomas and Mudroch 1979.
[b]Cleveland concentrations, shown for comparision, are from U.S. EPA 1978.

the arrival of man, together with the concentrations observed in modern sediments, and developed new guidelines for open lake dredged spoil disposal. Table 7.1 shows a comparison of their guidelines with the contents of the more-polluted of Cleveland Harbor's sediments.

Among the Lake Erie harbor sediments that have been sampled, those from Wheatley (Thomas and Mudroch 1979), Cleveland, Ashtabula, Fairport, Conneaut, Munroe, and Lorain (U.S. EPA 1978) have been found to have excessively polluted sediments. Conneaut was first sampled in 1974 and again in 1977, while Cleveland was sampled in 1972 and 1977. Both harbors now show decreased concentrations of mercury, zinc, cadmium, chemical oil and grease, and chemical oxygen demand in their sediments.

Heavy Metal Contaminants

Many modern contaminants are chemicals that have only recently been synthesized for the first time, elements that were previously uncommon in man's environment. Since life evolved in the virtual absence of these exotic materials, the higher forms of life have evolved no protective mechanisms against these substances, making them inherently toxic to humans. Many environmental toxicologists are naturally concerned. For example, Schienberg (1979) writes about copper as follows:

> Copper thus appears to exemplify the fact that only when a metal has been selected as essential by the evolutionary process do specific, genetically transmitted mechanisms develop that buffer the organism against environmentally induced deficiency and toxicosis. No such mechanisms appear to have evolved to protect human beings against the toxicosis of nonessential metals.

Other metals, such as mercury, lead, and cadmium, were apparently absent from the human environment during the formation of its genetic code, so that protective mechanisms and barriers against these metals also were never developed.

Ten or more trace metals are currently causing environmental concern, but only five have been investigated to any major extent in Lake Erie. These metals are lead (Pb), mercury (Hg), cadmium (Cd), copper (Cu), and zinc (Zn). There has been a steady increase in the loading of these important trace metals into the lake since 1850, and the concentrations of these metals in the sediments are now much higher than the precolonial background levels (Kemp et al. 1976; Nriagu et al. 1979).

An indication of the increase in loading of these elements can be obtained from the data of Kemp et al. (1976). Figure 7.2 shows the data from station U-42 (see Fig. 5.10), where the buildup of the five metals in the sediments has been somewhat greater than in the rest of the lake. On average, the modern concentration of mercury in the sediments is approximately 12.4 times that of precolonial sediments; lead is 4.4 times; zinc, 3.0; cadmium, 3.6; and copper, 2.5. The actual increase of loading to the lake is greater than the increase in sediment concentration because there has been a simultaneous dilution of metal content by increased sediment loading in recent times.

Of the above five metals, mercury, lead, and cadmium are the most toxic to man and should be kept at the lowest possible concentrations in water supplies and edible fish. Mercury attacks the brain and central nervous system; lead affects the blood, numerous organs, and the nervous system; while cadmium causes the painful Itai-Itai disease, among other effects (Clayton and Clayton 1981; Great Lakes Water Quality Board 1981a). Zinc and copper are essential micro-nutrients to humans, and these two elements are seldom found in concentrations dangerous to man in natural waters.

The problem of establishing dangerous concentrations of toxic trace metals is not simple. One cannot simply measure the concentration of a metal in water and then state whether the observed concentration is safe or not for humans or biota. For example, the measured concentrations of copper and zinc may be very high, but these elements may be chemically complexed with other materials (ligands), making them relatively harmless.

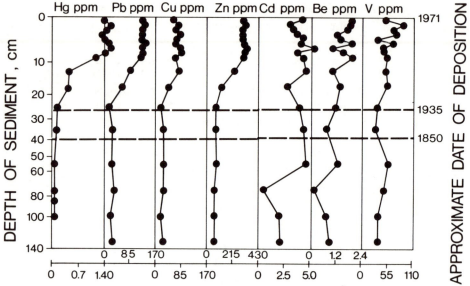

Figure 7.2 Profile of concentration versus depth of sediment at station U.42 in the West Basin for mercury (Hg), lead (Pb), copper (Cu), zinc (Zn), beryllium (Be), and vanadium (V), showing markedly increased concentrations in the recent sediments. (Kemp et al. 1976.)

Similarly, the water may be hard and the lead may be in the form of lead carbonate, which is not toxic. Unfortunately, the corollary to this situation also exists: very low levels of a metal present in water may be dangerous because of the chemical form of the metal. Bioaccumulation of low concentrations of the methylated forms of toxic metals can occur in levels dangerous for humans. Examples of this type of compound are methyl mercury (CH_3Hg), tetramethyl lead ($(CH_3)_4Pb$), or the methylated forms of arsenic, selenium, and tin.

Methylated forms of metals can be found in measureable amounts in water. They are formed in sediments containing high concentrations of the metals (Beier and Jernelov 1979: Chau and Wong 1978) and then move into the overlying water from the sediments. Thereafter they enter the foodchain by being adsorbed onto seston (suspended particles), which are ingested. Methyl mercury behaves in this manner but is also absorbed directly through the gills of fish, with the absorption rate being about ten times greater than that of the ionic form of the metal (Huckabee, Elwood, and Hildebrand 1979). Tetramethyl lead is also readily taken up directly from water by rainbow trout and is stored in the intestinal fat of the fish (Wong, Chau, Kramer and Bengert 1981). The ingestion and depuration rates of the ionic and methyl forms of mercury are also quite different (Huckabee, Elwood, and Hildebrand 1979), and this is probably the case for the other metals as well. The ionic form is taken up more slowly and

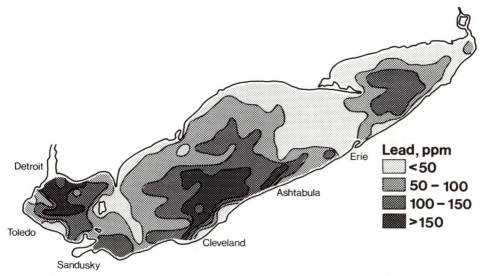

Figure 7.3 Concentration of lead in the surface sediments of Lake Erie, showing the six major point sources of input (ppm means mg of lead per kg of sediment). (PLUARG 1978; Thomas and Mudroch 1979.)

depurated at a higher rate than the methyl form. Thus the equilibrium concentration of mercury in the body of a fish exposed to ionic mercury is always much lower than the concentration in a fish exposed to similar levels of methyl mercury.

Both methylated and ionic forms of metals can be released from sediments, so the distribution of metals in sediment is important. The distribution of lead found by R.L. Thomas (PLUARG 1978) in Lake Erie sediments is shown in Figure 7.3. This shows quite clearly that the main sources for the element in the lake are the population centers of Detroit, Toledo, Sandusky, Cleveland, Ashtabula, and Erie. The main reason for the clear sediment distribution pattern is that the majority of the lead in the lake system is associated with organic particulates, and these settle out fairly rapidly. About 65 percent of the lead loaded into the lake is retained there (Nriagu et al. 1979), and has fairly wide distribution throughout the lake. This is possibly caused by transport of the previously settled particulates, but may also result from the fact that a great deal of the input of lead to lake is from the atmosphere, as shown in Table 7.2.

The measurement of lead concentrations in lake waters is difficult due to contamination problems, with concentrations often reported as being 10- to 100-fold greater than they really are (Great Lakes Science Advisory Board 1980a). Lead levels have only recently been reliably measured in Lake Erie, at an average of 0.2 mg m^{-3} (Leslie and Lum-Shue-Chan 1982) in the center of the lake. The values are far below the Canadian maximum

Table 7.2   Inventory of Sources and Sinks of Heavy Metals in Lake Erie

Source	Flux Rate (10^3 kg yr^{-1})			
	Cadmium	Copper	Lead	Zinc
Detroit River (import from Upper Lakes)	—	1640	630	5220
Tributaries, U.S.A.	—	100	52	271
Tributaries, Ontario	—	31	19	140
Sewage discharges	5.5	448	283	759
Dredged spoils	4.2	42	56	175
Atmospheric inputs	39	206	645	903
Shoreline erosion	7.9	190	221	308
Total, all sources	—	2657	1906	7776
Export, Niagara River, and Welland Canal	—	1320	660	4400
Retained in sediments		1157	1246	3376

Source: Nriagu, Kemp, Wong, and Harper 1979.

tolerable level for lead in drinking water (50 mg m^{-3}) and are close to the preferred concentration of 1 mg m^{-3}. Thus it is unlikely that drinking water drawn from Lake Erie would contain dangerous amounts of lead, unless there has been a large industrial release of the element within the proximity of a city water intake.

Nevertheless, people living in the industrial basin of Lake Erie probably have a total intake of 29 μg Pb day^{-1} while living their normal daily lives, compared with a prehistoric intake of less than 0.2 μg day^{-1}, as outlined by the National Academy of Sciences (1980). By their estimates, water plays a small part by contributing only 1.5 μg to the total daily intake, compared to food, which accounts for 21 μg, and air, 6.5 μg. Lake Erie fish contain about 0.15 μg Pb g^{-1} wet weight (Great Lakes Science Advisory Board 1980a). This may be a relatively safe level for consumption of fish, but it is difficult to judge because the old 10 μg g^{-1} guideline for fish has been cancelled and is yet to be replaced by a newer and (probably) much lower guideline. (The present guideline in England is 2 μg g^{-1} wet weight of fish.)

Lead is unique in the Great Lakes in that the recommended safe levels of the element vary with each lake. The present objectives for concentrations of lead in water, with the new proposed lower objectives of the Great Lakes Science Advisory Board (1980a) shown in parentheses, are as follows: Lake Superior, 10 mg m^{-3} (2); Lake Huron, 20 mg m^{-3} (3); Lakes Erie and Michigan, 25 mg m^{-3} (4); and Lake Ontario, 25 mg m^{-3} (5). In freshwater systems, lead carbonate complexes ($PbCo_3$) dominate the inorganic chemistry of dissolved lead (Rickard and Nriagu 1978) so that

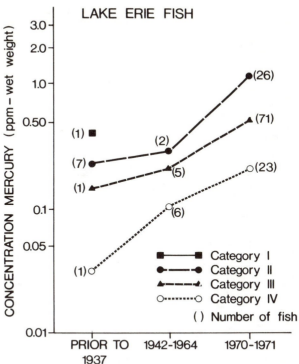

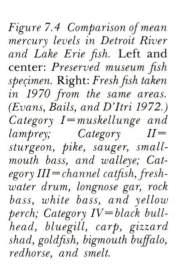

Figure 7.4 Comparison of mean mercury levels in Detroit River and Lake Erie fish. Left and center: Preserved museum fish specimen. Right: Fresh fish taken in 1970 from the same areas. (Evans, Bails, and D'Itri 1972.) Category I = muskellunge and lamprey; Category II = sturgeon, pike, sauger, smallmouth bass, and walleye; Category III = channel catfish, freshwater drum, longnose gar, rock bass, white bass, and yellow perch; Category IV = black bullhead, bluegill, carp, gizzard shad, goldfish, bigmouth buffalo, redhorse, and smelt.

between pH 6–8, lead will be complexed increasingly with higher concentrations of carbonate in the water. Since carbonate content and hardness of water increase as one moves down the Great Lakes chain, the recommended safe levels are relaxed from the upper to the lower lakes.

The distribution of mercury in the sediments, as shown in Figure 5.8, indicates Buffalo, Erie, and Cleveland to be significant sources of mercury to the lake, with the Detroit River being the main source of the contaminant. The realization of the mercury problem was forced on the inhabitants of Michigan, Ohio, and Ontario when information about high mercury levels in Lake St. Clair and Lake Erie fish was released in 1970 (D'Itri and D'Itri 1977). One of the first actions taken was to close all fisheries on Lake St. Clair and those for two species on Lake Erie. Upon investigation, the source of the mercury was found to be chlor-alkali plants situated on the St. Clair River upstream of Lake St. Clair. Steps to combat the problem were taken immediately upon public disclosure of the mercury sources, but the mercury releases had probably begun 30 years earlier, when a chlor-alkali plant was started in Wyandotte, Michigan, in 1939. Another plant opened in Sarnia, Ontario, in 1947. The increase in mercury content of fish began to occur after the opening of the chlor-alkali plants, as indicated by the data in Figure 7.4.

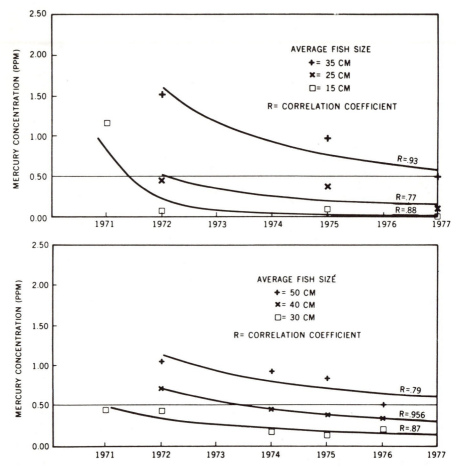

Figure 7.5 Declining mercury levels in fish from western Lake Erie. Top: *white bass;* bottom: *yellow pickerel. (Great Lakes Water Quality Board 1978c.)*

At present Lake St. Clair has no permanent sediment accumulation, and the mercury in the sediments of that lake is continually moving downstream (Thomas, Jaquet, and Mudroch 1975). Thus, Lake St. Clair is now a source of mercury to Lake Erie, even though most of the original industrial sources have been traced and shut off. The content of mercury in Lake St. Clair waters and sediments is decreasing, as well as the level in the fish (Thomas, Jaquet, and Mudroch 1975); however, Thomas and Jaquet (1976) have expressed the fear that the mercury pollution in Lake Erie could become worse as the mercury-laden sediments move from Lake St. Clair to Lake Erie. Luckily, this does not seem to have happened, as shown by the data in Figure 7.5. Mercury content values for yellow pickerel (walleye) of 50 cm length in the West Basin have declined from about 1 µg g^{-1} in 1972 to 0.15 µg g^{-1} (ppm) in 1979 (Great Lakes Water Quality Board

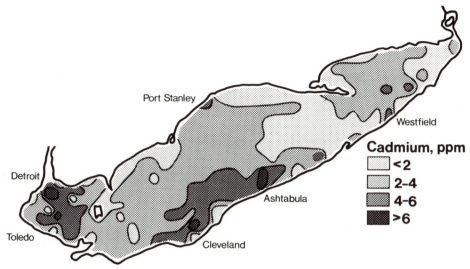

Figure 7.6 Distribution of cadmium in surficial sediments of Lake Erie, showing the six most prominent point sources of the element. (Thomas and Mudroch 1979.)

1980). A major reason for the decline is the decreasing external loading from industrial sources. In addition, the degree of adsorption and complexation of mercury onto organic carbon in the West Basin is high (Thomas and Jaquet 1976), leading to removal of mercury from the water by sedimentation of the organo-mercury complex. Once the organically adsorbed mercury settles onto the sediments, it is subducted quite deeply into the sediments by the activity of the benthic biota (10 to 15 cm). It is also diluted by the large load of fresh sediment entering the West Basin.

Cadmium is another toxic metal loaded into the lake. Again, a sediment distribution map of Thomas and Mudroch (1979) indicates the sources quite clearly. They are the Detroit River, Toledo, Cleveland, Ashtabula, Westfield, and Port Stanley (Fig. 7.6) As well as indicating the sources of the element, such highly localized areas of high concentration close to the sources of input suggest that cadmium settles out of the water column relatively quickly. Thus concentrations in the lake water are not likely to be high, averaging about 0.1 mg Cd m^{-3} (Leslie and Lum-Shue-Chan 1982). The relatively few measurements on concentration in the water show the levels of cadmium in the Detroit River to be less than 1 mg m^{-3}. Another reason for the low lakewater concentrations of cadmium is that the loading of the element to the lake is relatively small and is estimated at 44.0 (Nriagu et al. 1979) and 41 tonnes yr^{-1} (Thomas and Mudroch 1979). The data in Table 7.2 indicate that the sources of this metal are not well known.

One disturbing question in regard to cadmium and other toxic metals released by industry is that even when concentrations of the metal in open lake waters meet drinking-water standards, we do not know the concentrations of the elements at city water intakes. This question is pertinent because many of the city intakes are relatively close to city outfalls and mouths of rivers that flow through cities. Relatively few measurements of heavy metal concentrations at water intakes have been done, but the available data show the occasional day when unacceptably high values of one or another metal are present (U.S. FWPCA and Ohio Dept. of Health 1970).

The National Academy of Sciences (1974), when considering the effects of contaminants on fish and humans, has listed mercury (Hg) as being the most dangerous in relation to the other heavy metals as follows : $Hg^{2+} >$ $Ag^+ > Ni^{2+} > Pb^{2+} > As^{3+} > Cr^{3+} > Sn^{2+} > Zn^{2+}$. Little silver (Ag) is wasted, and the concentrations of silver in the Detroit River are less than 1 mg m^{-3} (Great Lakes Water Quality Board 1978c), but those of nickel (Ni) have been measured between 15 to 31 mg m^{-3} in the same river. Thomas and Mudroch (1979) have indicated high concentrations of nickel in the West Basin sediments but lower concentrations in the other basins. Waldechuck (1974) points out that if we consider the toxicity of metals to the most-sensitive stages of marine organisms, the order of relative metal toxicities changes to $Hg^{2+} > Ag^+ > Cu^{2+} > Zn^{2+} > Ni^{2+} > Pb^{2+}$ $> Cd^{2+} > As^{2+} > Cr^{3+} > Sn^{2+}$. Since we are interested in the well-being of the biota in the lake as well as the lake as a suitable source of water for people, we must consider the situation regarding copper and zinc.

Copper is an interesting trace metal in that concentrations of labile or ionic forms of copper as low as 0.5 mg m^{-3} are toxic to algae (Gächter, Lum-Shue-Chan, and Chau 1973), but healthy populations of algae can be found growing in water with 10 mg Cu m^{-3} (Atkins 1932). This paradox occurs because copper ions are strongly adsorbed or complexed by clays and organic matter in natural waters (Leckie and Davis 1979) and are thereby rendered harmless to algae. Most of the copper in a normal lake or river will be complexed and thus be not toxic, although the total concentrations may be well above 0.5 mg m^{-3}. The process of adsorption or complexation, however, takes time, so that an addition of Cu So$_4$ (copper sulphate) to small lakes and swimming pools effectively kills algae because the concentration of ions temporarily remain high enough to be toxic. After some time, the ions are complexed and the treated water is no longer toxic to algae. This means that, within limits, it is not the concentration of copper in water, but the chemical form of the copper in the water that is of major concern. Thus, a municipal sewage treatment plant releasing copper at 30 to 40 mg m^{-3} in an organically rich solution may do less harm to freshwater biota than an industry releasing a smaller amount of inorganic waste containing copper in ionic form.

Thomas and Mudroch (1979) showed that the distribution of zinc in Lake Erie sediments is different than that of cadmium and lead, with the areas of high concentration of zinc being more widespread. Evidently zinc

Table 7.3 Comparison of Heavy Metal Concentrations in the Surficial Sediments of the West Basin Between May 1970 and May 1979

	1970	1979
Cadmium	5.6 ± 3.5	3.0 ± 2.4
Copper	79 ± 46	51 ± 30
Chromium	177 ± 118	69 ± 49
Zinc	224 ± 152	200 ± 131
Lead	86 ± 48	56 ± 36
Arsenic	7.9 ± 2.5	6.5 ± 3.0
Mercury	1.14 ± 1.28	0.60 ± 0.42

Note: Measurements shown are mg metal per kg of sediment.
Source: Great Lakes Water Quality Board 1980.

does not settle out of the water as readily as the other elements. Only about 43 percent of the zinc loaded into the lake remains there (Table 7.2), with more than half remaining suspended in the water and leaving the lake. Zinc is known to effect biota adversely at concentrations greater than 50 mg m^{-3} (Weatherly, Lake, and Rodgers 1980), and concentrations of between 65 and 89 mg m^{-3} have been measured in the Detroit River (Great Lakes Water Quality Board 1978c). These quantities are probably not much over the toxic limit because zinc complexes with other material in the water, much as copper does. Thus, the actual concentration of zinc ions in the water would be considerably lower than the total concentration of zinc.

The average concentrations of six heavy metals in the sediments of the West Basin are showing a decline (Table 7.3), probably because of the improved level of sewage treatment in Toledo and Detroit. Many industries dispose of their chemical wastes in the municipal wastewater systems. These end up in the treatment plants, where they are precipitated and removed along with the organic wastes. Thus the waters being discharged to the lake now probably contain considerably lower concentrations of metals than before the improved levels of treatment were implemented.

In two recent studies, a number of trace metals were added simultaneously to lake water to produce concentrations at the legal limit for each metal. They have shown definite suppression of the algal systems (Gächter and Associates 1979; Wong, Chau, and Luxon 1978). The former study, which lasted for 18 months, showed initial suppression of photosynthesis. As the study continued, large shifts occurred in the species composition, from the original species to metal-tolerant types, so that eventually photosynthesis in the metal-laden system was at the same level as the uncontaminated control. In the Wong, Chau, and Luxon study, the algal population was dosed only once with a mix of metal salts at the maximum concentration levels considered tolerable under the Great Lakes Water Quality Agreement.

A large suppression of photosynthesis was observed in the unadapted algae. In addition to the complication of algal adaption, toxic metals have synergistic effects, and this factor will have to be considered seriously in the setting of limits for maximum concentrations of metals in water.

Obviously, much more research is needed on toxic trace metals in lacustrine systems to define realistic safe concentration limits. These limits should restrict industrial disposal to levels that will not harm the biota, and will leave the fish safe to eat and the water safe to drink.

Radioactivity

The electric power generating stations around the Great Lakes that are energized by nuclear reactors release radioactive particles to the air and water. Losses from these stations, when added to background levels of radioactivity remaining from nuclear bomb testing, could reach levels harmful to the people living around the Great Lakes Basin, particularly in the case of an accident or breakdown at one of the nuclear facilities. For this reason the 1978 Great Lakes Water Quality Agreement has set a maximum permissible radiation of 1 millirem per year for a person who consumes 1.1 liters of water per day from the Great Lakes. The rem is a complex measure of radiological dosage and is based on the amount of alpha, beta, and gamma radiation received. The dosage of each type of radiation is multiplied by factors dependent on the harmfulness to humans of each of the different types of radiation to determine the rems of radiation received.

Lake Erie has the Davis-Besse nuclear plant operating near Locust Point with two more stations planned for the near future, the Fermi station near Monroe in the West Basin and the Perry station near Painsville. Two additional large stations are on the Lake Huron Canadian shore, the Douglas Point and Bruce Stations, and since Lake Erie draws its water from Lake Huron, leakages from these stations could affect it. Nevertheless, in 1980 Lake Erie waters had the lowest potential for radioactive dosage of all the Great Lakes, at 0.06 millirem per year using a standard of 2.2 liters of water ingested per person per day (Great Lakes Water Quality Board 1981a). Thus, at present, there seems to be no danger of contamination by radioactivity. Some leakage of radioactivity has been detected from a former nuclear fuel processing site at West Valley, New York, into Cattaraugas Creek, but not at excessive radiation levels.

Non-toxic Organic Contaminants

As well as the inorganic contaminants of salt and heavy metals, industry and agriculture in the Lake Erie Basin have loaded many organic chemicals into the lake. The compounds listed below have been found in the lake (Great Lakes Water Quality Board 1978c) and are not considered toxic to man in low concentration, but many probably do have chronic effects; that is, they are not obviously toxic in nature, but they do affect man after prolonged exposure.

Alachlor	Metribuzin	Diethylhexylphthalate
Atrazine	Pentachlorobutene	Eptan
Benzopyrene	Prometone	Hexachlorobutene
Camphor	Tetrachlorobutadienes	Hexadecane
Chloroisopropyl ether	Tetradecane	Methyl-t-butyl ketone
Dicyclohexane	Trichloroethylene	Methylene chloride
Dichloroethane	Benzofluoranthene	Methylpalmitate
Dicamba	Butylphthalylbutyl	Methyltheobenzo-
Dimethyl decane	glucolate	thiazole
Fluoranthene	Carbofuran	Pentachlorobutadienes
Hexachloroethane	Cyprazine	Pentachloroethane
Indenopyrene	Dibromochloro-	Simzaine
Methyleicosane	methane	Tetrachloroethane
Methylethylhexanoate	Dichloromethane	Tetrahydrofuran
Methylstearate	Dichlorodifluoro-	Trichlorofluormethane
	methane	

Additional chemicals not included in this list are continually being found in the lake. Some of the compounds, such as the gases that comprise natural gas, do not appear to be harmful in the concentrations found. It is quite likely, however, that some of the yet-undiscovered compounds are dangerous.

An investigation into the distribution of lightweight hydrocarbons in Lake Erie was undertaken to check whether the lakewater was being polluted by the many gas wells that have been drilled in the lake. Virtually all the drilling and gas production has been done on the Canadian side of the lake, since the U.S. state governments have forbidden drilling and hydrocarbon production on the American side. They consider the possibility of pollution too high to be worth the risk of production, but some states are presently reconsidering this decision. This natural gas was formed by the marine deposits laid down during the Silurian period 400 million years ago. Reserves of oil, generated from the same deposits, also exist under the lake but are not being extracted at present.

Zapotosky and White (1980) found methane, ethane, propane, isobutane, n-butane, and some other residual hydrocarbons to be present in the lake waters above normal background levels at a number of sites. All these gases were found in low concentrations except methane. High concentrations of methane were found in association with measurable concentrations of ethane in some areas where there is current exploration and production of gas. The Canadian waters had ten sites with above-background concentrations of ethane, propane, and isobutane. The absolute concentrations of the petroleum gases reported in this study were low, and so far have had no obvious effect on the biota of the lake.

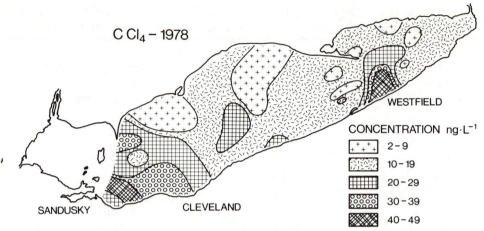

Figure 7.7 Distribution of carbon tetrachloride in Lake Erie in 1978, showing the high concentrations found along the south shore. (Kaiser and Valdmanis 1979.)

Toxic Organic Contaminants

The following organic compounds have been observed in Lake Erie (Great Lakes Water Quality Board 1978c) and have been listed in the Great Lakes Water Quality Agreement of 1978 as hazardous or potentially hazardous:

Aldrin	Dibutylphthalate	Polychlorinated bi-
Dieldrin	Malathion	phenyls (PCB)
Endrin	Trichlorophenoxy-	Phenol
Heptochlorepoxide	acetic acid	Chloroform
Methoxychlor	Chlorodane	Diazanon
Benzene	DDT and metabolites	Endosulfan
Carbon tetrachloride	Heptachlor	Styrene
Chlorpyrifos	Lindane	Xylenes

In a 1979 investigation into volatile chlorocarbons in Lake Erie, Kaiser and Valdmanis found widespread distribution of chloroform and carbon tetrachloride. The concentrations observed were low and probably not dangerous, but both compounds are known to have pronounced human physiological effects at higher concentrations. The chloroform was more or less evenly distributed, but high levels of carbon tetrachloride were found in the vicinity of Sandusky, Cleveland, and Westfield, as shown in Figure 7.7.

The organic chemicals currently causing the greatest concern are the polychlorinated biphenyls (PCBs) and long-lived insecticides such as DDT, Dieldrin, and their metabolites. The efforts to minimize the amounts of these chemicals in the environment arise from the known detrimental effect of these compounds on wildlife. The report by PLUARG (1978) states,

> Environmental concern with PCBs centers in their ability to cause gross deformities in primates used as test animals and reproductive failure in fish-eating birds (herring gulls). These birds over the past few years have exhibited a sharp decline in egg hatching. Young birds are often deformed, particularly their bills, rendering them incapable of eating.

DDT and its metabolite, DDE, cause eggshell thinning (Gilbertson 1974) and thus breakage of many eggs during incubation. Death of embryos in unbroken eggs was also found to increase with DDE content of the eggs. Breeding success per pair of herring gulls in 1972 was 0.08 to 1.2 young in Lake Ontario and 0.35 to 0.52 young in Lake Erie, compared with 0.8 to 1.2 for gulls on the New England coast (Gilbertson 1974). Obviously, some of the Great Lakes gull colonies were not breeding successfully.

One cause for the movement of these toxic materials up the foodchain is their insolubility in water as compared with their solubility in oil. DDT, for example, is 8×10^7 times more soluble in olive oil than water. Their affinity for oil causes PCB, DDT, and other insecticides to collect in the fat globules found in phytoplankton and the fatty material and tissues found in zooplankton and fish. Fish gills, too, are unfortunately extremely efficient at removing insecticides from the water (Reinert 1970), and thus fish can end up containing considerable amounts of toxin. Fish species containing a lot of body fat usually have higher PCB and DDT levels than less-oily species. Also, as fish grow older they generally carry higher concentrations of toxin—not because of age but because of size, since large individuals of a species usually contain more fat than smaller ones. Although the concentration of insecticide found in the oil of fish of different ages remains about the same, it is found to be dependent on the concentration of insecticide in the water where the fish live (Reinert 1970).

Because of their insolubility, most of the organochlorine pesticides are strongly adsorbed onto suspended particulates in water. These particulates settle out, carrying pesticides and PCB to the sediments. This process, together with the fact that PCBs and the DDT-type pesticides do not degrade easily, has led to the accumulation of large amounts of these pesticides in the sediments. The persistent nature of these chemicals also means that these accumulations will be present for a long time in the future, and in this way the sediments act as a reservoir of these materials. In addition, the larvae of many aquatic insects that live in muds are sensitive to DDT and may be weakened or killed by these insecticide accumulations in the sediments.

Sediment samples from Lake Erie have been analyzed for DDT plus metabolites and PCB and the distributions are shown in Figure 7.8. Since PCBs are industrial chemicals and the effluents containing them originate

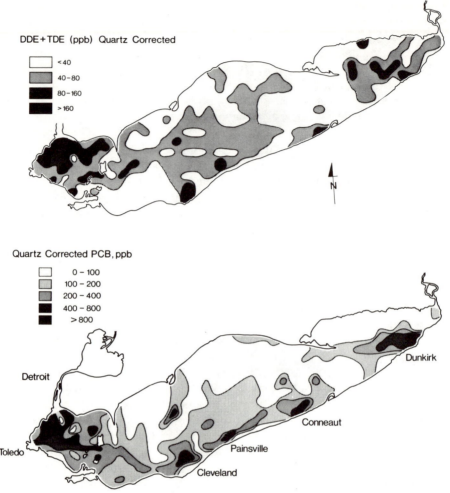

Figure 7.8 Top: *Distribution of the breakdown products of DDT—DDE and TDE—in the surficial sediments of Lake Erie, showing the result of high agricultural usage in the West and East Basin hinterlands.* Bottom: *Distribution of PCB showing the six cities closest to the areas of high concentration. (Frank et al. 1977.)*

largely from Detroit, they remain in the westerly segment of the Detroit River flow and can therefore be found near the west shore of the Basin. The elevated concentrations near the south shore of the West Basin probably originate in Toledo, while other high PCB concentrations appear to be associated with Painsville, Conneaut, and Westfield. On the other hand, DDT is largely used in agriculture, and the material in the West Basin probably originates in the farmlands of southwestern Ontario. Much DDT was also used in the tobacco lands along the north shore of the

East Basin, and the high concentrations in the sediments there result from both sources.

In 1967, the average concentration of total DDT (DDT + DDE + DDD) in smelt in Lake Erie was 1.59 μg g^{-1} (Reinert 1970), compared with recent values of 0.04 to 0.13 (GLWQB 1980). Restrictions on the use of DDT were first implemented in 1970 and then extended, so that by 1972 the material had been banned for use in Ontario and most of the United States. DDT in fish has declined noticeably to concentrations below the 1.0 μg g^{-1} wet weight guideline of the Great Lakes Water Quality Agreement of 1978 (GLWQA). Recent monitoring has shown no further decline because the sediments remain a source of the material for a long time after its use.

The PCBs, however, remain a real problem, since the sediments are not the only source of the material. Concentrations of PCBs in fish appear to be increasing and are well above the GLWQA guideline of 0.1 g g^{-1} wet weight (GLWQA 1978). The increase is related to the amount of PCB loaded from the air. For example, in the mid-70s the estimated loading of PCB to all the Great Lakes was 0.77 tons yr^{-1} from tributaries and 0.31 tons yr^{-1} from urban sources, while the direct deposition to the lakes from the atmosphere was estimated to be between 5 and 50 tons yr^{-1} (PLUARG 1978). Lake Michigan suffers the highest PCB concentrations with a mean PCB content in fish of about 10.2 μg g^{-1}. The corresponding values for the other lakes are approximately 2.4 for Lake Ontario, 0.9 for Lake Erie, 0.8 for Lake Huron, and 0.6 for Lake Superior (PLUARG 1978). While efforts are being made to control the tributary and urban inputs of PCB to the lakes, inhabitants of the Great Lakes Basin can do little to decrease atmospheric loading of this material to the lakes. A continent-wide program to control the use of this chemical is needed.

We are just beginning to realize some of the ramifications of the toxic materials in the Great Lakes. For example, a woman who ate about 5 kg of Lake Michigan fish per year was found to have about 80 μg kg^{-1} of PCB in her breast milk. Assuming that her child had a birth weight of 3 to 5 kg and drank about 0.4 kg of the mother's milk per day, the child would be consuming between 10 and 6 μg PCB per kg body weight per day. This infant would be taking in between six to ten times the maximum safe amount of 1 μg per kg of body weight daily, as recommended by the U.S. Food and Drug Administration (Swain 1981). The situation around Lake Erie is not as severe as around Lake Michigan, where the concentration of PCBs in the fish is much higher, but many people living around Lake Erie eat considerably more than 5 kg of fish per year, so PCB accumulation in these people could become excessive.

Spottail shiners taken from nearshore sites showed a decrease of about 60 percent in both PCBs and total DDT from 1975 to 1979. Moreover, recent evidence shows a decrease in PCBs in other species of fish and herring gull eggs. Since herring gulls do not migrate and keep to a fairly

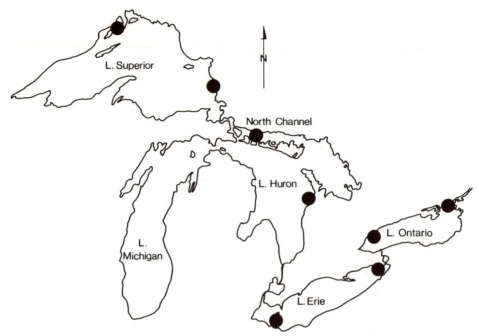

Figure 7.9 The eight sites in the Great Lakes where seagull eggs have been collected and monitored for content of toxic organic chemicals, with the results shown in Table 7.4.

specific feeding ground, their eggs can be used as a monitor of environmental conditions. Concentrations of most of these contaminants in gulls' eggs have dropped in logarithmic fashion since the efforts to diminish inputs began in recent years. This pattern of decrease has permitted the calculation of half-lives, that is, the time taken for the concentrations to halve. Data from Mineau et al. (1984), shown in Table 7.4, demonstrate that the eastern Lake Erie site has the longest half-life of DDE and DDT in the Great Lakes, because material draining from the tobacco fields maintains concentrations in the lake. The half-life of PCBs at Middle Island in the West Basin is also long because Detroit funnels a heavy load of these chemicals into the lake. With mirex, the half-life is long in the east because the Port Colborne gulls forage in the Niagara River, the main source of this material in the Great Lakes. The reason for the longevity of the HCB in the system is not known, but Dieldrin is a widely used agricultural pesticide, even more so in Lake Erie's West Basin than the East Basin.

Lake Erie receives a heavy burden of organic contaminants, so the question is often asked why Erie's fish do not contain higher concentrations of contaminants than they do. The present speculative answer is that the eutrophic state of the West Basin results in high concentrations of organic material in the water, which causes the contaminant concentration in the organic matter to be low. Thus, if the contaminant concentration in the

Table 7.4 Computed Half-lives of Major Organo-chlorine Contaminants in Great Lakes Herring Gulls, 1974–1979

Location and colony name (see Fig. 7.9)	Half-life of Contaminant (yrs)					
	DDE	DDT	PCB 1254/1260	Mirex	HCB	Dieldrin
East Lake Ontario (Snake I.)	3.7	1.4	3.7	2.5	N.S.	5.2
West Lake Ontario (Muggs I.)	3.4	1.7	3.5	2.6	4.6	7.2
East Lake Erie (Pt. Colborne Bw.)	4.5	2.1	6.8	4.0	4.7	9.2
West Lake Erie (Middle I.)	4.4	1.7	10.0	1.6	3.0	N.S.
South Lake Huron (Chantry I.)	1.9	2.3	4.8	1.5	2.7	7.9
North Channel (Double I.)	2.2	1.8	5.6	1.9	2.8	4.8
East Lake Superior (Mamainse)	3.6	1.4	N.S.	2.0	3.5	N.S.
West Lake Superior (Granite I.)	2.6	2.2	N.S.	2.3	N.S.	N.S.

Note: Calculation of a half-life entails a significant (P 0.05) first-order decrease over the period. N.S. means that a significant fit was not obtained.
Source: Adapted from Mineau et al. (1984).

primary element of the foodchain is low, the concentration of contaminant can be expected to be lower all through the foodchain. In addition, since many of the contaminants are adsorbed onto particles, the rapid settling out of particulate matter from the water column of the shallow West Basin provides an effective system of eliminating contaminants from the lake. In this way, the eutrophic state of the West Basin could be diminishing the problem of toxic materials in Lake Erie.

Summary

The disposal of the dredgings from the industrialized harbors of Lake Erie has to be done with care. Slightly polluted sediments can be disposed of by open lake dumping, while badly polluted sediments should be dumped in special containment areas; because of leaching problems, severely polluted sediments must be dumped on land.

Mercury has shown itself to be the most-dangerous metal contaminant in the lake and in 1970 led to a ban on the commercial fishing of two species in the west end of the lake. Serious efforts to curtail the release of the metal have led to a drop in the concentration in fish, so mercury pollution is no longer a serious problem. To the present there are no obvious problems posed by any of the other trace metals, but this may be due to lack of careful monitoring of city water supplies and lack of knowledge of the behavior of these materials in the lake system.

The organic contaminants, both known and unknown, are dangerous. PCBs exceed the safe limit in some species of fish and are the most serious contaminant problem. They have harmed the birds and people living around

Figure 7.10 A nest of double-crested cormorants from Big Chick Island, one of the small, uninhabited West Basin Islands. These birds migrate, so do not provide perfect evidence for changes in Lake Erie, but much greater breeding success has been noted for these birds recently. (P. Mineau, personal communication.)

the lake who eat the fish, but this danger is diminishing at present (Fig. 7.10). Many different organic compounds have been found in the eggs of gulls around the lake. Much industrial effluent is released to the lake that contains a number of chemicals that the scientific community has yet to learn to detect in the water or biota of the lake. Other contaminants also exist for which the long-term chronic effects are not known. This is a dangerous situation when one considers the millions of people who drink the water from Lake Erie and the other Great Lakes.

The bioaccumulation of pollutants in the Lake Erie foodchain remains to be fully characterized. Even the forms of the metals in the lakewater are still unknown, and the susceptibility of the biota of the lake to key toxicants needs to be carefully assessed.

We do not understand many aspects about toxic materials in lakes. One of the most-fruitful areas of research for the next decade would be the investigation of the cycling of heavy metals and organic contaminants through lake ecosystems. Medical research into the chronic effects resulting from environmental contaminants should be increased, particularly into the incidence of cancer. A start on this problem has been made by the Committee on the Assessment of Human Health Effects of Great Lakes Water Quality, who published a report in 1981 on a "Workshop on the Compatibility of Great Lakes Basin Cancer Registeries."

III

THE BASINS AND
THEIR BIOLOGY

The Basins of Lake Erie

The three basins of Lake Erie are very different in their physical characteristics (see Fig. 1.2). In fact, they are so different they could almost be considered as three separate lakes that happen to be contiguous with each other. Not only do the basins have different depths, sizes, and water retention times, but they have different land forms and shorelines surrounding the basins.

The vital statistics of the three basins are shown in the table below. The West Basin is small and shallow and receives huge inputs of nutrients and sediments. The waters of this basin are therefore turbid and productive of many forms of life. The Central Basin is much larger but is only a little deeper despite its size. It receives much smaller quantities of nutrients from the surrounding land and is not nearly as polluted as the West Basin. Nevertheless, its waters are enriched by the inputs from the West Basin. The East Basin is smaller and deeper than the Central Basin and also receives the smallest inputs of sediment and nutrients of the three basins. The offshore waters of this part of Lake Erie are clean and clear. Only the nearshore waters are turbid on occasion because of sediment or algae.

Hydraulic and Morphometric Data for Lake Erie and Its Basins

	Total lake	West Basin	Central Basin	East Basin
Surface area (km²)	25,220	3,680	15,390	6,150
Volume (km³)	468	28	274	166
Mean depth (m)	18.6	7.6	17.8	27.0
Maximum depth (m)	64	14	26	64
1970 flow-through (km³yr^{-1})	197	189	193	197
Mean water residence time (yr)	2.4	0.2	1.4	0.8

8

The West Basin

Historical Change in the Sandusky River System

A number of reports on the Sandusky River system record many of the changes that have occurred in the West Basin hinterland. All the forested lands, except along some of the river banks, have been cleared, drained, and made into good agricultural land. The marshes in the Sandusky River Basin have also altered and so has the large, shallow Sandusky Bay. A comparison between the descriptions of the Sandusky area made by the pioneers and those written by present-day naturalists will enable the reader to understand how the lands surrounding the West Basin have changed, and thus to understand the changes in the waters of the basin.

The land in the Sandusky River Basin is a little higher than that of the Maumee Basin and consists of three parts: the upland area, which is interspersed with bogs; the river and the marshes around it; and the relatively large Sandusky Bay into which the river drains. The upland areas before settlement were described as follows by Smith (1799);

> From the mouth of the Sandusky to the falls [at Fremont, Ohio] is chiefly first rate land, lying flat or level, intermixed with large bodies of clear meadows, where the grass is exceedingly rank, and in many places three or four feet high. The timber is oak, hickory, walnut, cherry, black-ash, elm, sugar-tree, buckeye, locust, and beech. In some places there is wet timber land—the timber in these places is chiefly water-ash, sycamore, or button-wood.

The early woods and river described by Keeler (1904) must have been a wonderful system: "Except where the 'plains' smiled to the sun in grass and flowers the Sandusky country was densely wooded. Great oaks, elms, walnuts and hickories were interspersed with beech, masswood, maple and sycamore." Nowadays the dense woods have been cleared and replaced with pastures and ploughed land. Few of the former impressive forests remain.

Many of the wet areas were bogs.

The most extensive cranberry bog, comprising some 2,000 acres, was in Cranberry Township, Crawford County, two miles south of New Washington. Before 1820, hundreds of bushels of cranberries were gathered and sold commercially for 20 to 25c per bushel. In 1850 cranberries brought $2.00 a bushel, but by 1855, the plants no longer grew in sufficient abundance for commercial purposes (Perrin, Battle and Goodspeed 1888, pp. 179, 624, 627–628; Dachnowski 1912, p. 46). This bog is now totally drained and under cultivation in agricultural crops [Stuckey 1976].

Sandusky Bay was described by Thorndale (1898) as being edged

with the tall, feathery plumes of the wild rice plant, intermixed with rank reeds, rushes . . . 'cat-tails,' . . . and the wild Rose of Sharon (*Hibiscus moscheutos*, swamp mallow) in full bloom. . . . Acres of wild rice and reeds pricked above the surface, and vast floating islands of water lilies bowed gracefully their broad leaves and creamy blossoms to the incoming swell. . . . Marine plants flourished luxuriantly under the water, and trailing masses of weed, vivid green in color, floated to the surface and frequently impeded the paddle wheels of the small tugs and steamers that ventured through the upper bay to the river beyond.

Sandusky Bay has changed during this century as described by Stuckey (1976), who explains the three main causes that have led to the deterioration of the bay and surrounding marsh:

The waters of Sandusky Bay have become quite muddy and turbid within the past century, as noted by Pieters (1901), Langlois (1954, pp. 97–104), Lowden (1967, 1969), and doubtless other sources not cited here. These conditions have come about by: (1) runoff from the extensive erosion of the soil from the once-forested uplands of the Basin that were cleared primarily for agricultural purposes; (2) the introduction of carp (*Cyprinus carpio* L.), a species of fish that uproots and destroys aquatic plants and contributes to the overall continued turbidity by stirring up the bottom silt and keeping it in suspension; and (3) the dredging, diking, and draining of large portions of the marshland around the Bay for private, industrial, agricultural, and wildlife areas. The silted conditions and continued high turbidity levels bring about a situation, as pointed out by Langlois (1954, pp. 97–104), Lowden (1967, 1969), and Stuckey (1971), where sufficient light does not reach the submersed plants, and, consequently, submersed species sensitive to open clear waters are eliminated or drastically reduced in numbers.

Not only the aquatic plants in the bays and streams have been affected, but fish too, since they are very sensitive to their environment. The tremendous abundance of fish in the early Sandusky system has been described as follows by Trautman (1976), after he studied the early literature.

The following published accounts are used as illustrations of the abundance of fishes in former times. Col. James Smith (Howe, 1900:589–90) was a captive of the Indians between the years 1755 and 1759. One spring he and others travelled down the Sandusky River until they "came to a little lake (Sandusky Bay) at the mouth of the Sandusky" stopping at a Wyandot town called Sunyedenad. There they caught "rock-fish" in a small tributary, which were migrating "up the creek to spawn," the first night catching "scarcely enough for present use." Mr. Thompson, a prisoner from Virginia, told Smith that he could "catch more fish than the whole town could make use of." He felled a tree so that it dropped across the creek, placing stakes along its prostrate trunk "to prevent fish from passing up, leaving only a gap at one side." He sat beside this gap at night with a "hoop net of elm bark" frequently "hauling out two or three rock-fish that would weigh about five or six pounds each." After capturing "about a wagon load" of fishes, he closed the gap before daylight, thereby preventing fishes from migrating. The next morning when the Indians saw the large heap of fish which Thompson had caught and the large number "confined in the water" they spent the "chief part of that day in killing rock-fish." Having no salt to preserve them, they left many of the fishes lying on the bank. "After some time great numbers of turkey buzzards and eagles collected together and devoured them." The literature records various other types of brush dams that were used by the white man. One on the Great Miami River, Butler County, Ohio made possible the taking of "5,000 weight," on 3–4 September, during the downstream migration of 1793 or 1794 (Wilson, 1935:53–54).

The abundance of fish in early times was also described by Keeler (1904):

What the people along the river most wanted in those early days was salt, more especially as the river teemed with fish. "Every spring," says Dr. Brainard's manuscript (1816), "the pickerel (walleye) and white bass were found in such multitudes all along the rapids, that it was often quite impossible to ride a horse across the ford till much exertion was made to drive them away and make room for his feet. Fish had in the meantime become a good article for traffic with southern teamsters, who occasionally came in with six-horse wagons loaded with flour to exchange. Hence in addition to the much-needed flour, at times a good deal of cash was paid for our choice fish, and our town became noted not only for its romantic situation, its productive soil, and the history of its inhabitants, but for its extensive fisheries."

The present-day distribution of fish in the Sandusky River and Sandusky Bay has also been studied by Trautman (1976). He has found that the

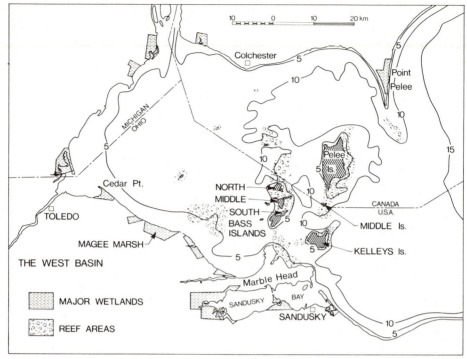

Figure 8.1 The bathymetry of the West Basin, showing the location of the reef areas and major wetlands. Depth in meters.

earlier fish populations have been severely reduced and has given these reasons for this damage:

> More than half of the 88 fish species recorded for the Sandusky River have decreased in numerical abundance since 1850 or have been extirpated. These include those species prevented from migrating upstream to spawn because of dams; those whose spawning habitat has been largely destroyed by agricultural practices, ditching and draining; those which require considerable aquatic vegetation; and/or those intolerant to turbidity. Many species of former economic importance, such as Sturgeon, Muskellunge and Walleye, have been largely or entirely eliminated.

Sandusky Bay was an important feature in the ecology of the West Basin because it is large, with a shoreline of 73 km, an area of 162 km², a width of 6 km, a length of 25 km, and a mean depth of 1.6m (Figures 1.2, 8.1). Before the hinterland was cleared, the mean depth was probably about two meters. The bay was then the huge, deep marsh described above, and was a nursery area for many types of fish. The plants prevented large waves from striking the shoreline, but nowadays, the absence of plants

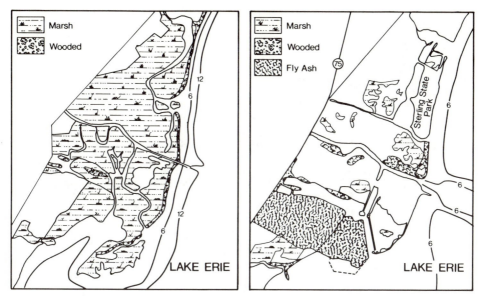

Figure 8.2 Left: *Wetlands adjacent to the Raisin River in 1915.* Right: *The vicinity of the Raisin River in 1975. (After Jaworski and Raphael 1976.)*

together with the relatively large amount of open water allows waves of about a meter to be generated. These waves have caused the banks around the bay to erode at a rate varying between 0.3 and 1.0m yr^{-1} (Carter, Benson, and Guy 1976). The material from these banks, together with that brought down by the river, is filling in the bay at the rate of 0.55 cm yr^{-1}. This shallow water body is easily stirred by wind, which together with the bottom of fine clay and silt, causes the water in the bay to be continually muddy whenever it is not frozen over. Thus, in about 100 years, Sandusky Bay has changed from being a huge, clear-water marsh populated by all manner of plants, fish, and birds to a virtual mudhole with crumbling banks and relatively few plant and fish species. Let us hope it may once again return to its former state.

Changes in the West Basin

Changes in the wetland areas have not only been caused by siltation and turbidity, but also by the draining, diking, and filling in of wetlands as the human population increased from 1.6 to more than 7 million in the West Basin hinterland during this century. An example of how the wetland around the Raisin River along the Michigan shore has been drained and used as a factory and disposal site is provided by Jaworski and Raphael (1976) in Figure 8.2. In Ohio territory around the West Basin, for example, only 12,000 of the original 40,000 hectares of Lake Erie marshes remain (GLBC, App. 17, 1975).

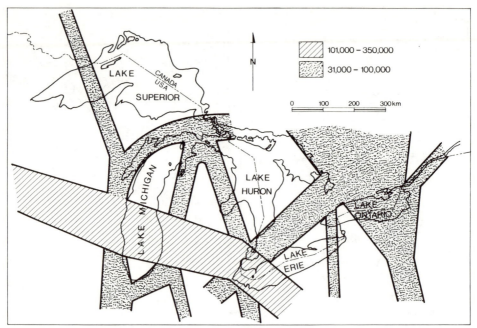

*Figure 8.3 The fall migration corridors of dabbling ducks in the Great Lakes area.
(Adapted from Bellrose 1968.)*

The loss of wetland is not only unfortunate for fish, but also for ducks, geese, muskrat, mink, raccoon, turtles, and the other many animals and birds that use wetlands. This is particularly the case for birds such as diving ducks, dabbling ducks, and the Canada, blue, and snow geese, whose migration corridors pass over the West Basin. A map of the migration corridors of the dabbling ducks, Figure 8.3, illustrates these corridors converging on the West Basin area. The migrating birds use the wetland areas for rest and feed before continuing their flights.

In the West Basin, shooting clubs existed even in the last century, primarily for duck hunting. These clubs have had a substantial effect on the ecology of the area because they caused about 40 percent of the wetlands around the Great Lakes to be diked (Herdendorf and Hartley 1980, vol. 1). The dikes enable the clubs to control the water level in the ponds and thus increase the growth of the wild plants favored by the waterfowl. The diking of the wetlands undoubtedly increases the harvest of ducks and geese, but it also alters the nature of wetlands. The Great Lakes wetlands are normally subject to many water-level changes because of seiches and the cyclical change of lakewater levels. This prevents the aging of these areas, in contrast to the steady senescence and terrestrialization of inland wetlands. The process of rejuvenation is altered by the diking and controlled succession of plants. Unfortunately, the dikes often erode

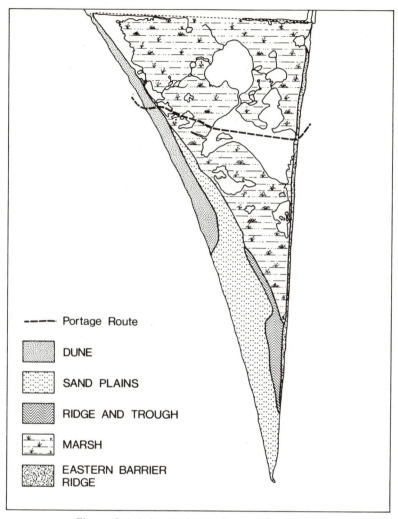

Figure 8.4 Pelee Park. (Parks Canada 1980.)

on the side facing the open water; built from the fine clay of the marsh, they cause considerable turbidity in the water as they erode.

Figure 8.1, a map of the West Basin, shows the major wetlands in existence today as drawn from Herdendorf and Hartley (1980, vol. 3). Point Pelee on the north shore is a National Park of Canada visited by many people, and is one of the unexpectedly beautiful parts of modern Lake Erie. Point Pelee lies on the same latitude as northern California, and this relatively southern position, together with the modifying influence of the surrounding water, gives rise to a Carolinian forest with a surprising diversity of plants and animals. A map of the park is shown in Figure 8.4. It is only 15.6

km² in area, but has 19.0 km of good sand beach and 1100 hectares of wetlands as well as forest and archeology sites.

Point Pelee, an area of overlap of both the Atlantic and Mississippi flyways, is at the end of a series of islands stretching across the lake.

> The Point is one link in a chain of stepping stones that lie across Lake Erie. Other links include Pelee, Hen, Middle, and Kelley's Island, the Bass Island and the south shore peninsula of Marblehead. Together the islands and peninsulas separate the central and west basins of Lake Erie and form a kind of incomplete bridge across the lake. In early history this "bridge" made crossing the lake feasible for Indian canoeists. The sections of open lake are small, and shelter from unpredictable storms was nearby. Consequently, a well-travelled route developed between Point Pelee and the adjacent mainland, and the south shore of Lake Erie [Stewart and Ross 1977].

The smaller species of migrating birds find this path for crossing the lake as safe and convenient as the earlier canoeists did. At times their numbers can be astronomical, with 20,000 birds of one species being observed in one day, and with about 200 different species migrating through the park. The mammals found at Point Pelee are deer, coyotes, raccoons, skunks, squirrels, rabbits, moles, foxes, and bats. Of course, there are also many nuisance insects, such as mosquitoes, black flies, and deerflies. More species of turtles are found in the park than anywhere else in Canada, as well as snakes, lizards, frogs, and salamanders. Few of these animals, especially the mammals, are found on the agricultural land just north of the park. We are very fortunate that this area was made into a park in 1918, since it has become a place of refuge for many wild creatures. If the land had not been appropriated by the government it would have continued to be farmland, running domestic animals and containing orchards. Few wild animals would now be found, while the marshes would probably have become private hunting preserves.

In the Point Pelee National Park nature conservation, and in some cases nature enhancement, is occurring while the park receives about 500,000 visitors a year. One of its special features is the marsh boardwalk, which gives people a chance to observe the marsh without disturbing the creatures living in it. Stewart and Ross (1977) describe it as follows:

> Patience and stealth on the marsh boardwalk bring results, especially early in the day, when animal life is active. Turtles, frogs and snakes hunt in the shallows, or along the edge of the cattail mat. Raccoons, weasels, and mink are part of the complex energy and food web, which includes all marsh life. On quiet evenings one can hear muskrats munching cattails or spadderdock roots. Bowfin, carp, northern pike, grass pike and largemouth bass are some of the larger fish that are frequently seen cruising the ponds. Painted, spotted, musk, Blanding's and snapping turtles lurk in their favourite haunts. With

Figure 8.5 The boardwalk and marsh at Point Pelee National Park. (Photo by Parks Canada, courtesy R. Watt.)

such a variety of living things, the marsh is an experience that can never be stale.

Point Pelee provides an example of what can be done to bring back part of the former beauty of the Lake Erie natural system. The achievement of this goal requires the expenditure of capital and careful thought by government officials, naturalists, and concerned citizens. Similar efforts should be made to restore some of the large wetlands along the southern shore of the West Basin and to develop a park emphasizing nature observation. This is possible because some of these wetlands are already state parks.

In general, the land around the West Basin not maintained as wetland, is now either farmed or urbanized, with little original vegetation left. The higher ground has been mostly cleared. Cover, where it is found, is brushy, consisting of idle farmland, small woodlots, and wooded stream bottoms. Stream gradients are very gentle and streams are wide, shallow, and slow-moving. The tree and shrub species are those of the eastern deciduous forest: oak, hickory, maple, beech, ash, elm, hawthorn, aspen, alder, and dogwood (GLBC, Ap.17, 1975).

The Islands of the West Basin

In summer the temperatures of the lakewater range between 20° and 25°C, with winter temperatures about 0.1° to 0.3°C. From January to March the basin is usually completely covered with ice, which can be thick enough for automobiles to be driven on it. Small villages of ice-fishing huts spring up near the shore and large islands. Many people enjoy the winter activity of sitting in one of these heated huts, quietly passing time with friends while tending their lines through a hole in the ice. Yellow perch (*Perca flavescens*) is the main fish caught, and large catches are not uncommon.

The West Basin has the highest average sedimentation rate in the lake, with the finest sediments collecting in the southeast segment of the basin. The topography of the bottom is not smooth like that of the Central Basin because of the Findlay Arch of limestone and dolomite (see Fig. 3.3). This emergence of a harder type of rock gave rise to the islands and the reefs that constitute almost three translake systems. The most easterly runs from Marblehead to Point Pelee (Fig. 8.1). The second reef system runs from the Bass Islands to Colchester, while the third consists of the reefs further to the west. These reefs are major spawning sites and contribute greatly to the production of fish from the basin.

Kelleys, Pelee, and the three Bass Islands support year-round human populations, while some of the other islands are owned as summer resorts, and still others are only large enough for day visits. They are generally flat-topped with steep, rocky sides varying from 1 to 4m in height

Figure 8.6 The Marblehead light in early spring. Built in 1823, it is the oldest lighthouse in continual operation on the lakes. (Photo by J.P. Barry.)

(Fig. 8.7), with bays and beaches existing at different sites. Today, even in their present overutilized state, they look lovely.

Kelleys Island was originally bought in 1814 by the Kelley family, who lived by cutting timber and farming. When the timber was exhausted, the lands were planted with grapevines and local wine was produced. Later, when limestone quarrying became the main business, a significant fraction of the island was removed. The island has two interesting features: the rocks bearing the grooves scraped out by the glaciers, and the Inscription Rocks discovered by Olmstead in 1833.

> A learned Indian, Shingvauk, who understood pictography, interpreted them to be the rather complex story of the Erie Indians: their occupation of the islands, the coming of the Wyandot tribe, the invasion of the Iroquois, and the evacuation in travail of spirit of the Erie from their temporary home in Lake Erie early in the seventeenth century. The carving presumably dates from about 1625 [Hatcher 1945].

Pelee Island supplied much timber when it was first deforested, and also many furs from the Big Marsh, up to 6000 muskrat skins in a year. After draining, the marsh became a rich market garden area, but recently a

Figure 8.7 The eastern end of Gibralter Island, a small dolomite island forming part of the harbor of Put-in-Bay on South Bass Island. (Photo by CLEAR.)

large part of the island has become a rich man's preserve for pheasant hunting.

South Bass Island has always been a vacation spot. Put-in-Bay is the harbor for the island, and many boats now crowd its waters. This harbor was used by the guests of the Hotel Victory, which unfortunately burned down in 1919. The following excerpt, from *Sketches and Stories of the Lake Erie Islands* by Theresa Thorndale, illustrates the importance of the Bass Islands in the last century.

The Hotel Victory was erected in 1892 and advertised as the largest and most luxuriously appointed summer hotel in the United States. It stood on a twenty-one-acre plot of high landscaped ground near the southwest shore overlooking Stone Cove, once known as Victory Bay. An electric railway connected it with the boat landing at Put-in-Bay. It could accommodate 1,500 guests at one time. People came from all over the country, especially from the southern states, and, as a contemporary, wrote, "in contemplation of this architectural marvel—its size, design, and magnificence—they are lost in wonder." It was 600 feet long, and the central portion surrounded a courtyard garden 300 feet square. It had three elevators, electric lights, steam heat, eighty private baths, an ornate dining hall that could accommodate 1,200 at one sitting; a vast lobby, a ballroom for dancing, a grand piazza along the full length of the main structure, a rustic bridge over the ravine, an electric fountain, and a boardwalk to the lake shore.

Today the grand style is gone forever. Most of the accommodation for visitors consists of a few small hotels and boarding houses, along with many privately owned or rented cottages. This is just one of the places on the Great Lakes where a once high-quality resort area has changed to a shadow of its former state, largely from changes in lifestyle and economics, but also partly as a result of the degradation of the water quality in the area. In contrast, the Grand Hotel built on Mackinac Island in 1880 on a similar scale to the Victory Hotel is still surrounded by clean water and is a thriving resort to this day.

One of the changes in lifestyle that has occurred over time is the increased popularity of boating in the Great Lakes area. The islands give the West Basin a character totally different from the other parts of Lake Erie, as far as people seeking recreation are concerned. Island harbors provide protection within short distances of each other and the mainland shore, so people can go out safely in power boats to fish. Many of these boats, while not seaworthy in a storm, are fast and can return quickly to any harbor in case of an impending storm. In the Central and East Basins, the harbors of refuge are fairly distant from each other and there are no islands; in the interest of safety, boaters must remain fairly close to the harbor they depart from. Because of the West Basin's relative safety, it is heavily used by boaters and sports fishermen. In fact, the requirements of the anglers are now so heavy that commercial fishing in the American waters of the West Basin has been prohibited and the fish catch is completely recreational. On weekends, the channels between the islands may have so many boats traveling through them that they resemble highways.

Much of the early limnology on Lake Erie was carried out from the facilities of the Stone Laboratory on Gibralter Island in Put-in-Bay. This laboratory, donated to Ohio State University by F.T. Stone, housed the scientists who first pointed out the dramatic changes occurring in the West Basin as man increasingly polluted Lake Erie. Not as much research is now conducted from this laboratory, but Ohio State does operate a school of limnology on the site each summer. It is also the field headquarters for the Center for Lake Erie Area Research (CLEAR).

Chemical and Biological Changes

Limnologists use nine primary variables as indicators of change in the trophic state of a lake. They are: the external loading of nutrients, total nutrient element concentration, soluble nutrient concentration, phytoplank-

Table 8.1 Total Phosphorus Concentrations in the West Basin

Year	Total phosphorus concentration (mg P m^{-3})	Data source
1942	14.7	Chandler and Weeks (1945)
1958	33	Beeton (1961)
1959	36	Beeton (1961)
1968	50	U.S. EPA (1970)
1970	50.9	Burns, Rosa, and Chan (1976)
1976	44.9	Fay and Herdendorf (1981)
1980	28.8	Fay and Herdendorf (1981)

ton and *Cladophora* biomass, phytoplankton species, chlorophyll *a* concentration, zooplankton concentration, oxygen concentration, and changes in benthic organisms. In addition, the change in concentrations of toxic materials in selected organisms indicates change in the degree of entry of these materials into the food web of the lake. Primary production can also be used as an indicator of change of trophic state, but it is fraught with methodological problems, and comparable values are not easily obtained. All these components of limnology have been monitored in the West Basin in the past, and some of them now give a good idea of the alterations that have occurred. The changes in the indicator variables give consistent evidence of increasing eutrophication from early times to the seventies, while some of the most-sensitive indicators of change are now showing signs of a very recent decrease in the degree of eutrophication.

NUTRIENTS

Total phosphorus concentration can be a good indicator of change, but unfortunately it was not measured during the 1929 and 1930 surveys of Wright (1955). Therefore we do not know the early phosphorus values, since the first published are those measured in 1942 by Chandler and Weeks (1945). Table 8.1 lists reliable total phosphorus data, with most of the values from samples taken in the island area between July and December of the various years. The values increase to about the year 1970 and then remain more or less steady to the mid-seventies, declining again in 1980. This response of the West Basin to decreasing phosphorus loads (see Fig. 6.10) is most heartening, although it will take some time for the full ecological consequences of this change to become apparent. There are no comparable values for total nitrogen or particulate organic carbon.

The concentrations of the soluble nutrients, except ammonia, are variable through the year, as the percentage-standard deviation values in Figure 8.8 indicate. Thus the time of sampling and the sampling frequency would have to be very similar during each year before time trends in nitrate plus nitrite, or soluble reactive phosphorus, could be compared feasibly. Data

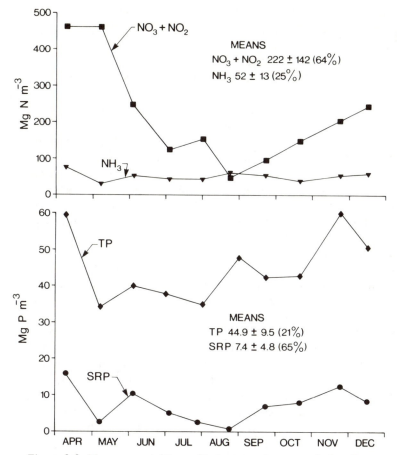

Figure 8.8 Mean concentrations of important nitrogen and phosphorus nutrient forms in the West Basin during 1970. (Burns, Rosa, and Chan 1976.)

over an extended period are not available. The data for ammonia, however are adequate and show an increasing trend to 1970. The values observed in 1930 were 17 mg NH_3-N m^{-3}; in 1942, 36; in 1948, 33; and 1970, 52 mg NH_3-N m^{-3} (International Lake Erie Water Pollution Board 1969; Burns et al. 1976a).

PLANKTON AND ALGAE

Although the phytoplankton of the West Basin have been more extensively studied than any other such community in the Great Lakes, it is difficult to describe the changes that have occurred over time. This results from almost every investigator using a different system of units for measuring population densities. Also, the sampling and counting procedures in most early studies missed many of the small organisms we now know make up a large fraction of the population, according to Munawar and Munawar (1976, 1980). Their 1976 study provides a good picture of the characteristics of the variability of the phytoplankton population in the basin during a year. The data in Figure 8.9 show that the diatoms were the dominant phytoplankton type in the spring and produced very high quantities of biomass. The diatom population then decreased during the summer when the green algae and the cryptomonads became more important. In the late summer these two groups were displaced by blue-green algae, which were co-dominant with diatoms. In the fall, the diatoms once again became dominant, a position they maintained through the winter (Burns, Rosa, and Gedeon 1978). A major growth pulse of diatoms sometimes occurs in March (Chandler and Weeks 1945). The highest chlorophyll *a* and primary production values were measured in the summer, not in the spring when the biomass is the highest.

The most-complete study of phytoplankton on the Great Lakes was carried out by Chandler (1940, 1942a, 1942b, 1944; Chandler and Weeks 1945), who examined the phytoplankton in the island area for the five years from 1938 to 1942, sampling throughout each year. His findings indicate that comparison of phytoplankton data from year to year is difficult, because "Each year the quality and quantity of the phytoplankton have been different." Although he studied all the important physical and chemical variables that could have affected the phytoplankton populations, he was not able to account for the population variability; nor was he able to develop very definite cause-and-effect relationships for the changes in the phytoplankton population he observed (Chandler and Weeks 1945). The problem of the factors controlling algal population fluctuations remains largely unsolved, even at the present time.

Although a large increase in phytoplankton density in the West Basin cannot be demonstrated by comparing earlier and recent values, the older scientists who have followed changes in this basin over a long period have reached a consensus that the phytoplankton density has increased significantly with time. As well as a general increase in biomass, some other differences between 1929–30 and 1970 are obvious. Wright's (1955) data for 1930 showed that the fall or late summer pulse contained many green algae, whereas Munawar and Munawar's (1976) data show that the mid-summer green population was almost completely replaced in the late summer by blue-greens in 1970. There have also been some major species changes to the more eutrophic types. Verduin (1969) has stated that the three dominant species in 1950 were *Asterionella formosa*, *Tabellaria fenestrata*, and *Melosira ambigua*, which are known to be oligotrophic species. By 1961–62 species had changed to *Fragilaria capucina*, *Coscinodiscus radiatus*, and *Melosira binderana*, and by 1970 *Fragilaria capucina* had been replaced by *Fragilaria crotonensis* (Munawar and Munawar 1976). These last-named species are known to be common in mesotrophic and eutrophic waters.

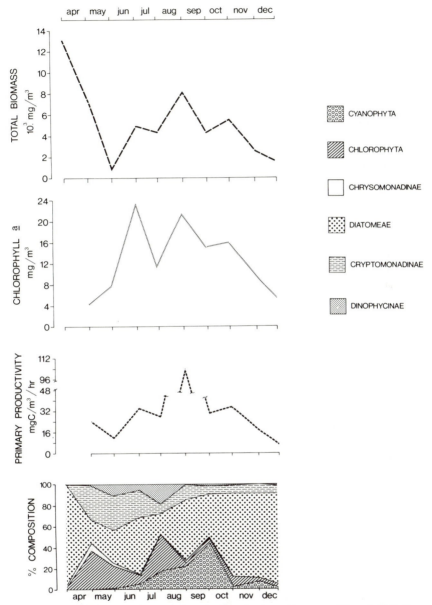

CYANOPHYTA

CHLOROPHYTA

CHRYSOMONADINAE

DIATOMEAE

CRYPTOMONADINAE

DINOPHYCINAE

*Figure 8.9 Seasonal fluctuations of phytoplankton biomass, chlorophyll "a",
primary productivity, and phytoplankton group composition in the West Basin
during 1970. (Munawar and Munawar 1976.) Common names are: Cyanophyta—blue greens, Chlorophyta—greens, Chrysomonadinae—chrysomonads, Diatomeae—diatoms, Chrytomonadinae—cryptomonads, Dinophycinae—dinoflagellates.*

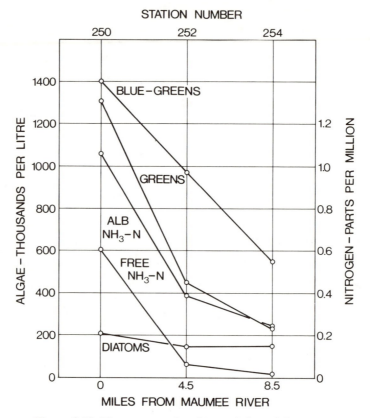

Figure 8.10 The average abundance of three different phytoplankton groups, and concentrations of albuminoid and free ammonia in the Maumee Bay area during July, August, and September 1930. (Wright 1955.)

An observation in 1929 that is similar to the present is the increasing importance of blue-green algae in the water near the nutrient-enriched rivers. Even in 1930, as shown in Figure 8.10, the greens and blue-greens increasingly out-competed the diatoms as the Maumee River was approached. This condition of nearshore dominance by blue-greens today extends along most of the south shore of the basin (Letterhos, personal communication).

Some small changes in the phytoplankton community have recently been observed that are indicative of change, because the same measurement techniques have been used with all samples. Five times in 1979 Munawar and Munawar (1980) resampled a station close to the Bass Islands that had been sampled nine times during 1970 and found a decrease in the overall biomass level (Fig. 8.11). Because of the variability described by Chandler, this difference cannot be considered to be definitive of change. They also found, however, that three species favoring eutrophic conditions were less abundant in 1979 than in 1970, and that seven species preferring oligotrophic

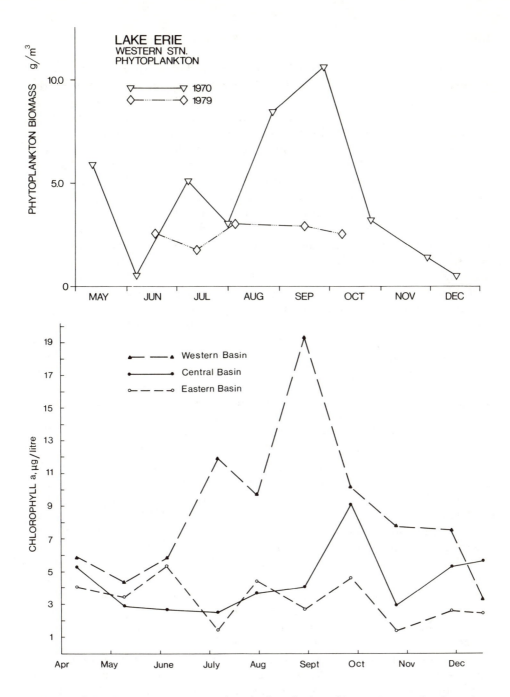

Figure 8.11 Top: *Measurements of total phytoplankton biomass in samples from the West Basin mid-lake station, taken in 1970 and 1979. The same measurement techniques were used, and the results show an apparent decline in biomass with time. (Munawar and Munawar 1980.)* Bottom: *Average chlorophyll "a" values measured in the different basins in Lake Erie. The large variability is especially apparent in the West Basin. (Glooshenko, More, and Vollenweider 1974.)*

conditions were more abundant in 1979. This indicates that there has been a recent response in the nature of the phytoplankton community to the lower phosphorus loads that have occurred since 1972. Nicholls, Standen, and Hopkins (1980) have also reported a decrease in greens and blue-greens in recent years at the Kingsville water intake on the north shore.

The pattern of *Cladophora* trends in the West Basin is not as clear. Early photographs (from Taft and Kishler 1973) show fairly heavy *Cladophora* wash-ups on beaches during the last century and early in this one. Evidently the nutrient availability was sufficient for the alga to use the light filtering through the clear water prevailing at that time to grow on many of the reef areas. The response of *Cladophora* to reduced phosphorus concentrations in the West Basin is difficult to predict. Because reduced phosphorus availability will result in reduced phytoplankton populations and thus improved water clarity, further growths of *Cladophora* are possible. The *Cladophora* situation is a complex one because stands of this alga can be found whenever soluble reactive phosphorus concentrations are consistently above 2 mg P m^{-3}. When the phosphorus availability is high the growth of the material is vigorous, and much of it sloughs off and causes large wash-ups of organic material on beaches. When phosphorus is less available because of decreased loadings, large stands of *Cladophora* can exist, but the growth rate, sloughing off, and wash-ups of the alga become much smaller (M. Auer, personal communication). If *Cladophora* grows under conditions of low nutrient availability, its nuisance value reduces considerably and it can become a more beneficial part of the ecology of the West Basin.

The data in Figure 8.11 (*bottom*) show that chlorophyll *a* concentrations are quite variable and many samplings of this parameter are needed for a statistically meaningful average. The data available for estimating June to November averages yield the following values: 1970, 10.3 mg m^{-1}; 1974, 14.6; 1975, 18.3; 1980, 10.4 (Fay and Herdendorf 1981), suggesting that peak concentrations were observed in the mid-seventies, although the uncertainty in these values weakens any observed trend.

Lake Erie's zooplankton population, which grazes on the phytoplankton, is dominated by short-lived opportunistic species with high reproductive potential. They occur in pulses of one, two, or more generations that are triggered by environmental factors (Watson 1976). The short life cycles are probably a result of both temperature and phytoplankton populations changing fairly rapidly in the lake. This pattern of behavior makes the zooplankton population fairly difficult to use as an indicator of change, but a few general patterns of change are discernable. Patalas (1972) carried out a survey of the Great Lakes zooplankton and found that the numbers of zooplankton increase directly with chlorophyll *a* concentration in the Great Lakes, and thus one can deduce that the number of zooplankton would increase with increasing phytoplankton populations and eutrophication. Following from this, the number of zooplankton in the West Basin could be expected to increase with time, and the data collected by Bradshaw

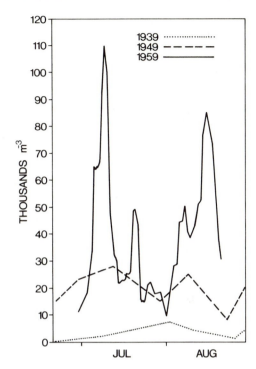

Figure 8.12 The distribution and abundance of Cladocera *in the Bass Island region during July and August of 1939, 1949, and 1959. The 1959 trace is a three-point moving average of daily collection totals. (Bradshaw 1964.)*

(1964) indicate that the copepods and also the cladocerans, shown in Figure 8.12, have increased with time. The four numerous cladoceran species in the West Basin are *Bosmina longirostris, Eubosmina coregoni, Daphnia retrocurva,* and *Daphnia galeata mandotae.* Of the cyclopoids, *Cyclops biscuspidatus thomasi* and *Cyclops vernalis* are the most important. Rotifers were not included in most surveys of the lake before Larson and Rathke (1980) measured substantial numbers of them in 1974, but there is no proof of change in these populations. The most important species found were *Keratella quadrata, Keratella cochlearis, Conochilus unicornis, Polyathra vulgaris,* and *Brahcionus angularis.*

OXYGEN AND BENTHIC ORGANISMS

Stratification occurs during calm periods in the spring and summer because then the sediments are always colder than the water and cool the water closest to them. Figure 8.13 shows a thermally stratified water mass that was observed after a five-day period with light winds, having a daily mean speed of about 3.0 m sec^{-1}. Sometimes the period of thermal stratification is initiated by a seiche causing thermocline water from the Central Basin, which is a little cooler than the West Basin water, to flow into the West Basin along the bottom. This water will remain on the bottom of the West Basin if conditions remain calm, causing temporary stratification.

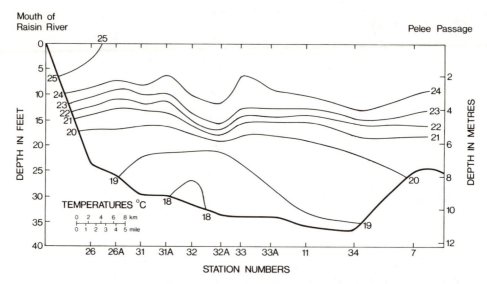

Figure 8.13 Profile of the West Basin of Lake Erie from the Raisin River to Pelee Passage, showing the thermal structure observed in the water along the transect. (Carr, Applegate, and Keller 1965.)

Temporary stratification results in depletion of oxygen from the near-bottom waters as the organic matter lying on the sediments decays. The lowest reported value in near-bottom waters is the 0.7 mg O_2 1^{-1} measured in 1953 (Britt 1955a) after 28 days of relatively calm weather. Many other occurrences of low oxygen concentrations in the West Basin have been observed, but in only one case was an oxygen uptake rate determined. This was done by Carr, Applegate, and Heller (1965), who found that the rate of oxygen loss from near-bottom waters was about 1 g O_2 $m^{-3}day^{-1}$ in 1963. Since oxygen uptake rates have not been computed for different years, it is not possible to state with certainty whether there has been an increase in the rate of sediment oxygen uptake with time. Nevertheless, other circumstantial evidence points to an increase in the uptake rate and resultant incidence of low oxygen concentrations. Wright (1955) surveyed the West Basin during 1929 and 1930. During that two-year period, the lowest oxygen value observed was 4.9 g m^{-3} in August 1930, with most values being greater than 7.0 g m^{-3}. Since that time, the frequency of low oxygen occurrences has increased markedly with, for example, two separate observations of oxygen concentrations of less than 3.0 g m^{-3} being observed in the same year, one in July of 1973, and another in August (Zapotosky and Herdendorf 1980). Britt, Skoch, and Smith (1968) report a similar finding in 1966.

The low, near-bottom oxygen concentrations are dependent on both the accumulation of organic material on the sediments and the length of the calm spells. Carr, Applegate, and Keller (1965) stated that a five-day period of weather with mean wind speed less than 6 knots and maximum windspeed less than 13 knots, together with temperatures above 18°C, will cause temporary thermal stratification about three times per summer, on average. In the early part of the century calm spells of this type were of little consequence because near-bottom oxygen concentration remained high enough for the organisms living in the sediments to survive. Nowadays, however, with higher oxygen uptake rates, these calm spells cause very low oxygen concentrations to occur.

Scientists, sporadically measuring oxygen concentrations in the West Basin, cannot describe with certainty the changes in the prevailing oxygen regime. But the benthic organisms that are sensitive to oxygen concentrations can be reliable indicators of change in seasonal oxygen minimum concentrations. Indirectly, they are also good indicators of the trophic state of the lake because the three types of benthic organisms in the West Basin exist under different oxygen regimes. One is the oligochaetes (aquatic earthworms) that feed in a manner similar to a terrestial earthworms, ingesting large quantities of sediment, digesting the suitable organic matter, and excreting the inorganic material. They are usually positioned vertically in the mud with the head downward. This organism absorbs oxygen through its skin; when oxygen concentrations become low it moves upward and extends its tail into the water to increase oxygen absorption. These worms, especially *Tubifex tubifex*, are often found in polluted environments, such as sewage-polluted rivers, where there is much available organic matter. Tubificid worms can survive when conditions become anoxic because they become quiescent and can exist for more than a month without oxygen (Pennak 1953).

The second type of benthic organism is the larvae of chironomids (midges), which are also common in the sediment in the West Basin. They live in tubes that are open at both ends and obtain their food and oxygen by flushing water through these tubes. The genus *Procladius* is tolerant of polluted waters and feeds on tubificid worms (Carr and Hiltunen 1965).

Another organism important to the ecology of the West Basin is the mayfly *Hexagenia bilineata*, which spends most of its life as a nymph (Fig. 8.14A). This insect also digs a burrow open at both ends through which it pumps water, and feeds on organic material strained from the passing water. These organisms are usually found in well-oxygenated water of less than 15m in depth. When mature, they come out of the water in the subimago form (Fig. 8.14B) and must alight on some object to shed an exocuticle before emerging in the final mating form. This organism and the midge larvae are important food items for fish (Pennak 1953).

Wright (1955) considered the density of oligochaetes to be an indicator of the degree of pollution, with 100 to 1000 individuals m^{-2} indicating light pollution, 1000 to 5000 indicating moderate pollution, and more than 5000 m^{-2} indicating heavy pollution. Carr and Hiltunen (1965) used these criteria to describe the changes in the benthic fauna from 1930 to 1961

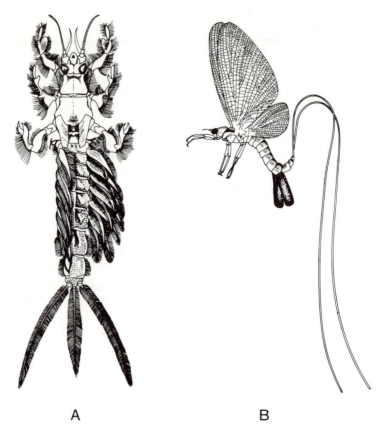

A   B

Figure 8.14 Left: *A mayfly nymph of a species common in the West Basin,* **Hexagenia bileneata.** Right: *An emergent subimago form that is very similar to the mayfly in its final mating form. (Pennak 1953.)*

in the region near the Maumee River. Figure 8.15 shows that the zones of heavy and moderate pollution increased enormously during the period. Britt, Pliodzinskas, and Hair (1980) found in 1973–74 that the zone of moderate pollution covered the entire West Basin.

The oligochaete density throughout the West Basin now varies between 1000 and 3000 m^{-2} except near river mouths, where it is higher (Britt, Pliodzinskas, and Hair 1980). This is much greater than the average of 5 oligochaetes per square meter counted by Wright (1955) in the island area in 1930. These openwater-type oligochaetes, primarily species of *Limnodrilus*, are different from the *Tubifex* species found mostly near the Detroit River at present. In addition, Carr and Hiltunen (1965) found that the chironomid density had increased substantially in all the areas they examined, except at the mouth of the Detroit River. The present midge population consists

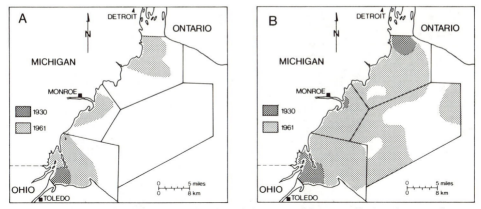

Figure 8.15 Left: *Changes in the size of the zone of heavy pollution (greater than 5000 oligochaetes per m²) from 1930 to 1961.* Right: *Changes in the size of the zone of moderate pollution (1000 to 5000 oligochaetes per m²) from 1930 to 1961. (Carr and Hiltunen 1965.)*

mostly of *Procladius* and *Chironomus* species (Britt, Pliodzinskas, and Hair 1980).

The largest observed change in benthic organism populations in the 31-year period from 1930 to 1961 was in the mayfly population, which crashed in 1953, so that the 1961 population was less than 1 percent of what it had been in 1930, as shown in Figure 8.16. The decline of the *Hexagenia* is almost certainly due to the increased sediment oxygen demand, which caused increased occurrence of low near-bottom oxygen concentrations. In 1953, the year of the well-known 28-day calm spell, Britt (1955a) visited a site where the oxygen concentration had dropped to 0.7 g $O_2 m^{-3}$ and found all the mayfly nymphs dead at a density of about 465 m^{-2}. When

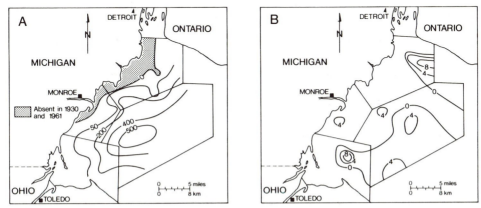

Figure 8.16 Distribution of the mayfly, **Hexagenia** *(num. per m²), in the West Basin (A) in 1930; (B) in 1961. (Carr and Hiltunen 1965.)*

Figure 8.17 Before the demise of the mayflies, they could assume nuisance proportions for the residents of Lake Erie islands, as shown by this collection on South Bass Island sometime in the 1940s. (Photo by N.W. Britt.)

other areas further afield were sampled a week later, the findings were similar. In 1954, after the eggs laid the previous year had hatched, the number of live mayfly nymphs was found to be almost double that of 1953, and there was hope that the population would recover from the natural catastrophe (Britt 1955b). Nevertheless, in the following years the population dwindled so that surveys conducted across the West Basin in 1973 and 1974 did not find a single mayfly (Britt, Pliodzinskas, and Hair 1980). This change denotes a tremendous ecological degradation, considering the huge number of these insects once populating the basin (Fig. 8.17).

Some people have questioned the thesis that the low oxygen concentrations, resulting from the increased load of organic materials to the sediments, caused the extirpation of the mayflies. They postulate that the chief cause was the increased concentration of DDT and its by-products in the sediments, because these chemicals exist in concentrations of 30 to 50 µg per kg of sediment in the West Basin (Great Lakes Water Quality Board 1980). This insecticide may indeed have helped kill the mayflies, but it is unlikely to have been the main cause. N. Wilson Britt (personal communication) has taken sediment from the West Basin in recent years and successfully cultured mayflies in it by ensuring that the water in his tanks was well oxygenated. Thus the loss of oxygen from the near-bottom waters does appear to be the most-important factor controlling the loss of the mayflies from the West Basin.

The mayfly story is not ended; they have given us some new information of great importance. A fairly large hatching of mayflies was seen in the island area in 1981 (Britt, personal communication), so conditions in the West Basin appear to be improving and the mayflies are going to survive.

To complete this discussion on oxygen, mention should be made that the longest calm spell in the West Basin occurs in the winter when the basin becomes completely covered by ice. Four stations were sampled in February 1977 after six weeks of complete ice cover to determine if the oxygen concentrations dropped during the winter to the extent that some of the biota could suffer by the end of the season. In the winter of 1976–77, one of the coldest in recent history, the ice thickness in the West Basin varied between 75 and 100 cm. Much to everyone's relief, the oxygen concentrations on 15 February 1977 were found to average about 90 percent of saturation (Burns, Rosa, and Gedeon 1978). Some of the highest concentrations were actually measured close to the sediment, where a layer of live algae lying on the bottom was probably producing a little oxygen by photosynthesis, since the water under the ice in mid-lake was very clear. Evidently the low temperatures (0 to 1.0°C) kept the rate of organic degradation low, and the small amount of oxygen taken up by decomposition was partially compensated for by photosynthesis under the ice.

Thus, of the nine trophic state indicators listed earlier, all, except for chlorophyll a, have showed a drastic deterioration of the West Basin environment since 1930. Some people, acting on their concern about the degradation, worked to bring the Great Lakes Water Quality Agreement into existence, which is a first step in rehabilitating the Great Lakes. In response to these actions, we now see decreased loadings of phosphorus and resultant decreases in concentration occurring in the waters of the West Basin. Changes in the phytoplankton and benthic communities are also giving us some indications of recent improvement in the system.

The Fish Community

Lake Erie has the most-productive freshwater fishery, in terms of commercial harvest, in the Great Lakes and probably the world. Only occasionally has the total harvest from any of the other Great Lakes been greater than that of Lake Erie. In terms of yield per unit area, this lake is about ten times more productive than the others. This is illustrated by the following average yields for the commercial fisheries from each of the lakes for 1960 to 1969 in kg of fish per hectare: Ontario, 0.52; Huron, 0.62; Superior, 0.69; Michigan, 2.68; and Erie, 9.20 (Smith 1972). This pattern of yield

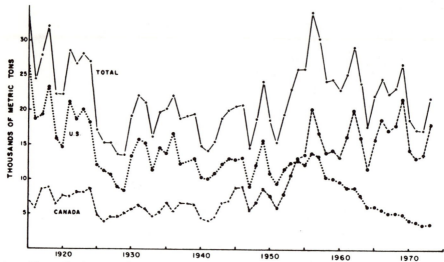

Figure 8.18 Canadian, U.S., and total commercial fish production (all species) from Lake Erie from 1915 to 1973. (Leach and Nepszy 1976.) The increase in the Canadian production has compensated for the decrease in the American.

has changed little from the last century, except that yields from Lakes Huron and Ontario were slightly higher then.

One reason for Lake Erie's productivity is that the West Basin, even today, serves as a good nursery for many of the fish in the lake (Hartman 1972). In addition, the shallowness of the lake, together with the supply of nutrients from the drainage area, has kept the waters fertile. In the early days, the many marshes and rivers around the West Basin as well as the numerous reefs and sandy shoals were superb breeding grounds for fish. At present, the reefs and shoals provide the best breeding areas for the fish currently living in the lake. The species of fish in the lake have been estimated at 138, with 114 of them native to Lake Erie. This is a remarkable diversity, considering that there are only 177 freshwater species in Canada (Leach and Nepszy 1976).

Fairly good records of commercial catches have been kept, but records of recreational fishing catches are poor. This is unfortunate because smallmouth bass (*Micropterus dolomieui*), largemouth bass (*Micropterus salmoides*), northern pike (*Esox lucius*), and muskellunge (*Esox Masquinongy*) were reserved for the sports fishery at the turn of the century along the American side of the lake. There are now no records of population change in these species. Commercial fishing effort in the United States has been decreasing, while that in Canada has been increasing (Figure 8.18). This is a result of the recreational fishery in the U.S. becoming more important than the commercial fishery.

While the total output of the Lake Erie fishery has remained fairly constant (see Fig. 8.18), the important species have changed dramatically since the last century. The first commercial species were mainly highly valued large fish, but most of these are no longer available and have been replaced by smaller, lower-valued fish. Nineteen species of fish have been considered important to the commercial fishery at one time or another (Leach and Nepszy 1976), but in 1975 there were only ten important commercial fish types (Ridgley 1976). Six species have gone from major commercial importance to insignificance, and some have been extirpated completely.

STRESSES ON THE FISHERY

Fishery problems in Lake Erie surfaced long before eutrophication problems. By 1900 two important species had become commercially extinct, the sturgeon (*Acipenser fulvescens*) and the lake trout (*Salvelinus namaycush*). A report on a conference held in 1928 to discuss this problem stated, "It is believed that material progress has been made in stimulating research on the problems of conservation and the rebuilding of a valuable but sadly depleted fishery in Lake Erie" (Higgins 1928).

The limnological surveys of the West Basin carried out by Wright (1955) and co-workers Tiffany and Tidd in 1929 and 1930 were a result of the 1928 conference. These investigators were commissioned to find out whether the pollutional inputs of the cities in the West Basin had caused the decline of the fishery. In the resulting report they identified areas that were polluted around the major cities, but they considered that the detrimental effects of the city inputs were offset by the increased biological growth and supply of fish food resulting from the nutrient inputs. Their final conclusion was probably correct: "that it seems highly improbable that pollution in Western Lake Erie has been the primary and controlling factor in the depletion of the fishery" (Wright 1955).

We now know far more about the factors affecting the West Basin fishery and the stresses on the fish. The problem is intensified because the factors are synergistic; that is, each stress worsens the effects of the other stresses. They do not affect the different species equally. Some species of fish are very vulnerable to the particular stresses occurring in the West Basin and declined in number many years ago; other species are only now showing signs of declining populations; and some of the less-desirable species have actually been increasing in number. The very fact that many commercially desirable species have disappeared or diminished while undesirable ones have flourished indicates that overfishing and not pollution has been the dominant stress. As can be seen in Table 8.2, the major stress affecting the fish community has been overfishing; i.e., that more biomass of a particular species is being harvested than can be produced on a continuing basis. Overfishing can reduce the number of spawning adults and thereby affect future population size. Even without exploitation, the success of year classes is affected by weather or other conditions. If excessive harvesting continues, the average age of the fish caught decreases, and the annual

Table 8.2 Summary of Cultural Stresses Affecting Commercial Fish Species in Lake Erie

| | Stresses | | | | |
Species	Commercial fishery	Nutrient loading	Nonnative species	Erosion and siltation	Tributary and shoreline restructuring	Entrainment at intakes
Lake sturgeon	X			X	X	
Lake trout	XX	X	X(?)	X		
Lake whitefish	X	X		X		
Lake herring	XX	X		X		
Sauger	XX	X		X	X	
Blue pike	XX	X	X			
Walleye	XX	X	X	X	X	
Yellow perch	XX		X			X

Note: X = moderate effect; XX = severe effect.
Source: After Leach and Nepszy 1976.

catch begins to vary greatly, because it depends more and more on the survival of a good-year class rather than on a large, stable background population. If overfishing does not cease, the fishery usually collapses abruptly with the removal of the last, strong year class, as has occurred with a number of species in Lake Erie.

The effects on the fish populations of heavy nutrient loading and increased eutrophication are much less dramatic, but are nevertheless dangerous. The prime effect is the increase in the amount of organic material settling on the bottoms of rivers or lakes, either directly from city wastes or indirectly from increased phytoplankton growth as a result of nutrient loading. When this organic material lowers the oxygen concentration near the bottom, it increases the probability of suffocation of fish eggs lying on the sediments, or death of fish-food organisms such as mayfly nymphs. There also appears to be an increase in number and abundance of fish parasites in Lake Erie associated with increased eutrophication (Leach and Nepzsy 1976).

The non-native or introduced species in Lake Erie at the present time are the sea lamprey (*Petromyzon marcinus*), alewife (*Alosa psedoharengus*), smelt (*Osmerus mordax*), white perch (*Morone Americanus*), and Pacific coho salmon (*Oncorhynchus kisutch*). All these species have affected native populations in the Great Lakes. In Lake Erie, the smelt have affected some important native species by their competition and predation on young fish. The white perch is a recent invader and its effects on other species have not yet been assessed.

Erosion and subsequent siltation affect the sandy or gravelly spawning areas of fish, the fish themselves, and also the plants some fish feed on.

The effect of soil erosion on some species of fish has been dramatically illustrated by Trautman (1977) as follows:

> Before 1890 the "May sucker," as the commercial fishermen called it, apparently was captured in some numbers in the Scioto River in central Ohio (Trautman 1957:263). It was sufficiently numerous in the Blanchard and Auglaize Rivers [tributaries of the Maumee River] of northwestern Ohio during August of 1893 for Kirsch (1895:326) to collect "many young" in the Blanchard River "just below Ottawa" in Putnam County.
>
> Kirsch (1895:326) described the Blanchard River at this locality as containing whitish clay along the "banks as well as the bottom of the channel" and that in "some places the bottom is covered with sand and fine gravel." The stream was "remarkably clear" of rubbish. Water-willow (*Justica americana*) and "dartweed" were common.
>
> On July 7 1929 the late Prof. James S. Hine and I visited this locality and found the substrate uniformly covered with silt. With shovels we dug through the silty substrate approximately 15 inches (38 cm) and uncovered the sand, gravel, and whitish clay mentioned by Kirsch. The transition between silt and the original substrate was sharply delineated, indicating that heavy silting occurred immediately after the land had been plowed. The remarkably well preserved blackened rootlets of plants still remained in the buried sand.
>
> It seems obvious why the harelip sucker was extirpated from this locality. This species had a highly specialized, small subterminal mouth and a broad isthmus widely separating the restricted opercles. These prevented a supply of water sufficient enough to remove the accumulated mucus and silt from passing between the gills. In contrast the largemouth blackbass, with its huge mouth and widely flaring opercles, has the ability to flush readily the accumulating silt and mucus from the gills. I have repeatedly observed members of the closely related genus *Moxostoma* (redhorses) dead, with their gill chambers packed with silt and mucus, immediately following a brief summer shower that caused cornfield silts to be washed into the stream.

The draining and filling of marshes caused destruction of many of the fish breeding habitats of shallow water species. The large, shallow, and prolific Sandusky and Maumee Bays have been completely changed by turbidity caused by silt, which has indirectly killed many of the macrophytic plants in these bays. Also, many of the spawning streams were blocked by hundreds of dams built during the last century for sawmills, gristmills, and flood control (Hartman 1972).

Entrainment of fish into the cooling water intakes of thermal- and nuclear-powered electrical generating stations is a recent source of stress. Particularly unfortunate in this regard are the St. Clair River, Detroit River, and West Basin with the greatest concentration of these power-generating stations in the Great Lakes. Many of the larger fish are killed by impingement on powerplant screens. Kelso and Milburn (1979) conservatively estimated from powerplant data that approximately 23 million fish are killed annually by impingement in powerplant intakes in Lake Erie

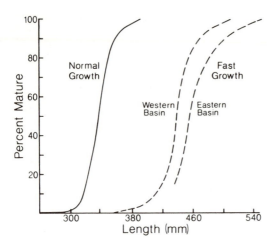

Figure 8.19 The different relation-
ships between length and percent ma-
ture female walleye in Lake Erie under
conditions of normal and fast growth.
(Schneider and Leach 1977.)

(exclusive of the plants on the Detroit and St. Clair Rivers). The impinged fish have a similar species distribution to those taken by the commercial fishery and an average weight of 75 g. This means that the fish biomass lost from the fishery by impingement is about 1700 metric tons, or about 10 percent of the total commercial fish landing. The number of larval fish entrained into the system is much greater and is estimated from data at about 255 million fish. If one in ten of these small fish survived to adulthood, then the loss by entrainment would be approximately equal to the loss by impingement, that is about 25 million fish. This means that the powerplants in Lake Erie are uselessly eliminating a number of fish equal to about 20 percent of the commercial catch. This amount is greater than the quantity of fish taken by the sport fishery as, for example, the Ohio sports fishery is estimated at 18 million fish per year (GLBC, App. 8, 1975). Fish entrainment and impingement is probably the most-underestimated problem in Lake Erie, particularly since the synergistic effects of the different stresses magnify the losses. For example, the loss of larval fish by entrainment would be greatest during the years of greatest spawning success because much of the spawning is done in shallow water near the intakes. When a fishery is struggling, it really needs these successful year classes to fill the void left by the unsuccessful years.

Another synergistic effect is the interaction between eutrophication and overfishing. Eutrophication increases the number of zooplankton and forage fish in the water and hence the food base for grazing fish. Walleye in the West Basin utilize this resource and have been shown to have a much higher growth rate in the period from 1964 to 1966 than during 1927 to 1933. Increased growth rate would normally be considered advantageous for a species, but this is not the case in an exploited fishery. In the West Basin, the fishery was permitted to take walleyes longer than 394 mm., and the data in Figure 8.19 show that during 1927–33 the fisheries would not have taken immature female walleyes. In the 1960s, with the greater growth rate, virtually all the females of that length would have been sexually immature, and under these conditions the fish were taken before they had a chance to spawn. The data speak for themselves, as follows:

> The western half of Lake Erie long sustained the best walleye (*Stizostedion vitreum vitreum*) fishery in the Great Lakes, if not in the world. Commercial harvest was relatively stable at about 1,000 tons from 1885 to 1939 (Baldwin and Saalfeld 1962). Walleye catches then increased almost steadily until 1954 and sharply after 1954, to nearly 7,000 tons in 1956—the record year. By 1969, however, the catch had dropped precipitously to 213 tons. The population recovered after commercial fishing was banned in 1970 [Schneider & Leach 1977].

The collapse of the walleye fishery was probably not due only to the interaction of eutrophication and overfishing, because the introduction of non-native species also played a part. The smelt, which invaded Lake Erie about 1935, spread and become an important forage fish for walleye, blue pike (*Stizostedion vitreum glacum*), and sauger (*Stizostedion canadense*). Part of the increased growth rate of the walleye was certainly due to this additional source of food. The adult smelt also prey on larval walleye (Regier and Hartman 1973), and thus the two species are mutual predators. When fishing pressure caused the stocks of sauger, blue pike, and walleye to weaken, the smelt population was able to expand from lack of predation, and then the smelt added severe grazing pressure on the declining stocks of the preferred fish.

HISTORY OF THE FISHERY

The action of the stresses on the different species of fish can best be illustrated by a brief history of the more important species. Fishing with seine nets (Fig. 8.20) began in 1815 in Maumee Bay, but there was often a 95 percent release after the local needs had been met. Commercial fishing became important in 1830 and increased in 1850 with the use of pound nets (see Fig. 8.20). The onset of the Civil War in 1857 resulted in a big increase in the demand for fish (GLBC, App. 8, 1975).

Many lake sturgeon were caught in the pound and seine nets. These fish were often huge, weighing more than 50 kg, and were frequently older than the men who caught them. (A sturgeon of 94 kg and 154 years of age was caught in 1953 in Lake-of-the-Woods [Scott and Crossman 1973].) Unfortunately, the sturgeon tore the nets and were considered a pest by the fishermen, who devised heavy nets with a large mesh to capture and then destroy them. Some were stacked as cordwood on the wood dock at Amherstburg, Ontario (near Windsor); because of the oil in their bodies, they were used to fire the boilers of the steamboats plying the Detroit River (Scott and Crossman 1973).

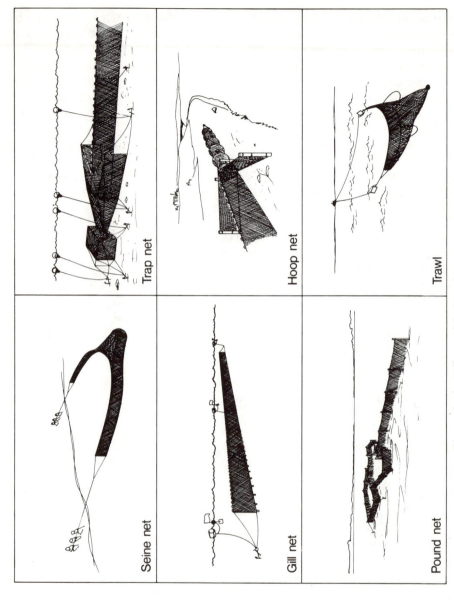

Figure 8.20 Different fishing techniques used in Lake Erie.

An immigrant from Europe with a knowledge of the fish's value taught the local people in the 1860s how to render it for its oil, smoke it, and make caviar from its eggs and isinglass from its air bladder. By 1870 the sturgeon had become a valued species, and the population soon thereafter became stressed. Many of the rivers flowing into the West Basin, the spawning areas of these fish, were being dammed and becoming laden with silt. And because sturgeon do not become sexually mature for at least 20 years and grow slowly, they were very susceptible to overfishing. These stresses took a heavy toll during the 1890s, and by 1900 the species was scarce.

In addition to the pound and seine nets, a hook-and-line fishery for bullheads and channel catfish (*Ictalurus spp.*) was started in 1850. In 1877 gill nets were first used in the West Basin. These nets, which are still used, are made with a mesh size appropriate to the type of fish to be caught. They are hung in straight lines from floats at the depths where the fish are most likely to be (see Fig. 8.20). The fish try to swim through the net, and when they find that the mesh size is too small, move backward and are caught in the net behind the gills. This has slowly evolved to become the most commonly used fishing technique in the lake.

At the turn of the century the West Basin fishermen were primarily taking lake herring (*Coregonus artedii*), lake whitefish (*Coregonus clupeaformis*), sauger, and blue pike. At that time fishing pressure was heavy, and the availability of individual species began to oscillate irregularly. Some fisheries experts began to work toward implementation of stringent regulations, but their arguments were weakened by fish culturists who believed that fish hatcheries could replace the stock taken by a heavy fishery. The hatchery concept won out, and the fishery continued to be virtually unregulated. Between 1867 and 1920, eighteen hatcheries were constructed in the Lake Erie Basin and utilized for different periods of time (Regier and Hartman 1973).

Fishing pressure continued to increase. By 1900 most gill netters were using steam-powered tugs with gill net lifters, and in 1905 a variation of the gill net, called the bullnet, was introduced and widely used. These nets, which were four to five times the depth of a normal net, were set with heavy weights along one edge while the opposite edge floated up from the bottom. These nets were particularly wasteful in that they took many immature whitefish and laketrout. The use of bullnets was banned by 1934.

The herring fishery collapsed in the West Basin in 1920, primarily because of overfishing (Hartman 1972). This was a very heavy blow to the fisherman because herring had been the most important species in the fishery. Simultaneously, the populations of whitefish dropped and the annual catch oscillated, partly because their spawning areas were being increasingly limited by pollution and siltation. Lake whitefish successfully spawned in the Detroit River and Maumee Bay until about 1890 (Trautman 1957), but by 1900 the runs into the Detroit River had apparently been stopped by pollution. The ever-increasing silt load in the Maumee River began smothering whitefish spawning areas in Maumee Bay in about 1900, and those populations were essentially destroyed by 1918 (Trautman 1957; Hartman 1972).

The fish hatchery programs in place at that time were proving to be inadequate to the needs of the fishery. As Langlois (1954) points out, the Ohio hatchery on South Bass Island produced 150 million whitefish fry in 1942. An average female whitefish lays 35,000 eggs per year, and at this rate only 4,272 females, spawning naturally, would produce this number of fry. The Ohio catch in 1942 was approximately 174,000 females, so that the hatchery was making up for only 2.4 percent of the females caught. In the case of the walleye, the hatchery could replace the fry of only 0.0006 percent of the females taken. Unfortunately, the implementation of stringent regulations, which was the alternative management strategy to the hatchery program, was not carried out when the inadequacy of the hatcheries was realized. The costly hatchery program was merely dropped, and nothing was substituted for it.

The sauger populations started a slow, steady decline in 1915 just before the herring fishery collapsed in 1920. At this time the blue pike populations began to oscillate wildly and continued to do so for many years. In 1925 the catch of yellow perch went up as fishermen began to concentrate on this fish after the loss of the herring. Both of these fish have good flavor, but where the lake herring varied in length between 20 and 30 cm and weighed between 250 and 750 g, the perch vary between 20 and 25 cm and weigh between 120 and 310 g, on average (Scott and Crossman 1973). This size difference makes the perch less desirable to fishermen than the herring.

In 1930, the catch of walleye began to increase. In 1935 rainbow smelt were first seen in Lake Erie, but their numbers did not build up significantly until 20 years later. The lake herring staged a surprising comeback in 1946, and 1946 and 1947 were two good years, based on a strong year class in 1944. This was the last year class to contribute to the fishery. Over 7,000 tons were taken in 1946, while virtually none were taken in 1968 (Baldwin and Saalfeld 1962).

In 1949 nylon gill nets were introduced and increased the efficiency of the fishermen manyfold. In the 1950s the catch of sauger diminished to zero and the lake whitefish harvest was reduced drastically; the blue pike fishery collapsed in 1958. Walleye production dropped from almost 7000m tons in 1956 to 800m tons in 1960 (Baldwin and Saalfeld 1962). These changes cannot be attributed to any one cause, but are probably the result of increased growth rate, increased smelt predation on larval fish, and overfishing with the nylon gill nets (Nepszy 1977).

It is interesting that although sauger (*Stizostedion canadense*), blue pike (*Stizostedion vitreum glaucom*), and walleye (*Stizostedion vitreum vitreum*) are genetically compatible, they maintained their separate species identity in the past by spawning at different sites and times (Nepszy 1977). Blue pike are now extirpated from Lake Erie; a possible reason is that after the population crashed, introgressive hybridization occurred between the blue pike remnants and the walleye (Regier, Applegate, and Ryder 1969). Since the sauger also disappeared, it is presumed to have undergone the same fate. An encouraging note is that introductions of sauger by the state of Ohio into Sandusky Bay have shown appreciable survival and exceptional growth (Nepszy 1977).

In 1960 the Government of Canada introduced a test program of trawling for smelt (MacCallum and Regier 1970). The results from this program were good and trawling for smelt is now an established part of the Central and East Basins fisheries. The smelt population is apparently being kept under control by this fishery.

In 1970 commercial fishing for walleye was banned in the West Basin because mercury content of the fish was too high for human consumption. Ontario allowed limited landings in 1974 as mercury levels declined. Ohio and Michigan have continued to prohibit commercial fishing in favor of the angling fishery, and the Ohio sport fishing catch of walleye (see Fig. 8.21) is now much higher than the Ontario commercial catch (J.H. Leach, personal communication). The moratorium on fishing for the walleye permitted the species to recover substantially, and the 1981 Ontario West Basin catch was 840 tons (J.H. Leach, personal communication)—still very low compared to the catches in the early 1950s but high compared to the catch of 75 tons in 1969, just prior to the fishing ban.

The walleye in the West Basin now appear to be doing well because of an interagency quota management system implemented in 1976. Walleye quotas were set for commercial fishing in the West Basin at 11.36 tons per boat in 1979 and are preventing overfishing because, as one fisherman said in 1979, "it took only three lifts of their nets to bring in a year's quota" (Berkes and Pocock 1980). In 1981 the quota was raised to 15.9 tons per boat. Comparison of this new situation with the collapsed walleye fishery of the 1970s illustrates the real need for good regulation of the fishery.

From 1956 to 1980 the Ontario yellow perch catch for the West Basin was variable, ranging from 3000 tons in 1969 to 260m tons in 1976 and back up to almost 2000 tons in 1980 (Ridgley 1976; J.H. Leach, pers. comm.). The populations of the fish of minor economic importance, such as white bass, channel catfish, and carp, appear to be steady or increasing (Leach and Nepszy 1976).

Summary

The West Basin is a tremendously important body of water to the people who live around it. They use the waters for commerce and recreation as well as a source of food. Large ports have been developed, and the cultivation of the surrounding land is extensive. The area is also important to many

Figure 8.21 A walleye caught by an angler in the West Basin. (Photo by CLEAR.)

birds who use the shoreline marshes as vital resting areas during their migrations. The West Basin of Lake Erie has suffered violent ecological abuse but is showing a surprising resilience in responding to recent improvements. If a sustained effort is made to correct many of the numerous mistakes man has made, there is no doubt that this part of Lake Erie can be rehabilitated. The walleye fishery, for example, is responding to proper control measures. The West Basin can become a fine body of water once again and continue to be a source of pleasure and food for many people.

9

Changes in the Central Basin

Characteristics of the Basin and Its Surroundings

The land to the north of the Central Basin of Lake Erie is flat and very similar in nature to the agricultural lands surrounding the West Basin. Unexpectedly, though, the height-of-land in this flat area is very close to the northern shoreline of the lake, and the streams run northward away from it to join the Thames River and thence flow westward to Lake St. Clair. Because of this situation, the land at the lakeshore is fairly high, giving rise to the steep cliffs of glacial till that stretch almost the whole length of the northern shoreline of the Central Basin (see Frontispiece). Nevertheless, a number of very short streams do flow south to the lake from the higher land, and they cut deeply into the till cliffs, making steep-sided, wooded ravines with a small beach at the runout into the lake. Except for Erieau Beach, Point-aux-Pins, and the few harbors along this shore, these ravines provide the only easy access to the lake along the 180 km of shoreline from Wheatley to Port Burwell.

In contrast to the West Basin, the Central Basin shoreline has few low-lying areas and wetlands, except along the east shore of Point Pelee and around Rondeau Harbor. Point-aux-Pins, which forms Rondeau Harbor, is the only unusual feature along the north shore and is a relict landform that has remained from the Erieau moraine (Fig. 3.5). It is growing along the east shore of the point by the sedimentation of sand derived from the erosion of the nearby bluffs.

The south shore has bluffs similar to those of the north shore, but they are lower and its drainage basin extends about 35 km south of the lakeshore.

As one moves eastward through this hinterland, the country changes from the flat lowlands of the West Basin to rolling country that continues to increase in elevation. Many streams run through this land directly into the lake, but tree cover is extensive and these short rivers draining the well-covered slopes do not carry heavy silt loads into the lake (Figs. 1.3, 3.6). There has been some filling and restructuring of the shoreline, but in the Central Basin most of man's actions have been taken to preserve the lakeshore from erosion. But except for the most-expensive and large-scale construction near harbors, the lakeshore has not been stabilized. A few private property owners, after spending large sums of money, have managed to save some of their land.

In contrast to the relatively small, irregular West Basin, the Central Basin is a large, rectangular-shaped basin about 100 km wide by 200 km long, with no islands and a simple bathymetry. The fine sediments of the basin are surrounded by sand and gravel deposits; the Pelee moraine is on the west, the Long Point (Norfolk) moraine is on the east, and gravel deposits are in the wave zones along the north and south shores (see Fig. 3.5). The edges of the basin are relatively steep, so a depth of 20m or so exists within a few kilometers of the shoreline. The depth then increases gradually by 5m over distances of 40 to 80 km to a depth of 25m in the middle of the basin, making this large central area very flat (see Fig. 1.2).

The winds sweep over long fetches, creating large, steep waves, and with the absence of islands and protective landforms, the Central Basin can become a very dangerous body of water. This observation is confirmed by comparing the nature of the scientific investigations carried out in the West and Central Basins. The large majority of the research in the West Basin has been done by individual scientists going out frequently in small boats, investigating problems of their own interest. Virtually all the research done on the Central Basin, however, has been done from large ships carrying a crew and a complement of scientists. Until 1970 most of these investigations consisted of surveys of the basin, with the ship visiting a number of stations on a regular schedule and taking samples of water and biological specimens. During 1970, investigations of particular problems of the basin were started, and almost all this research has been carried out from a large ship. The "C.S.S. Limnos" has been the most-used research vessel on the Central Basin. All subsequent special topic research has also been done from large ships (Fig. 9.1). Few operators of small powerboats would dare to stay out overnight in the offshore waters of this basin.

The sometimes wild nature of the lake is illustrated by the events of 20 October 1916, known as "Black Friday" among the older sailors of Lake Erie (Ratigan 1960). On that day, the Canadian steamer "Merida" was seen to be having difficulties and then sank with the loss of 23 lives. The lumber carrier "Marshall F. Butters" sank, but her crew of 13 was saved by another freighter. The only wooden ship of the four to be lost that day was a

Figure 9.1 The working deck of the "Limnos" during a research cruise. The heavy equipment used in Great Lakes research necessitates the use of large ships. (Photo by W. Booth.)

schooner, the "D.L. Filer," which sank in the shallows near the Detroit River. One of the crew of six survived because he held onto the mast, which stuck out of the water. The whaleback steamer "Colgate," with twenty-four years of service on the Great Lakes, had her hatches torn off near Long Point and sank, taking 24 of her 25-man crew with her. Ships are still lost on Lake Erie from time to time, but far less frequently now because of improved technology.

The Central Basin has no rocky spawning reefs close to shore, and since the silt burden of the rivers is not heavy, silt pollution causes relatively little damage to the basin's ecology. The only reef areas existing in the

Central Basin are the sand-and-gravel area southwest of Erieau and the cross-lake sill lying north of Erie, Pennsylvania. These areas are not seriously affected by the large silt load from shoreline erosion that has always entered the lake. The disturbance of the lakewater by wave action in these areas generally prevents the fine sediment from remaining settled on these sand-and gravel-reefs for any significant period of time.

Most of the harm to the Central Basin by pollution is caused directly by the dumping of substantial amounts of garbage, oil, chemical wastes, sewage, and nutrients into the basin via rivers or outfalls and, indirectly, by the flow of enriched lakewater from the West Basin. Perhaps the biggest difference between the West and Central Basins is the fact that the Central Basin stratifies strongly for about 100 days during the summer, while the West Basin stratifies only sporadically for a few days each year. The hypolimnion layer of cold water on the bottom of Central Basin averages only about 4m in thickness. These differences result in the Central and West Basins having different natural susceptibilities: the West Basin, with its heavy nutrient loading and small volume, is naturally prone to problems of excessive algal growth, while the thin hypolimnion of the Central Basin is naturally susceptible to problems of deoxygenation.

Research on the Basin

C.C. Davis (1964) summarized the research situation on the Central Basin in 1966 as follows:

> As one would expect, most of the limited scientific work that has been accomplished to date in the Central Basin has been closely associated with practical matters, and hence has dealt with hydrology, fishes, searches for commercially useful sand deposits, shore erosion, or pollution. Few published documents have considered the Central Basin alone and as a whole; usually they have been portions of reports dealing with the whole lake, or with the Eastern and Central Basins together. Often only local portions of the Central Basin have been considered.

Luckily, the small amount of research has proved adequate to describe most of the major changes that have occurred, particularly when the older data is interpreted with the knowledge gained from recent research.

The first basin-wide surveys of the Central Basin were conducted from tne "Shearwater" in 1929 (Fish and Associates 1960). They placed little emphasis on nutrients but carefully measured temperature, oxygen, carbon dioxide, alkalanity, chloride, and turbidity. The next series of surveys was conducted out of Erieau by the Fisheries Research Laboratory of the University of Western Ontario, London, Ontario, between 1947 and 1952 (Powers et al. 1960). From that time on, data on the Central Basin became more available as the Great Lakes Institute of the University of Toronto,

Ontario (1964, 1965), Rodgers (1962, 1963) and the U. S. Federal Water Pollution Control Administration (FWPCA) carried out investigations in 1963 and 1964. The results of the FWPCA surveys were published in the "Lake Erie Report—A Plan for Water Pollution Control" (U.S. FWPCA 1968) and showed an area in 1964 of 6700 km² of the Central Basin that was virtually devoid of oxygen in the hypolimnion.

The discovery of the large area without oxygen, together with the fact that oxygen is essential for higher forms of life, caused journalists and environmentalists to state that Lake Erie was dead (Dambach 1969). This description of the lake has puzzled many people, because the lake now has more living organisms in it than ever before, although many of the present fish and phytoplankton are not as desirable as those they have displaced. Nevertheless, when an anoxic hypolimnion is examined, as was done again in 1970, the adjective "dead" is appropriate. The bottom was found to be black, the water stank, and the only living things were anaerobic bacteria. Nevertheless, recent data from the eighties show both lower phosphorus concentrations and lower oxygen uptake rates, so that hypolimnion oxygen concentrations are now higher than previously. Lake Erie is improving and will survive.

When Dobson and Gilbertson (1972) determined the observed oxygen depletion rate of the Central Basin for each year from 1929 to 1970 for which suitable data could be obtained, they found an erratic but definite increase from 1929 onward (Fig. 9.2). This finding correlated with another (by Gilbertson, Dobson and Lee 1972), which indicated annual increases in the phosphorus loading to the lake during the same period (see Fig. 6.10). This information, together with Vollenweider's 1968 report that generally implicated phosphorus as the leading culprit of accelerated eutrophication in most bodies of freshwater, led to the conclusion that high phosphorus loads to the Central Basin were the indirect cause of the oxygen problem. In addition, the International Lake Erie Water Pollution Board in 1969 recommended that phosphorus inputs to the lake be severely cut back to decrease the excess production of organic materials in the lake, and thus the rate of oxygen depletion resulting from this material.

In 1969, scientists from the Cleveland office of the U.S. Environmental Protection Agency and from the Canada Centre for Inland Waters conferred about the problem of anoxia in the Central Basin hypolimnion after the city of Cleveland experienced serious difficulties with the quality of its municipal water whenever hypolimnetic water reached a city intake (Potos 1968). Anoxic lakewater usually contains hydrogen sulphide (H_2S), which has a most unpleasant odor. Further, anoxic conditions cause the release of many essential plant nutrients from sediments to the overlying water (Mortimer 1971), thus encouraging plant growth and increasing the state of eutrophication. At this meeting of scientists in 1969, an investigation of the processes affecting the uptake of oxygen and the regeneration of nutrients in the Central Basin of Lake Erie was planned. The scientists

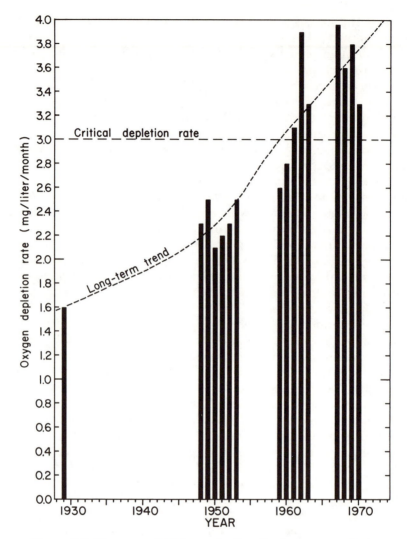

Figure 9.2 The mean depletion rates for dissolved oxygen during summer in the bottom-waters of the Central Basin, as calculated by Dobson and Gilbertson (1972). Note that the critical rate of 3 gm $O_2 m^{-3}$ month^{-1} was reached in 1961, and rates in excess of this produce widespread anoxia before the end of the stratified season.

involved felt that a more-thorough examination of the problem would be obtained if both organizations pooled their resources. A carefully coordinated investigation comprising physical, chemical, and biological components was implemented during July and August of 1970, with seven basin-wide ship surveys carried out between 1–26 August 1970. This study was the first large-ship research investigation on processes in the Central Basin and was named Project Hypo.

The study of physical processes during Project Hypo was carried out by Blanton and Winklhofer (1972), who stated the most unexpected finding that as the summer progressed, the hypolimnion volume could increase by the downward incorporation of thermocline water. This unusual phenomenon is largely a result of the average 17m epilimnion thickness being much greater than the 4 to 5m thick hypolimnion. The normal situation in a lake is for the epilimnion to be thinner than the hypolimnion or, at most, of a similar thickness. Under normal circumstances, wind-mixing of the water column usually causes hypolimnion water to be mixed upward into the thermocline, making the hypolimnion thinner. In this case, the unusual "upside-down" entrainment of the thermocline water into the hypolimnion caused the thermocline to move upward, increasing the volume of the hypolimnion. This phenomenon is very important to the Central Basin because it adds oxygen to the hypolimnion, since the thermocline concentrations of oxygen are higher than those of the hypolimnion, and oxygen is moved down with the thermocline water. This downward mixing also explains the fairly rapid hypolimnion temperature increase of about 1°C per month. Blanton and Winklhofer (1972) also found an occasional flow of well-oxygenated East Basin water flowing into the Central Basin hypolimnion. Further, the dominant hypolimnion currents flowed toward the northwest with speeds, averaged on a two-hour basis, in the 2.5 to 5.0 cm sec^{-1} range and with the maximum average speed once reaching 98.5 cm sec^{-1}.

Murthy (1972) studied dispersion within the hypolimnion and found the horizontal eddy diffusion coefficient to be about 10^3 cm^2 sec^{-1}. This is about two orders of magnitude lower than the same value for epilimnetic waters, which is about 10^5 cm^2 sec^{-1}.

Perhaps the most-startling finding of the study was the quantity of algae lying on the bottom. The biologists Braidech, Gehring, and Kleveno (1972) did much *in situ* sampling using diving techniques. In early August they found a layer of green algae about 2 cm thick lying on the bottom over almost the whole deepwater area of the Central Basin. Figure 9.3 was taken during one of their dives. The algae were sampled quantitatively at a station in the middle of the Central Basin, and the results are shown in Figure 9.4 with the comment that,

> The algae on June 16, 1970, were found to be 428 organisms/cm^2. Most of the algae were of the coccoid green type although some *Tribonema* were present. On August 8 the numbers of algae, which had been slowly increasing, rose to 11,875 organisms/cm^2 with *Tribonema* being the most numerous form. From then until September 1, 1970, algae displayed large fluctuations ending at a peak of 13,700 organisms/cm^2 with *Tribonema* again most abundant.

The intermittent periods of algal settling were termed "algal rains" and appear to have occurred at different times in the different parts of the

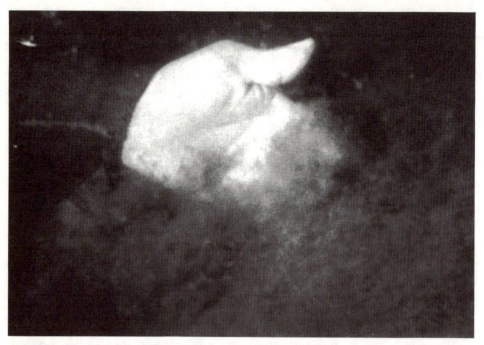

Figure 9.3 A photograph taken during a dive soon after the first heavy algal rain, showing the thick layer of phytoplankton that settled onto the lake sediments (Braidech, Gehring, and Kleveno 1972).

basin. When the algae first settled out in early August, the surface waters were very clear and the algae were able to get enough light to remain alive. As August progressed, the phytoplankton volume in the surface waters increased, so the hypolimnetic light levels decreased and the algae on the bottom died. They turned brown and compacted and the lower layers turned black, since the oxygen could not penetrate through the compacted algal mat. The black color was almost certainly due to the precipitation of ferrous sulphide, which occurs under anoxic conditions. Once the first algal rain died, any algae that subsequently settled out died quickly. By the end of August almost all the bottom of the western half of the basin, at a depth of more than 20 m, was covered with a black mat of decaying algae dotted with dead smelt.

During Project Hypo, sediment oxygen demand (SOD) was measured by Lucas and Thomas (1972), who placed both clear and dark chambers on the bottom which trapped some of the overlying water. They monitored the concentration of oxygen in the chambers and were able to measure the rates of oxygen uptake in them. Light was able to reach the algae lying on the bottom under the clear chambers. They found that:

In August, rates measured during daylight hours with the clear chamber

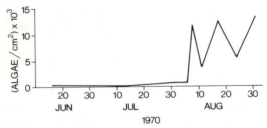

Figure 9.4 The number of apparently live algae found on the bottom near the middle of the Central Basin during summer 1970. (Braidech, Gehring, and Kleveno 1972.)

(0.0–0.4 g m^{-2} day^{-1}) were less than those measured at night with the clear chamber or during the day with the black chamber (0.7 to 1.0 g O$_2$ m^{-2} day^{-1}). Oxygen produced by photosynthetic activity of algae on the lake bottom offset the SOD during part of the day.

A summary diagram of their results is shown in Figure 9.5. Perhaps the most-interesting results of these experiments were recorded at station P at sunrise and at Station R at sunset in early August, just after the first algal rain. At station P the sediment oxygen demand rate in the clear chamber is seen to decrease with increasing daylight, and at Station R the oxygen demand was seen to increase with the decreasing light at sunset.

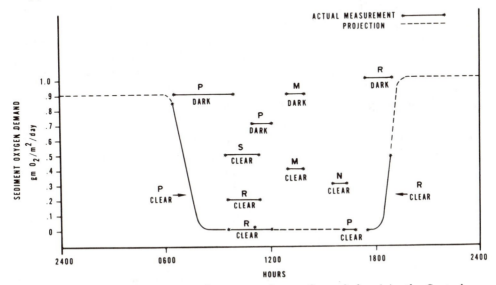

Figure 9.5 Sediment oxygen uptake patterns in gm O$_2$ m^{-2} day^{-1} in the Central Basin from 4 to 7 August 1970, showing the decreased oxygen uptake in the clear chambers during daylight hours. (Lucas and Thomas 1972.)

These effects were almost certainly due to photosynthetic activity of the algae on the lake bottom. This was unexpected because Station P was in the center of the basin at 24.5 m, and Station R, while closer to the shore, was 23m deep. Even so, the surface waters were quite clear and light penetration was good.

Menon, Marion, and Miller (1972) studied bacterial densities in the water column and at the sediment-water interface. The most-numerous bacteria throughout the water column were the aerobic heterotrophs. The smallest number of bacteria were found in the thermocline zone, while the algal remains at the sediment-water interface contained about two orders of magnitude more bacteria than the overlying hypolimnion water. The sulfate-reducing desulfovibrio bacteria were almost completely absent until the oxygen concentration dropped below 1 mg O_2 m^{-3}, when their numbers increased markedly.

The chemical part of Project Hypo, conducted by Burns and Ross (1972a), incorporated the findings of the other studies with their own to document the cause and effects of the occurrence of anoxic conditions. This study was quantitative in that the entire Central Basin hypolimnion was sampled using 25 stations, and the values from each station were multiplied by a specific volume, which when summed, equalled the total measured hypolimnion volume. The hypolimnion thickness was measured and the waters were sampled during seven surveys spaced four days apart during August 1970. By making an adjustment for the changes in the computed hypolimnion volumes, the changes in the quantities of chemical species in the hypolimnion were calculated. This enabled the changes caused by the chemical or biological reactions that took place during the six intervals to be estimated.

The cause-and-effect relationship between phosphorus loading and excess eutrophication in Lake Erie was concluded from broader-based studies, such as those of Vollenweider (1968) and the International Lake Erie Water Pollution Board (1969). Once phosphorus loading was accepted as the root cause of the oxygen problems of the Central Basin, the results from Project Hypo were able to indicate the significance of other important processes occurring in the basin, such as the difference in the rate of the nutrient releases under oxic and anoxic conditions. The phosphorus quantities released under these different conditions were then compared to the external loads, so that the effect of internal loading under anoxic conditions could be understood.

The following results of Burns and Ross's (1972a) contribution to Project Hypo are relevant to the limnology of Lake Erie.

     1. The massive algal bloom in the Central Basin during the last week of July 1970 caused a 2–3 cm thick layer of algae to be laid down on the floor of the basin and was the major cause of anoxic conditions which subsequently developed in the hypolimnion.

2. The net oxygen demand was variable, being influenced by the photosynthetic oxygen produced by the sedimented algae; the average oxygen areal demand was 0.40 g O_2 m^{-2}day^{-1}, which is close to the demand expected of a eutrophic lake. The observed change of oxygen concentration in the hypolimnion was approximately -0.13 g O_2 m^{-3}day^{-1} or -3.9 g O_2 m^{-3} month^{-1}.

3. Approximately 88% of the oxygen uptake was due to bacterial degradation of algal sedimentation, with 12% of the oxygen being taken up in the oxidation of reduced metallic species.

4. Since nutrients cause organic growth, with phosphorus often being the limiting nutrient, and since the oxygen depletion was largely due to organic decay, it can be concluded that a reduction of nutrients, especially phosphorus, would lead to a corresponding decrease in the oxygen depletion rate.

5. Anoxic regeneration of phosphate was observed to commence only when the oxygen concentration in the water fell below 0.6 g O_2 m^{-3}.

6. The oxygen contour maps show that complete oxygen depletion started at the western end of the basin during the week of 10 August and moved eastwards, with the eastward movement being more rapid in the shallow water and along the southern shore. By the 25th of August, one-third of the hypolimnion was anoxic and on the 23rd September 1970 the complete hypolimnion was found to be anoxic [see Figure 9.6]. The area and duration of observed anoxic conditions during the summer of 1970 was 25.2 $\times$ 10^{10} m^2 days.

7. The anoxic regeneration rate of soluble reactive phosphorus was 7.5 mg P m^{-2} day^{-1} and was approximately 11 times greater than the oxic rate, which was 0.7 mg p m^{-2} day^{-1}. [The processes causing these different rates were described in Chapter 6.]

8. The anoxically generated phosphate is largely the result of the dissolution of inorganic complexes that were insoluble under oxygenated conditions. In the Central Basin of Lake Erie a large part of the phosphorus regenerated under anoxic conditions apparently re-enters the life cycle of the lake.

9. During the oxic degradation of organic materials approximately only 45% of the nitrogen and 25% of the phosphorus contained in the organic material returned to the water in soluble form.

10. Under anoxic conditions there was a considerable loss of inorganic nitrogen nutrients, which were presumably converted to nitrogen gas. This loss decreased the quantity of nitrogen nutrients regenerated by 44%.

11. The anoxic conditions caused an internal loading of phosphate to the Central Basin equal to 111% of the external loading of phosphorus during the same period. This quantity, together with the oxic regeneration in the complete basin for the same period, caused the 2-month internal loading to equal 137% of the external loading. The Central Basin is now changing from being a settlement basin for phosphorus to a production basin for the element during the summer stratification period.

The estimates in point 11 were calculated in the following manner:

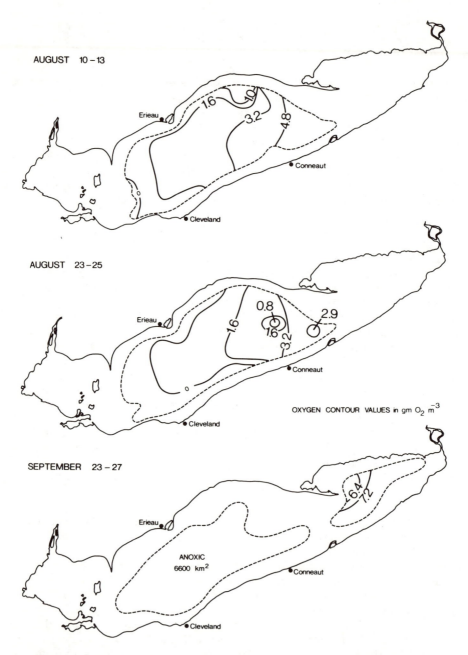

AUGUST 10 – 13

Erieau

1.6

1.0

3.2

4.8

Conneaut

0

Cleveland

AUGUST 23 – 25

Erieau

0.8

1.6

2.9

1.6

3.2

Conneaut

0

OXYGEN CONTOUR VALUES in gm O_2 m^{-3}

Cleveland

SEPTEMBER 23 – 27

6.4

7.2

Erieau

ANOXIC
6600 km^2

Conneaut

Cleveland

Figure 9.6 Hypolimnetic oxygen concentration patterns observed in Lake Erie in 1970. The west-to-east increase in oxygen concentration in the August maps is clearly seen. (Burns and Ross 1972a.)

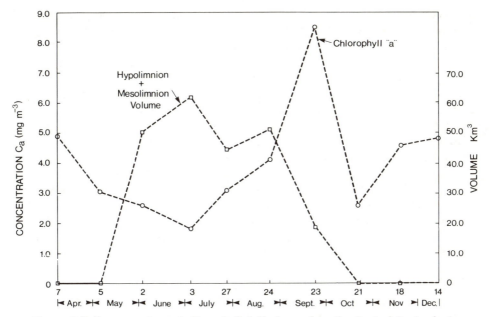

Figure 9.7 Concentrations of chlorophyll "a" observed in the Central Basin during 1970, showing the effect of the upward mixing of hypolimnetic waters during September on the chlorophyll "a" concentrations. (Burns and Ross 1972a.)

— Internal loading during August and September by oxic regeneration only=437m tons P.
— Internal loading during August and September by anoxic regeneration only=1914m tons P.
∴ Estimated total *internal* loading=2351m tons P.
— *External* loading during August and September from the West Basin and shoreline of the Central Basin=1720m tons P.

Normally, the net movement of phosphorus is from the water to the sediments, but in this case the phosphorus moved from the sediments to the water at an extremely high rate. In fact, this internal loading during August and September exceeded the external loading, causing the total loading to reach the massive sum of 4071 tons for two months. The regenerated phosphorus was mixed upward during September 1970 as the hypolimnion eroded upward. The growth resulting from this internal nutrient loading caused by the upward mixing of the hypolimnion waters with surface waters can be seen in Figure 9.7 in terms of a high chlorophyll *a* peak on the 23rd of September.

The findings of Project Hypo were reviewed by Burns and Ross (1972c); they strongly recommended that phosphorus loads to the lake be sharply reduced to diminish the high internal load of phosphorus. They considered that if no action was taken the lake would continue to deteriorate, with an accompanying increase in the extent of anoxic conditions and internal loading of phosphorus. If effective reduction in external loadings was made, the internal loadings would also decrease. Thus the total reduction in phosphorus load would be considerably greater than the reduction in the external load. These recommendations were seriously considered by both Canadian and American authorities. Project Hypo played a definite part in bringing the Great Lakes Water Quality Agreement into existence in 1972. One of the major aims of this agreement was to reduce the phosphorus loads to Lake Erie from 28,298 tons in 1971 to 14,600 tons in 1976.

An additional study on oxygen in the Central Basin was carried out in the winter of 1977 (Burns, Rosa, and Gedeon 1978), when the basin had been completely ice-covered for six weeks with no possible reoxygenation of the lakewater from the atmosphere. After the findings of 1970, scientists feared that the summer anoxic conditions would release a large quantity of nutrients, with an ensuing increase in organic growth, which would cause anoxic conditions during the following winter, particularly if the lake was completely covered with ice. The nutrients released under winter conditions would then engender more anoxia and more nutrient release the following summer, and so on, in a vicious cycle of self-sustaining anoxia. The winter study, however, showed that all the winter bottom oxygen concentrations in 1977 were greater than 70 percent of saturation and averaged over 90 percent. This means that there is no possibility of self-sustaining anoxia occurring in Lake Erie. It also indicates that the lake should respond quickly to significant remedial measures.

Physical limnologists have shown much interest in the Central Basin of late and one of the resulting investigations has been on the exchange of water between the East and Central Basins (Boyce et al. 1980). The mixing of these water masses is an interesting phenomenon. The two basins are separated by an underwater ridge averaging between 15 and 20m deep with a notch in the ridge just north of Erie, Pennsylvania. The depth here reaches 24 m, close to the Central Basin's maximum depth of 25 m. The high rate of hypolimnetic warming in the Central Basin helps create the situation where the Central Basin hypolimnion is at the same temperature and depth as the East Basin thermocline, as shown in Figure 9.8. Boyce et al. (1980) found that this resulted in most of the lower epilimnion and East Basin thermocline flows moving toward the Central Basin. Thus, substantial quantities of well-oxygenated water from the East Basin thermocline can be added to the Central Basin hypolimnion, which helps to keep the eastern part of the Central Basin hypolimnion better oxygenated than the central and western parts (see Fig. 9.6). Boyce et al. (1980) estimated that 13 km^3 of water moved into the Central Basin hypolimnion from mid-June to mid-July and about 7 km^3 during August of 1977. Since the Central Basin hypolimnion had an average volume of 45 km^3 during this time, these flows were quite significant. But Boyce et al. considered that dispersion and movement in the hypolimnion is not sufficient to

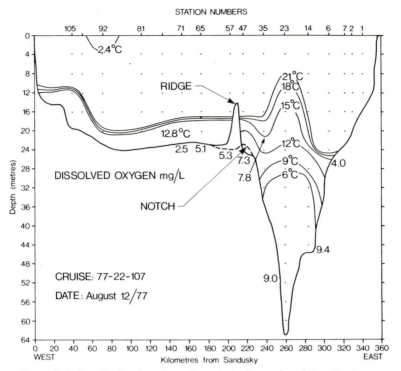

Figure 9.8 Longitudinal sections through the Central and East Basins, showing the distribution of temperature and near-bottom values of dissolved oxygen (Boyce et al. 1980). The height of the ridge between the basins is shown, together with the notch through the ridge.

distribute the oxygen associated with these flows beyond the eastern third of the Central Basin and this is confirmed by oxygen concentration distribution maps. This flow of water can alleviate low oxygen concentrations only in the eastern part of the Central Basin.

During 1979 and 1980, limnologists investigated the somewhat unique situation of the thin Central Basin hypolimnion sitting below a thick epilimnion in a shallow water body, open to long wind fetches. One of the first results of this work was a study by Ivey and Boyce (1982) on the earlier-noted downward entrainment of thermocline water into the hypolimnion (Fig. 9.9). They found that downward entrainment of water can occur when strong epilimnetic currents flow, if the hypolimnion and lower thermocline are protected from epilimnetic turbulence by a small secondary thermocline above the main thermocline (dashed line in Fig. 9.9). By using data collected over 270 km², Ivey and Boyce concluded that the downward entrainment happens simultaneously over a large part of the basin. It is not a phenomenon that occurs in one part of the basin with the down-mixed water then dispersing through the basin. Since the thermocline

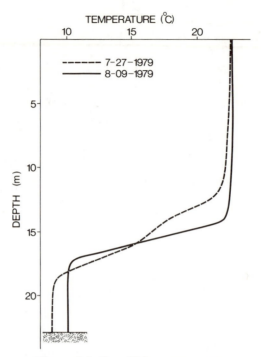

Figure 9.9 Two 48-hr average temperature versus depth traces taken 13 days apart at a station in the middle of the Central Basin, showing a simultaneous increase in hypolimnion thickness and temperature. (Ivey and Boyce 1982.)

water has an average oxygen concentration higher than that of the hypolimnion, this down-mixing phenomenon adds oxygen to the hypolimnion. Ivey and Boyce's estimate is that during this 13-day episode, the added oxygen accounted for about 10 percent of the daily demand during that period. If the small secondary thermocline is absent, epilimnetic currents cause normal upward entrainment of water, and the hypolimnion volume decreases.

Changes in the Basin with Time

A recent study by Harris and Vollenweider (1982) of diatom skeletons in a core from the middle of the Central Basin gives us some idea of long-term changes in the diatom community. From about 1700 to 1850 there appears to be no change in the record, which has a total of nine species of diatoms with *Stephanodiscus niagarae* as the most common. This finding is consistent with the little change in the lake basin during that period.

Deforestation of the lake basin began in 1850 and continued for about 30 years. Deforestation and the resultant agriculture caused an increasing load of nutrients from the land to the lake. The number of observed species increased slightly from nine to twelve by the turn of the century, with *Melosira islandica* being observed with greater frequency at this time. From about 1900 to the 1940s the number of species increased to fourteen, with *Fragilaria crotonensis* becoming another important species. These changes occurred when the population in the basin increased from about 3 to 8 million people. In recent years, *M. binderana*, an indicator of highly eutrophic conditions, has replaced *M. distans* entirely and *M. islandica* to some extent.

Another study of change in the Central Basin was that of Fish and Associates (1960), who set out to determine whether pollution had caused the demise of some of the fisheries in this basin. They did find some harbor areas that were polluted and would have affected the fish, but found no evidence of pollution in the open lake. Their conclusion was that the lake was not sufficiently polluted to have affected the fishing—a far cry from today's situation—and commented about the condition of the East and Central Basins in 1929 as follows:

> There is no evidence that silt from industrial and sewage outwash is invading the offshore spawning grounds or in fact affecting any part of the area investigated at distances of more than one mile from the shore, except in two instances. The lake is remarkably free from chemical and sewage pollution and only those species spawning in or about the mouths of certain streams are likely to encounter seriously unfavorable conditions.

People expected little change with time. Finally, in the fifties and sixties these preconceptions began to break down because, as Davis (1964) stated,

> It was widely held that the vast dilution factor characteristic of the world's largest lakes would prevent any clear indication of eutrophication in them. Recently however, concern has arisen that rapid eutrophication may be taking place in the lower Great Lakes, particularly in Lake Erie.

Changes in the basin have certainly occurred since the 1929 studies. One that has been documented is the phytoplankton density in the near-shore area of the Cleveland Division city water intake, about 5.9 km offshore from Cleveland. This was done by Davis (1964), and his results demonstrated a steady increase in the average concentrations of phytoplankton, from about 450 cells per ml in 1930 to about 1500 per ml in 1964. The increase has been so steady that it is unlikely to be caused entirely by changes in counting techniques. Davis also noted that the dominant species in the spring growth pulse changed from *Asterionella* in the 1920s to *Melosira* in the 1960s, and the autumn pulse changed from *Synedra* to a codominant group of *Fragilaria* and *Melosira*. This type of change denotes a definite alteration in trophic status from oligotrophic to more-eutrophic conditions.

One of the most-profound changes with time has been the slow but erratic increase in the Central Basin hypolimnetic oxygen depletion rate. The increase has been erratic because it is much affected by weather factors, some of which were described in the previous section. In fact, the perturbations have been so great as to call the trend into question. A debate arose on this issue, and has been resolved (Charlton 1979, 1980; Rosa and Burns 1982). The consensus of opinion is that there has been an increase in oxygen depletion rate with time as a result of increased phosphorus loads to the lake, and that the reduction of phosphorus inputs to the lake is desirable (Barica 1982; Lam, Schertzer, and Fraser 1983b).

Additional evidence confirms the decrease in the concentration of oxygen in bottom waters with time: the disappearance of mayflies from the Central Basin ecosystem. As mentioned in Chapter 8, mayflies require well-oxygenated water for survival, and their disappearance indicates that the oxygen content of the bottom waters has decreased with time. The following comment was made by C.A. Dambach (1969) on this matter:

> From the speaker's own personal experience, an obvious change involving the Central Basin comes to mind. It dates to the summer of 1924 when he marked time between calls to pick up telegraph messages for the Postal Telegraph Office in downtown Cleveland, Ohio, by impaling Mayflies to the walls both in and out of the building with common straight pins. A box of 500 pins was barely sufficient to pin all the Mayflies that would appear on a four by eight foot bulletin board in the course of a day. Nor were the horse-drawn dump wagons adequate for the loads of Mayflies which piled up overnight under the lamp posts during a warm summer evening as far uptown as Superior Avenue and the public square. Today, a box of 500 ordinary straight pins would probably be more than sufficient for a season's collection of Mayflies on the entire waterfront. And I suspect that the present members of the sanitary department in Cleveland have rarely, if ever, been called upon to shovel adult Mayflies from the street before the flow of traffic got underway in the early morning hours.

A decline in the number of mayflies invading Cleveland was noted in 1949, but they reappeared in 1950 and were reported yearly through 1957, after which time they finally disappeared (International Lake Erie Water Pollution Board 1969).

The Biota of the Basin

BENTHIC ORGANISMS

The ostracod provides a good general overview of sediment conditions in Lake Erie. These small creatures living on the bottom have two shells like a clam and are seldom more than 3 mm long. Unlike clams, some ostracodes, or seed shrimp species, as they are commonly called, can be mobile. The ostracodes of Lake Erie have been investigated by Delorme (1978), who found the interesting distribution of the three species shown in Figure 9.10. *Candona caudata* has a life cycle of months and can withstand low oxygen concentrations of down to about 2.3 g m^{-3}; *Cytherissa lacustris* has a life cycle of a year or longer and can tolerate a minimum of 3.0 g m^{-3} of oxygen; and *Candona subtriangulata*, with a similar long lifespan, requires a minimum of 5.6 g m^{-3} to survive.

Candona caudata is found over virtually the whole lake. Evidently the species survives the anoxic periods in egg form and hatches out after the waters have been reoxygenated. Because of its longer life cycle, *Cytherissa lacustris* cannot live in areas that go anoxic every year, but does seem to survive in areas that experience infrequent anoxia. Thus, we see that this species does not exist in the West Basin, the Sandusky subbasin, or areas along the south shore of the Central Basin, but is found in the rest of the lake. On the other hand, *Candona subtriangulata* requires well-oxygenated water and is found only in the deeper waters of the East Basin.

Benthic organisms were also sampled by Brinkhurst (1969) in 1963, who subsequently carried out careful species identification. *Peloscolex ferox* was found to be the most-important oligochaete in the Central Basin. Brinkhurst described the midge fauna in the West Basin as consisting of five genera indicative of eutrophic conditions. In the East Basin there are fourteen that include some indicative of oligotrophic conditions, while the fauna in the Central Basin was found to be intermediate between that of the other basins; the most common midge species in the Central Basin belonged to the *Chironomus* genus.

Britt, Pliodzinskas, and Hair (1980) sampled the Central Basin in 1973–74 and found no marked change in the species distribution when compared to that of the earlier studies, and they sampled frequently enough so that their organism counts can be considered as a reference set of values for the basin. The average number of oligochaetes in the middle of the Central Basin was between 1000 and 2000 oligochaetes m^{-2}, with higher values observed near the shorelines, such as 4000 to 5000 m^{-2} observed near Cleveland. The chironomids (midge larvae) were far less numerous, averaging between 0 and 500 individuals per m^2.

PHYTOPLANKTON

Glooschenko, More, and Vollenweider (1974) plotted the average distribution of chlorophyll *a* (corrected for pheopigments) as shown in Figure 9.11. The distribution of phytoplankton chlorophyll shows the chlorophyll levels increasing as the water moves away from the Detroit River, providing time for the nutrients added by the river to be converted into phytoplankton biomass. The peak levels in the open waters are observed around the island area, with the chlorophyll concentrations dropping considerably as the

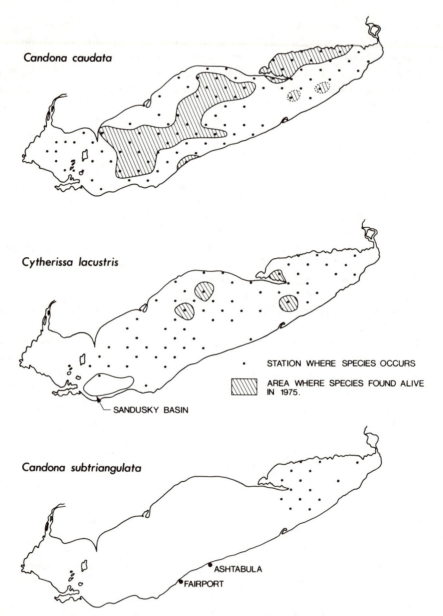

Candona caudata

Cytherissa lacustris

• STATION WHERE SPECIES OCCURS

▨ AREA WHERE SPECIES FOUND ALIVE
   IN 1975.

SANDUSKY BASIN

Candona subtriangulata

ASHTABULA
FAIRPORT

Figure 9.10 The distribution in Lake Erie of three different ostracode species with very different oxygen requirements. No living Candona subtriangulata *were found in 1975. (Delorme 1978.)*

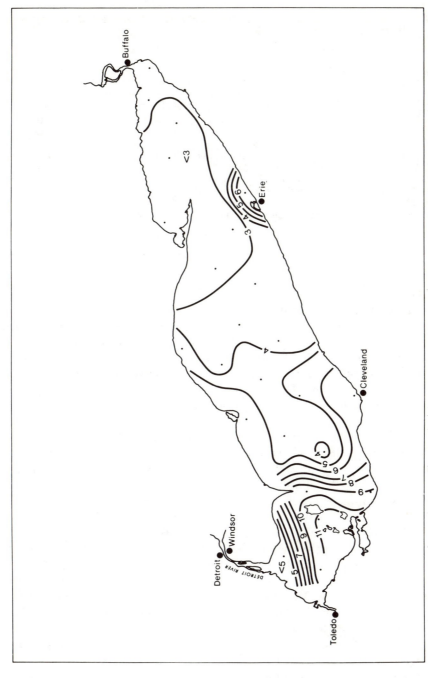

Figure 9.11 The average distribution of chlorophyll "a" in the surface waters of Lake Erie from April to December 1970. (Glooschenko, More, and Vollenweider 1974.)

Table 9.1   Seasonal Abundance of the Dominant Species of Phytoplankton in the Central Basin of Lake Erie during 1970

Date	Central Basin species	Mean % of total volume of biomass
Apr. 7–11	Stephanodiscus tenuis Hust.	34.0
May 6–10	Stephanodiscus niagarae	30.0
June 2–6	Gymnodinium helveticum	24.0
July 3–7	Cryptomonas erosa	34.0
July 25–Aug. 2	Ceratium hirundinella (O. Müll.) Schrank	37.5
Aug. 25–30	Ceratium hirundinella	31.0
Sept. 23–27	Fragilaria capucina (Desm.)	37.0
Oct. 21–26	Stephanodiscus niagarae	54.0
Nov. 25–30	Stephanodiscus niagarae	71.0
Dec. 14–18	Stephanodiscus niagarae	73.5

Source: After Munawar and Munawar 1976.

water moves into the Central Basin. Near Cleveland and Erie they are increased locally by the loadings from these cities. The mean level for the open waters of the Central Basin of about 4 mg chlorophyll a m^{-3} is low and not uncommon for oligotrophic small lakes. Secchi disk readings of 5 to 8m are normal in late June and early July, after the spring phytoplankton pulse has settled out, and indicate very clear water at that time. The maximum chlorophyll levels were observed in September and averaged 9.2 mg m^{-3}, still not very high by criteria commonly used for eutrophic lakes. There seems to have been a drop in these concentrations since 1980, which probably relates to the recent decrease in phosphorus loadings. Fay and Herdendorf (1981) report the 1980 average summer Central Basin chlorophyll a at 2.8 mg m^{-3} (1970 summer value 3.4), and the fall average of 5.5 mg m^{-3} (1970 fall value 5.9).

The most complete study on the phytoplankton of the Central Basin was carried out by Munawar and Munawar (1976), and their data is shown in Table 9.1 and Figure 9.12. In the Central Basin, they observed three peaks in the inshore region, while the offshore region showed only a single pulse during September. Diatoms were the major component in the inshore region for most of the year, whereas phytoflagellates were dominant in the offshore region during May to August, having practically replaced the spring diatoms. During February 1977, Burns, Rosa, and Gedeon (1978) sampled four stations for phytoplankton in the Central Basin. The winter biomass volume was low, measuring between 0.2 to 1.0 g m^{-3}, which is lower than the values (shown in Fig. 9.12) of between 0.8 to 6 g m^{-3}. The species observed were almost exclusively diatoms, with *Stephanodiscus niagarae* the most common, as it was during the fall. The early spring (7–13 April) and early winter period (13–21 December) data in Figure 9.12

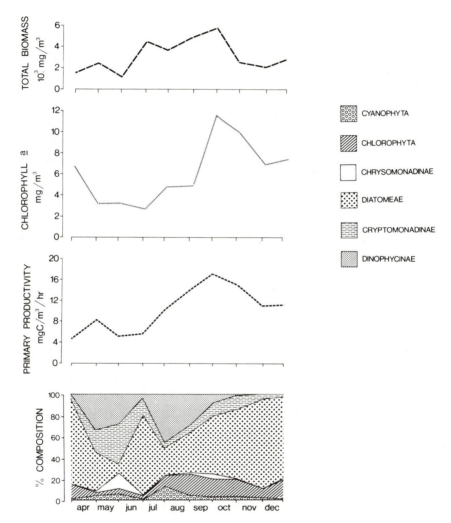

apr may jun jul aug sep oct nov dec

TOTAL BIOMASS
10^3 mg/m³

CHLOROPHYLL a
mg/m³

PRIMARY PRODUCTIVITY
mgC/m³/hr

% COMPOSITION

CYANOPHYTA

CHLOROPHYTA

CHRYSOMONADINAE

DIATOMEAE

CRYPTOMONADINAE

DINOPHYCINAE

Figure 9.12 Seasonal fluctuation of phytoplankton biomass, chlorophyll "a" (uncorrected), primary productivity, and group composition in the Central Basin, 1970. (Munawar and Munawar 1976.) Common names are: Cyanophyta—blue greens, Chlorophyta—greens, Chrysomonadinae—chrysomonads, Diatomeae—diatoms, Chrytomonadinae—cryptomonads, Dinophycinae—dinoflagellates.

also show the phytoplankton populations consisting almost totally of diatoms. These observations, together with the 1977 mid-winter data, indicate that the late fall, winter, and spring phytoplankton populations are all predominantly diatom communities; in fact, *Stephanodiscus* species appear to be dominant for half the year.

ZOOPLANKTON

The zooplankton, which are not primary producers but which eat phytoplankton and organic detritus, are the next major organisms in the food chain. These tiny creatures, generally between 0.2 and 3 mm long, constitute one of the basic food items of small fish. The order of zooplankton known as *Cladocera* are numerous in the Central Basin in mid-summer. This particular order responds favorably to eutrophication, and higher populations are found in the western half of the lake and along the south shore in the eastern half. *Bosmina longirostris* (Fig. 9.13 top), *Eubosmina corgoni*, and *Daphnia retrocurva* (Fig. 9.13 middle) are the most-common cladocerans observed (Larson and Rathke 1980).

Another zooplankton group with an annual cycle and population density similar to the *cladocerans* is the cyclopoid copepods (Watson 1976). One species of this group, *Cyclops bicuspidatus thomasi*, is the most-numerous single species in the lake. In a study of zooplankton in the Sandusky subbasin, Herberger and Reynolds (1977) found that this organism prefers to remain in the bottom waters, and that when the waters become anoxic their numbers collapse. This happens every year, but the species appears to be doing well because it is able to enter a summer resting stage within the bottom sediments and thereby survive the anoxic conditions.

The third major group of zooplankton species are the calanoid copepods, which reach only a tenth of the populations of the other two groups. In the Central Basin, the calanoids are largely made up of *Diaptomus* species. A fourth group of zooplankters, called rotifers, are often neglected because the individuals are so small, usually between only 0.1 and 0.5 mm in length. Nevertheless, they can comprise a relatively large fraction of between 6 and 40 percent of the zooplankton biomass (Larson and Rathke 1980). They are largely made up of *Keratella* and *Polyarthra* species. These small zooplankton are often the food for larger, carnivorous zooplankton such as *Leptodora* and *Polyphemus*.

FISH

Two exotic species of fish have invaded the Great Lakes and have caused problems. The alewife (*Alosa pseudoharengus*) is one of these fish: it in— vaded the Great Lakes system from the Atlantic Coast and enjoyed great breeding success leading to a tremendous population explosion. In spite of this success the individual landlocked fish is small, thin, and bony and thus not palatable to man. (Along the Atlantic Coast the fish is large, meaty, and edible [Scott and Crossman 1973].)

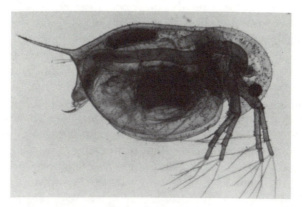

Figure 9.13 Types of zooplankton found in Lake Erie.
Bosmina (top), Daphnia, and mouthparts of a meso-
cyclops (bottom). (Photos by A. Chapman.)

The Great Lakes' alewives are not fully acclimatized to freshwater conditions and undergo huge die-offs in the spring when the temperatures in the lakes change rapidly (Scott and Crossman 1973). The numbers of floating dead fish can make large areas of the lake unpleasant as well as most of the beaches when huge numbers of them are washed up and rot. Water intakes in the lake can become badly clogged with dead fish. Lake Erie has been spared from this curse to a large degree, however; the lake is so shallow and the warming so rapid that the change in temperature appears to be beyond the capability of the alewife to handle. Also, the water in Lake Erie in winter is colder than that of the other Great Lakes, which adds an additional stress on alewives. The result is that Lake Erie is the only Great Lake without a problem-causing alewife population.

The other fish that has ravaged the other Great Lakes but left Lake Erie relatively unscathed is the sea lamprey, not be confused with the lake lamprey. There have always been lake lampreys in the lakes above Niagara Falls (Trautman 1949), but they did not distort the ecology of these systems. The sea lamprey, however, found its way out of Lake Ontario into the other Great Lakes, with the first specimen being caught in Lake Erie in 1921. Thereafter the lake trout fisheries in the Upper Lakes began to suffer predation from the sea lamprey. The sea lamprey evidently needs spawning conditions similar to those of lake trout in that the streams must have clear water, well-defined riffles, and sandbars and banks rich in organic debris for the young to feed on. These conditions used to exist in a number of Lake Erie streams, but the silt pollution that has damaged so many of these streams has inadvertently kept both the sea and lake lamprey populations below the danger level in Lake Erie. Consequently, they do not pose the same problem as in the other lakes. Possibly because of recent pollution abatement measures, numbers of larval sea lamprey are increasing in Conneaut and Cattaraugus Creeks (Mormon, Cuddy, and Rugen 1980).

The fisheries in the Central and West Basins differ somewhat, although the commercial fish species in both basins are the same. Perch is the most important, but smelt, and not walleye, is the second most-important fish of the Central Basin fishery. These differences are shown clearly in Figure 9.14. Quite a large amount of freshwater drum (sheepshead) are caught coincidently with the perch, but the market for these fish is not large. They used to be eaten, and efforts are now being made to revive interest in them as food for humans. Even without that interest, if the commercial market for pet food or mink farm food is active, a fairly large weight of these fish will be landed.

In the past, attempts at controlling the Lake Erie fishery included setting a minimum legal size of each fish species and keeping the number of commercial fishing licenses relatively constant. The fishery has intensified over the years, nevertheless, by operators buying up inactive licenses from small-boat owners and transferring them to increasingly powerful combination gill net–trawling vessels (Berkes and Pocock 1980). This largely

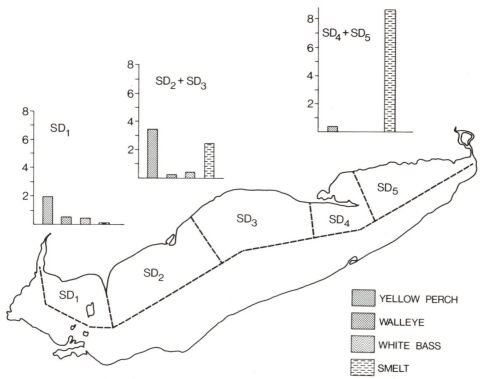

Figure 9.14 The Canadian commercial fish production, in 1000-ton units, for the different Lake Erie statistical districts in 1981. (J.H. Leach, personal communication.)

unregulated fishery has led to "gearing-up": investment of increasingly large amounts of capital in larger and more-efficient boats so these boats can capture the decreasing number of fish before the less well-equipped boats do. This process leads to disaster, with more and more "capital" chasing fewer and fewer fish, until the business becomes totally uneconomic and the fishery collapses. This situation can be prevented by a number of alternatives, but implementation of these measures has been slow.

The current, desired management scheme is the quota system, which has been applied to the walleye fishery. When this fishery was reopened in the West Basin in 1974 after the closure resulting from mercury contamination, a quota per boat was set. These quotas were deliberately set low, since it is much easier to raise a quota than lower it. The quota set in 1979 was 11,350 kg per boat for Canadian West Basin fishermen, and 1,700 kg per boat in the Canadian waters of the Central Basin. The Central Basin quota is lower than the West Basin quota, because the walleye spawn in the spring in the West Basin and only a small fraction of the population drifts over into the Central Basin later in the summer.

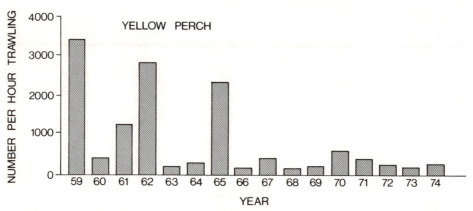

Figure 9.15 Average numbers of young-of-the-year yellow perch caught per hour of trawling in Lake Erie. (Leach and Nepszy 1976.)

The situation with yellow perch is quite different. The most valuable fish in the Central Basin (see Fig. 9.14), it has been intensely overfished. The population has been dropping as shown by abundance index for young-of-the year perch (Fig. 9.15). The success of the quota system for the walleye means that a quota system for yellow perch could be introduced in Canadian waters in 1984 (J.H. Leach, personal communication). Another problem with yellow perch needing resolution is that of the yellow perch young-of-the-year summer catch. There is presently an 8 inch (20.3 cm) size limit on perch that can be retained for sale. Unfortunately, in the summer many undersized perch get caught in the nets and are thrown away. Both the fisherman and authorities are looking for a regulation satisfactory to all concerned to prevent this wastage.

The smelt in the Central Basin provide a stable fishery. Each boat has a limit of 20 tons per week, which enables fishermen to make a reasonable living if the price paid for the fish is normal. Since there is a good but limited market for this fish, overproduction causes a rapid drop in price, so a large degree of self-regulation is built into this fishery. The present market requirements seem to be within the sustainable yield for the smelt, and no serious problems are foreseen at this time. White bass is another fish in a similar situation where the demand is not greater than the supply, and a small quantity of these fish are sold annually at about half the price paid for yellow perch.

Two presently overabundant species of fish are the freshwater drum (Fig. 9.16) and the gizzard shad. Both of these species grow rapidly when young and quickly pass through the stage when they are useful as forage fish to other species. When they are larger they are not considered desirable as market fish because both have soft flesh. For much of its lifespan, the freshwater drum eats the same food as yellow perch; if many drum were removed from the lake, a greater number of perch presumably could be

Figure 9.16 An average-size freshwater drum about 45 cms (18 in.) long. (Photo by CLEAR.)

sustained. If a large, profitable pet food industry were established, these fish would be worth harvesting. If the drum and shad were put under the same fishing pressure as the other species, a more-balanced fish community would result.

The Central Basin as a Resource

There is a considerable difference in opinion between Canadian and American authorities over the utilization of the fishery resource of the Central Basin. The Canadian regulations favor the commercial fisherman and enable him to take large quantities of fish. The American regulations for commercial fishermen are far more stringent, especially those passed in Ohio in November 1981 (Reuter 1981), and favor the sports fisherman. This is the main reason why Canadian commercial fish production is increasing while the American production is going down (see Fig. 8.18).

Broadly speaking, both the Canadian and American authorities are acting wisely in regard to the Central Basin when one considers the difference in the populations living along the north and south shores. The north shore of the Central Basin has no towns and only four village harbors along its 180 km of shoreline. In some areas there are cottages along the shore, but in most parts the farmlands run right to the edge of the clay bluffs. Although quite a number of vacationers use the few parks and holiday resorts along this shore, most of the residents are farmers or fishermen who do not use the lake much as a recreational resource. For example, when Wheatley Harbor was upgraded, two piers were laid out for the use of pleasure boats. A year or two later one of these piers was removed to make more space for commercial boats. The second pier had not been sufficiently used by the pleasure boaters. Also, when sailing along the north shore, one passes few pleasure boats. Actually, sailing along the north shore and then spending time in these harbors, with the occasional walk into the countryside, provides a unique opportunity to observe man in harmony with his surroundings. The farms are productive, and the rural setting with the occasional village or harbor is delightful.

The south shore of the Central Basin, on the other hand, has many towns, harbors, and a huge city. The majority of the residents of this area are industrial or office workers. When one sails nearshore on a weekday one can almost tell the time of day by the number of pleasure craft that come out on the lake soon after 4 PM. The many boats out on a good summer's day show the lake to be an important source of relaxation for the people in the industrial sphere. Some of them sail but many of them fish, so maintenance of a good nearshore recreational fishery is important. For similar reasons, the beaches should be accessible to the local inhabitants, with efforts made by those who use them to keep the beaches clean and safe from broken glass. The authorities have the responsibility to ensure that the lake waters are clean and safe for swimming. In an era of a strange, simultaneous increase of free time and stress in life, the lake becomes an increasingly valuable recreational resource.

A number of concerns require improvement in the Central Basin. Perhaps the worse problem is the one we know least about, the number of fish killed by impingement on the intake screens or by passing through the cooling water systems of large power plants. Figure 9.17 shows the twelve such installations along the south shore of the Central Basin, and they are known to kill many fish (Kelso and Milburn 1979). The effect of these generating station intakes should be investigated in greater detail. If the damage to fish life is excessive, the problem should be faced and a solution found.

Many of the waste treatment plants now meet the effluent standards of 1000 mg P m^{-3}, but this concentration is 50 to 100 times greater than the lake background level of 10 to 20 mg P m^{-3}. Effluents from lakeshore treatment plants should be pumped a few km offshore and released through diffusers situated above the hypolimnion at depths of 12m or so. Since dispersion of effluents in the hypolimnion is weak (Murthy 1972), undesirable concentrations of all nutrients in the hypolimnion would result with outfalls set at more than 15m depth. The 12m depth is deeper than the draught of the large lake vessels, but above the normal level of the hypolimnion and so is a suitable disposal depth. If all outfalls were far offshore, the nearshore water quality would be much improved. Also, every effort should be made to minimize dumping materials into the many rivers entering the south shore, whether oil, garbage, chemicals, or treatment plant wastes. The waters from these rivers move alongshore with little dilution if there is wind blowing in a westerly or southwesterly direction, as there often is. Many efforts are presently being made to control dumping, and the quality of life around Lake Erie is slowly improving. The August 1980 *National Geographic* showed a pair of "before and after" photographs of a site on the Cuyahoga River in Cleveland: a rotted, derelict pier surrounded by oil-covered water has now become a pleasant riverside marina with a restaurant and reasonably clean water flowing by.

The deeper waters of the Central Basin in midsummer are clear, warm, and lovely to swim in, but the real beauty spot of the Central Basin is Point aux Pins (Point of Pines), the 10 km peninsula forming the eastern shore of Rondeau Harbor (Fig. 9.18). The open bay, the marsh, and the land of the point became a Provincial Park in 1894, and although some of the eastern shoreline area has beachfront cottages, the majority of the park is in a remarkable state of preservation as described by Allen (1970):

> There are no untouched patches of forests left in the Great Lakes region. One that has probably been least altered is Rondeau Provincial Park on Lake Erie. Pines were taken from here as from everywhere else in the Great Lakes area, but this is still a beautiful old southern-hardwood forest, a kind of forest that appears in Canada only in this southwest section of the Great Lakes

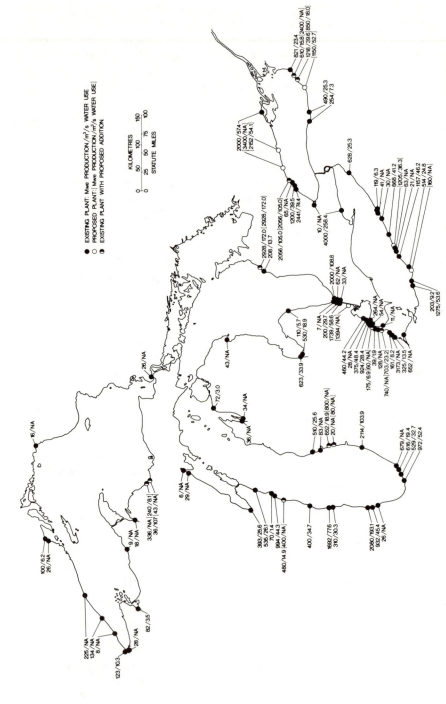

Figure 9.17 Thermal electrical generating stations using the waters of Lakes Michigan, Huron, Erie, and Ontario for once-through cooling, showing the large number of stations along the Central and West Basins and the Detroit River. (After Kelso and Milburn 1979.)

Figure 9.18 An aerial photograph of Point aux Pins shows how the land was formed from a number of sand ridges built up at different periods in the history of the lake. (Bukata, Haras, and Bruton 1975.) Figure 3.6 provides a frame of reference. Part of Rondeau Harbor and Bay are shown at the left of this picture, separated from the lake proper by a man-made breakwater at bottom (south).

region. The first thing you notice, about a mile south of the park entrance, is the height of the trees. The road goes through a deep green slot in the forest. Tulip trees, with leaves that look as if they had been cut off across the top, grow straight and black-trunked, a hundred and fifty feet high, with dark heavily ridged bark. These monumental pillars of trunks are forty inches in diameter, bare of branches near the ground.

Often Virginia creeper gives the trunks of trees in the park a feathery look, from a distance. Wild grape vines drape from the trees and form great green shrouds above the forest floor. In some regions of the park young ironwood trees with straight horizontal branches give the forest a peculiar wavy appearance, as if seen from underwater. There are enormous white oaks, which in open areas of the park develop huge serpentine branches, and a blue beech which foresters claim can be identified in the dark by soft ridges beneath the bark that feel like muscles. The blue beech trees with their elephant-like grey bark grow in the sloughs. The swampy ground in these low places is jet black with the rotting and decaying matter of the forest and covered with maidenhair fern. There are big-leaved basswood trees with sucker branches growing low on the trunk, and shagbark hickory, a tree found only in the southern hardwood forests of this part of Canada, and chestnut oaks which just barely make an appearance in Canada in the region of Lake Erie and Lake St. Clair.

The varied vegetational cover found at Point aux Pins derives from the formation of the land shown in Figure 9.18. The point has been building eastward with a series of high sand ridges interspersed with troughs that become swampy ground and with forest vegetation covering the ridges. Although less well known than Point Pelee, this park receives more than 500,000 visitors a year, who camp and picnic, fish in the bay, swim in the lake, or walk along trails through the lovely forest. This small part of the Lake Erie shoreline offers a welcome opportunity for people to experience nature once again.

Summary

The Central Basin can be a rough body of water, so most of the research is done from large ships in the offshore area. Investigations into the causes of the low oxygen concentrations observed in the bottom waters of this basin found that these conditions resulted from the large amount of algal material that settled out of the surface waters. The excessive algal growth is caused by the overloading of phosphorus from the surrounding cities to the lake. Unfortunately, the ensuing anoxia resulted in the release of large amounts of phosphorus from the sediments to the overlying water, making the problem worse. This led to the decision to diminish phosphorus loads to the basin.

Wind and weather cause a great variability in the behavior of the water masses in the Central Basin each year, and the annual rate of oxygen depletion. This variability has obscured trends of change and led to a debate on whether the rate of oxygen depletion was actually increasing with time. After allowance for the differences resulting from effects of the weather, the consensus is that the rate has been increasing with time, thus confirming the original decision to diminish the loading of phosphorus to the basin.

A large number of larval fish are killed in the cooling water intakes of power stations along the basin shoreline. This is a difficult problem that requires resolution because the fishery is valuable to both recreational and commercial fishermen. The Central Basin is a valuable resource to the many people living along its shoreline and needs careful management.

10

The East Basin

The East Basin Today

The land to the north and south of the East Basin has more variation in altitude than the land surrounding the other two basins (see Fig. 3.6). The Allegheny Plateau descends by a series of glaciated valleys to the narrow plain running along the south shore. Deer are found in the upland areas, while grapes grow along the lakeshore. In contrast, the north shore is flat for some distance inland; the area east of Port Dover consists of the Haldimand clay plain, while the area to the west consists of the Norfolk sand plain, a quite different soil type (Fig. 3.7). Farther north, the land rises via a glacial spillway that is the headwaters area for the Grand River, Ontario, the largest river flowing into the East Basin. The Haldimand clay soils support mixed farming, while tobacco is grown on the sandy Norfolk soils.

Figure 5.9 shows that the shoreline areas consist of thin bands of bedrock running parallel to the shore, which form most of the contact zone of the lake waters with the shore. This layer of rock at water level prevents extensive shoreline erosion. Along the south shore, the rock is overlain with three to five meters of soil, but there is relatively little erosion of this soil to the lake. Along the north shore there is almost no soil on the rock close to the lake, so this area consists of low, rocky shores interspersed with sandy beaches, although high clay bluffs do exist between Port Dover and Turkey Point. Much of the lake bottom in the nearshore zones is swept clean of recent sediment by the action of waves and currents, leaving areas of exposed, prehistoric glaciolacustrine clay adjacent to the rock outcrops.

The ancient Port Huron moraine crosses the lake from Long Point to Erie, which together with sand from the Central Basin bluff erosion has

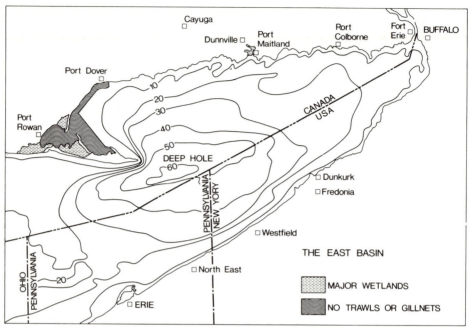

Figure 10.1 The bathymetry of the East Basin, showing the major wetlands. Depth shown in meters.

provided material to build two sand spits. The littoral drift along the south shore in the East Basin is strictly eastward and has resulted in Presque Isle migrating slowly eastward (Jennings 1930). This peninsula is large (9 km long) but is small compared to Long Point on the north shore, which seems to extend almost to the middle of the lake. Long Point peninsula receives sand from both the west and east (Fig. 4.7) and continues to grow at about 7m yr^{-1} (Sly and Lewis 1972).

The morphometry of the East Basin is deeper and has a different shape than either of the other basins. It does not have the islands of the West Basin nor the regular shape of the Central Basin, but has an irregular shape with two peninsulas. The East Basin is roughly 140 km long with a width of about 65 km, but because of its shape the tip of Long Point is within 14 km of the deepest part of the Basin (Fig. 10.1). The irregular shape of the East Basin has given rise to some major wetland areas behind Long Point and just to the west of it. The large bay formed by Presque Isle is too deep for wetlands, but there is a small marsh at the east end of the spit.

While the Central Basin bathymetry has the shape of a baking pan with relatively steep sides and a large flat area in the middle, the East Basin is shaped like an inverted cone. The water in this basin stratifies in late May, and the warm surface layer is usually about 20m thick. The thermocline

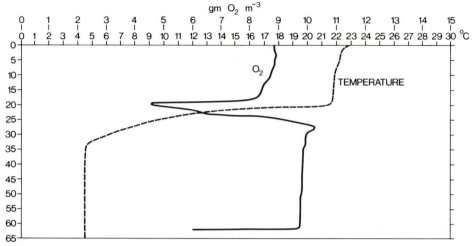

Figure 10.2 Depth profiles (in meters) of oxygen concentration and temperature taken at the deep hole of the East Basin on 31 August 1981. These data show a marked oxygen minimum near the top of the thermocline.

average thickness is 8 m, so the surface of the hypolimnion usually commences at a depth of about 28 m. The cold waters of the hypolimnion move in response to storms but are far less disturbed than those of the Central Basin. Because of this calmer situation, there is very little entrainment of the warmer thermocline waters into the hypolimnion and thus much less warming of the East Basin bottom waters. For example, in 1970 the mean temperature of this hypolimnion in the first week of June was 5.5°C and warmed to only 6.2°C by the third week of October, a rise of less than one degree in 4.5 months. In contrast, the Central Basin hypolimnion had warmed by more than 5° in 3.5 months. During the winter months the water in the East Basin is isothermal at 0.1°C.

The East Basin hypolimnion is not reoxygenated from above and this, together with the small temperature increase, means that the corrections required to standardize the oxygen uptake data for different years are minimal when one calculates annual oxygen depletion rates. The East Basin oxygen depletion rate thus could provide simple evidence of whether or not there has been an increase in the oxygen depletion rate with time. Unfortunately, there is not a great deal of data available but that which exists has been analyzed by Rosa and Burns (1982) and results indicate a probable increase of about 1g per year in this rate. This pattern of change in the East Basin is in agreement with the changes computed for the oxygen depletion rate of the Central Basin.

Another aspect of the oxygen regime is that quite substantial oxygen minima are seen in the thermocline of the East Basin. Figure 10.2 shows how temperature and oxygen concentrations change with depth at the deepest point of the East Basin. The data show a minimum oxygen concentration near the top of the thermocline. Similar minima have been frequently observed in Lake Ontario (Boyd 1980), while oxygen maxima have been observed in the thermocline in Lake Superior. The depth of occurrence of these phenomena is similar, about 20m from the surface, but the prevailing light intensities are different in the different lakes. The superbly clear waters of Lake Superior allow the one percent light level to be present at the thermocline depth of 20 m. Algae observed in this layer were photosynthetic and produced a slight oxygen supersaturation at 107 percent of saturation (Watson, Thompson, and Elder 1975). The clarity of the East Basin and Lake Ontario waters is less than that of Lake Superior, so the 1 percent light level in these waters is well above the thermocline—at about 11m in the East Basin (J. Jerome, personal communication). Thus, the material accumulating in the thermocline at 20m is subject to decay rather than growth, resulting in an oxygen minimum. The increase in density and viscosity of the water that occurs in the thermocline because of the temperature decrease causes material settling out of the epilimnion to settle more slowly as it enters the thermocline. This creates a higher concentration of organic material in this zone, and when this decomposes it reduces the oxygen concentrations noticeably. This decomposition also causes the flux of organic material leaving the thermocline to be less than that entering the thermocline. This result was indicated by Rathke et al. (1981), who measured the average flux of particulate organic carbon settling into the thermocline at 290 ± 74 mg m^{-2} day, and the amount settling out at 238 ± 47 mg m^{-2} day^{-1} during a number of experiments done between July and September of 1978.

The biology and chemistry of the East Basin are both dependent on the thermal stratification occurring during the summer. The heavy diatoms with their relatively high sinking velocities virtually disappear from the basin for the months of June, July, and August, with the May and September populations being very small (Fig. 10.3). During this period they are largely replaced by algal types that have some control over their vertical positioning, such as the blue-greens (cyanophyta) or flagellate species (chrysomondae, cryptomonadinae and dinophycinae), or alternatively by the greens (chlorophyta), which have characteristically low settling velocities (Burns and Rosa 1980).

The water quality of the open waters of the basin is excellent by any standard, and so most of the problems in the East Basin are nearshore. Surface blooms have never been reported in mid-basin, and during the summer the water is beautifully clear. The author can recall many delightful swims in these offshore waters from the deck of his research vessel. These waters stay clear all summer and become murky with sediment only when they have been turned over by storms in the spring and fall.

Although offshore concentrations of phosphorus are low, higher concentrations do exist in the nearshore zones close to the sources of phosphorus input. This is most unfortunate for the East Basin, because its shorelines

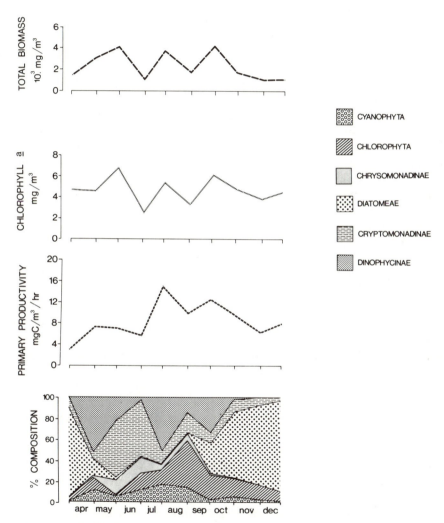

EASTERN

apr may jun jul aug sep oct nov dec

TOTAL BIOMASS 10³. mg/m³

CHLOROPHYLL a mg/m³

PRIMARY PRODUCTIVITY mgC/m³/hr

% COMPOSITION

apr may jun jul aug sep oct nov dec

CYANOPHYTA

CHLOROPHYTA

CHRYSOMONADINAE

DIATOMEAE

CRYPTOMONADINAE

DINOPHYCINAE

Figure 10.3 The annual variation in phytoplankton biomass, chlorophyll "a", primary productivity, and phytoplankton group composition in the East Basin during 1970. (Munawar and Munawar 1976.) Common names are: Cyanophyta—blue greens, Chlorophyta—greens, Chrysomonadinae—chrysomonads, Diatomeae—diatoms, Chrytomonadinae—cryptomonads, Dinophycinae—dinoflagellates.

are rocky and provide a good substrate for *Cladophora* growth. Just as the
Central Basin is susceptible to anoxic conditions because of its thin hypolimnion, the East Basin is naturally susceptible to massive *Cladophora*
growths because of its rocky nearshore zone (see Fig. 10.4). A 1981 report
by Kirby and Dunford found no improvement in the density growth of
Cladophora in a 10 km segment of shoreline near Nanticoke, which they
studied from 1971 to 1979. The problem of excessive amounts of *Cladophora*
in the East Basin is not going to be easy to solve, but should be tackled.
The area has tremendous recreational potential that is badly damaged by
excess growth of this alga (Fig. 10.5).

When considering the zooplankton of the basin, we find surprisingly
little difference between the zooplankton populations of the Central and
East Basins, even though the East Basin is less eutrophic than the Central
Basin. Watson's (1976) data show similar seasonal abundance and population
densities in both basins for cyclopoid copepods, calanoid copepods, and
cladocerans. The cladocerans are a little more numerous in the Central
than in the East Basin.

The East Basin fishery, like those of the other two basins, has declined
considerably over the last century but still provides many fish. There is
much sport fishing along the south shore, and many recently stocked Coho
salmon are taken. A small commercial fishery has an annual catch in New
York waters of about 50 tons of walleye (Schneider and Leach 1977). The
perch in the East Basin spawn in the rocky area along the north shore
shown in Figure 10.6 and also along the south shore. Commercial catches
of these fish are relatively small—less than 500 tons in 1981—and represent
about 10 percent of the commerical catch of perch for the lake. The most-
important commercial fish in the East Basin is the smelt, which spawns on
sandy beaches from Point Pelee eastward, with most of the spawning done
in the Central Basin region. Although smelt can survive in this basin all
year, they prefer colder water and thus tend to collect in the East Basin
toward the end of the summer, when the oxygen concentrations become
too low for them in the bottom waters of the Central Basin (MacCallum
and Regier 1970). They are caught in great numbers by the trawlermen
of the East Basin (Figs. 9.14, 10.7). There are now very few walleye or
sturgeon caught in the Canadian waters of the East Basin.

The extensive wetlands of Inner Bay provide a wonderful spawning
ground and nursery area for smallmouth (*Micropterus dolomieui*) and rock
bass (*Amblophites rupestris*), northern pike, bowfin (*Amoa calva*), bullheads
(*Octalurus sp.*), sunfish, and carp, as well as many other species. Inner Bay
has two fishing seasons, the summer holiday season from 13 May to 31
August when only anglers may fish, and the rest of the year when commercial
fishermen as well may fish with hoop-nets and seines. The anglers catch
many fish, mostly perch and bass, in summer and winter. The commerical
fishermen use small boats, hoop-nets, and long seine nets to catch bullheads,
bowfin, and sunfish (Table 10.1). The fact that the commercial fishery takes

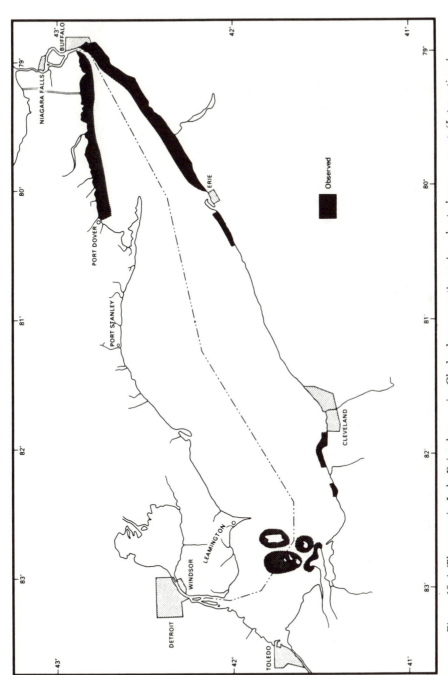

Figure 10.4 The areas in Lake Erie where major Cladophora *growths and wash-ups have occurred. (International Lake Erie Water Pollution Board 1969.)*

Figure 10.5 Cladophora *growing in excess at a site on the north shore of the East Basin, just west of Port Maitland. (Photo by J.P. Barry.)*

different species to those taken by the sports fishery enables the two to co-exist, although the commercial fishermen do become irritated when

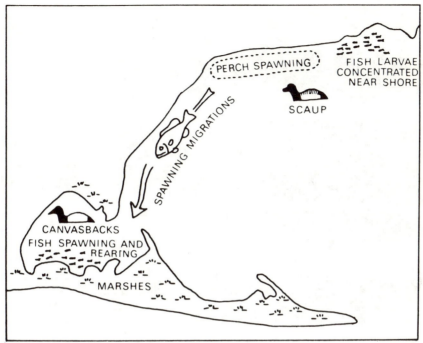

Figure 10.6 The ecologically sensitive areas in the northwest part of the East Basin. (Hamley and MacLean 1979.)

sports fishermen sell their perch catches to local outlets (Berkes and Pocock 1980).

The Inner Bay marshes are valuable as resting areas for migrating wildfowl. It is estimated that about one-third of eastern North American canvasbacks and a somewhat lesser proportion of redheads stop in this area each fall to feed on the abundant bottom vegetation (Hamley and MacLean 1979). Table 10.2 gives some idea of the importance of this resting area to waterfowl. The scaups remain in the Inner Bay at night, but migrate out to the lake to the area shown in Figure 10.6. Congregating into rafts of from 1000 to 10,000 birds, they stay fairly close to shore on water from 0.6 to 3.6m deep. From this vantage point, they dive down and eat the snails that are abundant on the rocky bottom (McCullough 1981). Unfortunately, much of the north shore of the East Basin, particularly the area close to where these ducks raft, is now on the threshold of massive industrial development, and the future for fish and wildlife remains uncertain.

Changes Wrought by Time and Man

Before settlement, the land around the East Basin was forested, except where water collected in low-lying areas and produced grassy meadows.

*Figure 10.7 Rainbow smelt (*Osmerus mordex*) from Lake Erie. The top pair are male. (Photo by J. Leach.)*

The land along the north shore was originally the home of a population of more than 12,000 Neutral Indians. Their culture was fairly advanced; although they hunted, their primary source of sustenance was crops grown on the lands they had cleared by burning. They lived in villages protected by earthworks and stakes and occupied the territory from about A.D. 1000 to 1650, when they were first weakened by the white man's diseases and then destroyed by the Iroquois. The land around Long Point, which had been the Neutral's hunting ground, became a no-man's land and was used on a "first come—first served" basis (Barrett 1977, 1981).

The first settlers to the northshore area took up land in 1786 and were followed by the Empire Loyalists, who arrived in 1796. Soon afterward, settlers arrived in Buffalo and the settlement of both shores of the Lake Erie Basin began. A settler in 1824 discovered that the flat land along the southern shore was suitable for growing the Concord grape, and over the years much of the narrow East Basin lake plain was transformed into vineyards. Some of the juice is used for wine, but much is still sold as unfermented grape juice. The settlers along the north shore planted wheat and developed orchards. Many chose lands close to the Long Point marshes because of the meadows in the vicinity. Their cattle ran wild throughout the area and thrived on the natural pasturage, but losses were high from wild dogs and poachers. Sometimes, many of the cattle were drowned when

Table 10.1 Fish Harvest from Long Point Bay

	Number of fishermen	Landed catch, kg (1977)
Commercial fisheries		
Outer Bay, gill net		
Yellow perch	83	133,879
Outer Bay, trawl		
Rainbow smelt	61	4,808,862
Inner Bay, hoop-net and seine		
Mixed (35% bullheads, 42% sunfish, some bowfin, carp, rock bass, northern pike, and yellow perch)	30	135,619

	Number of angler-trips	Catch in number of fish (1975)
Angling		
Summer, concentrated in the Inner Bay in June, off Turkey Point in July and August		
Mixed (43% yellow perch, 21% rock bass, 20% smallmouth bass, fewer northern pike and sunfish)	21,344	101,527
Winter, Inner Bay ice fishing centered at St. Williams		
Yellow perch (89% of catch)	6,475	79,000

Source: From Hamley and MacLean 1979.

Table 10.2 Waterfowl Use of Long Point Bay, Including the Marshes of Long and Turkey Points (in 1000s of waterfowl-days)

	Spring (Mar. 1–June 1)	Fall (Aug. 16–Jan. 1)
Mallards and blacks	252.0	1,168.5
Other dabblers	12.6	186.4
Canvasbacks and redheads	462.3	4,749.4
Scaups	104.2	222.7
Other ducks	90.9	40.1
Geese	125.3	198.7
Swans	41.3	9.9

Note: Waterfowl-day = one day spent in the area by one bird.
Source: Hamley and MacLean 1979.

they were caught out on the marsh and a storm caused sudden changes of lake level (Barrett 1977).

At first the only lumbering around the lake was done by farmers clearing their lands. Commercial lumbering began in 1840 and proceeded at a great pace, even to the extent of removing the trees from Long Point in 1860. By 1880 the whole Long Point and northshore area was logged out. The thin layer of soil covering the sand of the Norfolk plains was disturbed and Long Point itself was degraded; where the ridges of Long Point had been logged, wind and water combined to form immense blow-outs. Wind erosion also began to devastate the farmlands where magnificent forests had once stood. Now only huge gray stumps stood on the tip toes of their roots, for one to three feet (0.3 to 1m) of soil had blown out from under them to leave a desolate wasteland (Barrett 1981). Luckily, a reforestation program by Dr. Edward Zavitz restablized the area. In 1920, tobacco, which needs sandy soil, was introduced to the area and the land increased dramatically in value. Care has been taken ever since to preserve it (Barrett 1977).

But not all the changes have been wrought by man. In 1833, a November storm blasted a "cut" through Long Point. This was scoured out even more extensively by the water that funneled into Inner Bay after the winds stopped. In a little more than twenty-four hours, a channel 350m wide with a depth varying between 4 and 6m had been made. In 1865, storms opened another cut, which was further widened by subsequent storms to a width of about 1 km and a depth of about 6 m; it closed gradually in 1895. The first cut closed suddenly in 1906 as described by Barrett (1977):

> Nature continued her tricks. In 1906 a storm blew up, trapping John Backus and Austin Deduck in their duck-hunting cabin near the Cut. Galeforce winds blew, and heavy seas rolled under the cottage all night, threatening to carry it, and their punt, which was tied to it, into the Inner Bay. Towards morning the wind suddenly dropped, and, as quickly as it had risen, the lake dropped back to its normal level. Shortly after daybreak the hunters looked outside. Where the punt had ridden the night before in a fairly wide, deep channel there was no water to be seen. The punt, still tied securely to the cabin, sat on a broad expanse of solid lake sand. The Long Point cut, which had served the seamen of Lake Erie most of the time since 1834, had ceased to exist in a matter of a few hours. Long Point was once again just that—a continuous peninsula.

Inner Bay also changed with time. Whillans (1979a) has been able to reconstruct the variations in bathymetry of the bay over time. Some of his diagrams, shown in Figure 10.8, illustrate that the sediments were washed out of the bay when the cuts were made and that the bay silted up again after they were closed. The changes of depth in the marsh rejuvenated it and prevented aging by siltation. Most of the area where

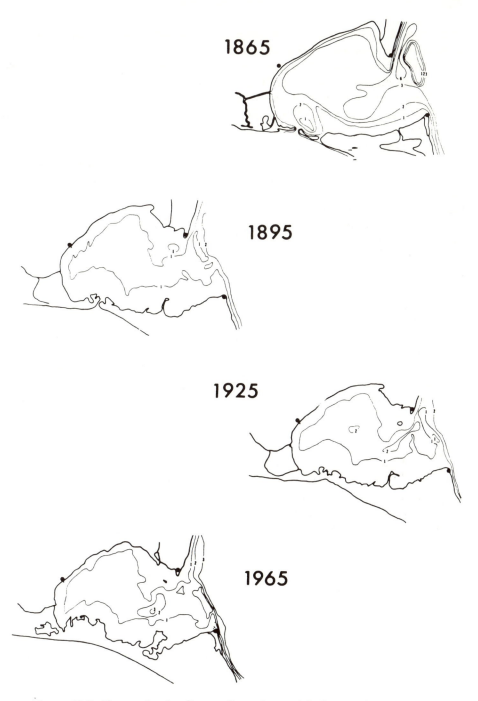

Figure 10.8 Changes in shoreline configuration and bathymetry in Inner Bay from 1865 to 1965. (Whillans 1979a.)

the "cuts" occurred is now stabilized with a road, cottages, and Provincial Park. It does not seem likely that we will see any massive "cuts" again in the near future. This will surely have some large, long-term effect on the Inner Bay marshes, but the nature of this effect remains uncertain.

Soil erosion and silt deposition in streams along the north shore is a real problem, especially in the sand plain area. MacCrimmon and Gordon (1981) found that 78 percent of the eggs laid by coho salmon (*Oncorhynchus kisutch*), brown trout (*Salmo trutta*), and rainbow trout (*Salmo gairdaeri*) in the stream did not survive, largely because they were suffocated by shifting sand. Inner Bay, an important nursery ground for many of the East Basin fish, has also been affected by both siltation and increased loading of phosphorus and nitrate from Big Creek. This creek drains into the west end of the bay and does not mix with the open waters of the lake, so the nutrients in the creek are utilized in the bay, leading to a big increase in the growth of plants. These nutrients come from the fertilizer used for the tobacco grown in the drainage basin of Big Creek, because the sandy soil has a low retention for dissolved ions. The present loading of Big Creek to the bay is about 15 tons of phosphorus and 175 tons of nitrate nitrogen per year (Ongley 1976.)

The Inner Bay recreational fishery is important, with up to 7000 fishermen observed on the bay on the opening day of bass fishing, and more than 500 cars once observed on the ice for winter ice fishing. Except for the changes associated with water depth, the changes in the Inner Bay fishery have been caused by man. The first users of Inner Bay were the Neutral Indians, who caught the abundant whitefish with nets woven by the women from the fibers of wild hemp and nettle. They would catch, fillet, and smoke the whitefish for storage for the winter. The nature of the fishery did not change until the arrival of the settlers. Whillans (1979b) has examined historical records and developed a detailed account of the changes in the Inner Bay fish community in recent years. A pound net fishery at the mouth of the Bay in the 1870s caused a decline in the number of northern pike and permitted an increase in the number of muskellunge. In the 1880s the yellow walleye lost its traditional spawning grounds in Big Creek due to silting over with sand, and sawdust and bark litter choking the waterway. Also about this time, a dam was constructed across the mouth of the creek, and the would-be migrants collected below the dam each spring in a futile effort to travel upstream to spawn. Just before the turn of the century, the herring and whitefish populations around Long Point collapsed (Whillans 1981). At the turn of the century seine fishing increased in the bay and the stocks of smallmouth and largemouth bass diminished, along with those of northern pike. White bass and carp increased at this time. The next major change was the virtual elimination of the sturgeon in the 1930s by overfishing. The blue walleye was extirpated from Inner Bay in the late 1950s, and these walleye appear to have been the last of their species in existence.

Of all the fishes that have graced Long Point Bay, blue walleye was particularly treasured. Blues, or blue pike as they are officially named, were restricted to the lower Great Lakes. They thrived in the waters around Long Point in late summer and autumn, and were prized for their tastiness.

Although blue walleye faltered at the time of herring and whitefish declines, they managed to hold on. During the Second World War blues filled rationed stomachs, and in the 1950s, tonnes were pulled from nets. Late in that decade, however, as fishing techniques became more efficient, the species crashed without warning. Blue walleye became extinct within 10 years—a frightening speed, unequalled even by the demise of the passenger pigeon [Whillans 1981].

In the 1960s, the enrichment of Inner Bay caused an increase in the amount of weeds. This is thought to have resulted in greater relative abundance of carp, yellow perch, white sucker, rock bass, and crappies. The most-recent change has been a decrease in smallmouth bass and an increase in the yellow perch. The warmer water, enrichment, and spread of vegetation provide the most-acceptable explanation of the recent concurrent increases by largemouth bass, yellow perch, white sucker, rock bass, black and white crappie, alewife, bullheads, catfish, bowfin, pumpkinseed, gizzard shad, freshwater drum, and northern pike (Whillans 1979a).

The phosphorus loading to the East Basin has decreased, largely because of the decrease in the load from the Grand River, Ontario, of 1044 tons of bioavailable phosphorus in 1970 to 551 tons in 1980 (see Appendix Table A.1). There has been a definite increase in soluble inorganic nitrogen (NO_3 + NO_2 + NH_3) concentrations in the lake, from 68.4 mg N m^{-3} in 1970 to 138.6 mg N m^{-3} in 1978. This concentration increase is probably caused by material derived from both land drainage and atmospheric fallout. An example of the increase from land drainage is given by Leach (1981), who found that the nitrate concentration in Big Creek has increased from 230 mg N m^{-3} in 1962 to 623 mg N m^{-3} in 1979. A major source of nitrogen to the atmosphere is the new industrial park at Nanticoke on the north shore, which is currently releasing about 58,000 tons of NO_2 per year to the air (Schuldt 1980). This combines with atmospheric moisture to form nitric acid (H NO_3), which then becomes part of the rain and snow.

The Nanticoke Project

The north shore of the East Basin is now undergoing a time of rapid change, as did the south shore of the Central Basin at the time of the American Civil War. Once again change to a rural area is being caused by the advent of steel-making and industrialization. A real test of man's intelligence is developing at Nanticoke. We have seen what happened to the lake and its surroundings during the 19th century, when man acted in haste and ignorance during the massive buildup of Detroit, Toledo, and Cleveland. In the case of the Nanticoke development, we have the information necessary for the preservation of an environment undergoing industrial development. The test is to see whether man will use his knowledge to build an industrial area without destroying or damaging the nearby lake, or whether the development will be allowed to destroy the ecology of the area. The necessity of profit may make the provision of funds for the maintenance of the water quality and biota of this region difficult to ensure.

At present, the five major components of the Nanticoke development are sited between Kitchen and Peacock Points (Fig. 10.9): the Stelco steel mill, the Ontario Hydro Electrical Generating Station, the Texaco Petroleum Refinery, the Stelco Industrial Park, and the new city of Townsend. From the start of the venture there has been a high degree of government involvement, which began in 1968 when Ontario Hydro announced the proposed construction of a large (4,000 megawatt), coal-fired electric power generating station. Land was then set aside for other industries that would want to locate nearby to utilize the power generated. The Nanticoke Environmental Committee was formed, consisting of members from a number of provincial government agencies. These agencies were given the responsibility of monitoring the biological and chemical condition of the lake adjacent to the development. In the early seventies, the Steel Company of Canada, Inc. (Stelco) and Texaco Canada, Inc. (Texaco) announced proposed construction of a steel mill and a refinery in the area. These industries now share membership with the Ontario Ministries of the Environment and Natural Resources on the Nanticoke Environmental Committee and have helped pay for a number of the environmental studies. Another joint government-industry venture, the Nanticoke Environmental Management Program now exists for the purpose of monitoring and advising on air quality requirements (Jeffs 1981).

Two major problems are associated with the Ontario Hydro thermal generating station: first, the damage to aquatic organisms living in the large volume of water that is cycled through the station (approximately 150 m^3 sec^{-1} at full load) and, second, the large quantity of by-products from the burning of coal, which can be consumed at 35,000 tons per day when the station is running at full load. The intake water is split into two parts, with 60 percent of the water cooling the condensers directly, and the other 40 percent merely added to the hot water from the condensers to temper it to the 8.3°C temperature increase permissable for release to the lake. The amount of water used for cooling in 1978–79 was about 2.1 km^3 per year, when the plant was operating at about 35 percent of capacity (Wianko 1981). Since the volume of the East Basin is 166 km^3, this plant cycled about 1.3 percent of the basin water through its systems each year, killing about 70 tons of fish, 98 percent of which was smelt. Many of the zooplankton passing through the system were also damaged, with the percentage of damage increasing with the size of the species. About 26 percent of the relatively large *Leptodora kindtii* suffered major damage (Standke and Monroe 1981). These quantities are not excessive when one

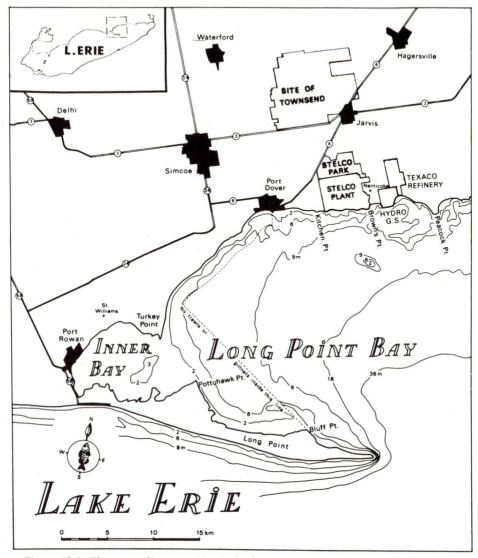

Figure 10.9 The area adjacent to Nanticoke that is currently undergoing development. (After Hamley and MacLean 1979.)

considers the mass of biota within the basin, but do represent the death of many live organisms. In particular, this northshore area is a favored spawning area, with many fish larvae concentrated close to shore in the zone where the power plant intakes are sited; thus many fish with considerable potential for growth are destroyed. The losses of both small and large fish could triple if the plant were run at full capacity for long periods of time. Ontario Hydro is concerned about these losses and is trying to find means to diminish them (Foster and Wheaton 1981). Perhaps this type of attitude on the part of the industrial managers is one of the more-unique features of the Nanticoke development; the managers are prepared to change and modify the plants to decrease environmental damage even after much time, thought, and expense has been expended during the initial planning and construction.

Many fish are damaged by impingement on the screens filtering the condenser water, but far more are killed by the high-speed impellers in the tempering pumps, which add lakewater to the condenser water to lower the temperature of the final effluent. Experiments are currently being conducted with an axial corkscrew-type tempering pump to try to reduce the fish kill. Another alternative being considered is the elimination of the tempering pumps altogether. In addition, the installation of large screens over the 6.5m diameter intakes situated in the lake is being tested and does appear to reduce the intake of fish. The huge quantities of ash generated are also a problem; they are made into a slurry with water and pumped into the ash lagoon to settle out for permanent storage. All other wastewaters from the site are also pumped into the supernatant lagoon, and this water is sampled and analyzed before release to the lake.

Stelco had to build a large dock running about 1.2 km into the lake to receive the large quantities of coal, limestone, and ore necessary for their mill. To minimize the disturbance of nearshore processes by the dock, the segment closest to shore, 322m long, was built in the form of a bridge and permits normal littoral currents and fish migrations to pass under it. The steel company will use about 18,000 m³ of water per day when at full production and is installing good water-purification equipment. Because of the possible release of many trace metals, extensive monitoring of this effluent and its effects will have to be maintained for a long time after the plant is in full production, to determine whether the installation is adequate or whether further water treatment steps must be applied.

Some green belt area has been maintained around the Stelco plant and adjoining industrial park since its inception. At the time construction started there was a sizable rookery of about 170 pairs of blue herons on the site (Spectator 1980). These birds are still present many years later and are being closely watched. Being fairly shy of people, they provide a natural barometer of the human pressure on the area.

In the planning of the Texaco refinery, the decision was made to minimize water use by using air cooling where possible. Thus the refinery uses in the range of 460 to 650 m³ per day compared to typical rates of 30,000m³ per day for comparable plants with once-through water cooling. The refinery came into operation in October 1978. Its environmental control systems are working well, with all discharges of contaminants within permissible levels (Jeffs 1981).

The development of the industrial park and the occupation of the specially designed city-site of Townsend have proceeded much more slowly

Table 10.3 Release of Gases That Cause Acid Rain at Nanticoke, Ontario

	Tons/year
Sulfur dioxide emissions	
Ontario Hydro–Nanticoke Thermal Generating Station (1978)	202,000
Stelco	8,000
Texaco–Nanticoke Plant (1979)	8,000
Total	218,000
Nitrogen oxides emissions	
Ontario Hydro–Nanticoke Thermal Generating Station (1978)	49,000
Stelco	8,000
Texaco–Nanticoke Plant (1979)	1,000
Total	58,000

Note: Stack emissions are as NO_2.
Source: Schuldt 1980.

than planned. Thus the pressure on the environment that will be exerted when these two developments are realized in full remains conjectural. The problem with modern industrial developments is that they seldom produce obvious catastrophic damage to the environment in a short time. Instead, they usually cause a small environmental degradation, which is then followed by another, and so on, with the sum total of change eventually adding up to an environmental catastrophe. Extreme vigilance is necessary to prevent this cancerous process from occuring at Nanticoke.

Since each of the three major industries has a large potential for creating air pollution, $100 million (in 1980$) has been spent on equipment to control air pollution. The concentrations of sulphur dioxide (SO_2), nitrous oxide (NO_2), ozone (O_3), and total suspended particulate matter in the air surrounding Nanticoke have not exceeded Ontario standards. Nevertheless, large quantities of these materials are released to the atmosphere, as shown in Table 10.3 (Schuldt 1980). Both NO_2 and SO_2 produce acids when combined with water, and the quantities of these gaseous oxides released at Nanticoke will produce much acid rain. Acid rain does not affect the waters of the Great Lakes markedly, because their limestone basins give rise to alkaline waters, which buffer the acidic effects of the rain. But the acid rain does affect the flora of the Great Lakes Basin and the small lakes northeast of Nanticoke, which are set in Canadian Shield rock and have unbuffered waters. These lakes will suffer from the Nanticoke emissions, just as they presently suffer from the effects of SO_2 from the Sudbury smelters. Acid rain causes much damage and as a result, the question has arisen whether to run the Nanticoke station at full power and export unneeded electricity, or to run at a reduced level sufficient to meet only local needs.

The more-important water chemistry parameters have been measured in the lake off the Nanticoke area since 1968 and have been reported on by Heathcote, Weiler, and Tanner (1981). Their opinion is that over the 10-year period 1968 to 1978, the water chemistry of the area has not really changed. This appears to be good news when one considers that three major industries started up during that period. But upon reflection, one realizes that the situation is not as rosy as it might appear. The north shore of Lake Erie is a prime recreational area (Figure 10.10); it has many fine beaches, and the landforms of Long Point and Inner Bay make fishing and sailing with small boats relatively safe. This area is also near the large population centers of Toronto, Hamilton, and Buffalo. The water quality was not satisfactory before the large industries started up, as indicated by *Cladophora* concentration in the nearshore waters, and although the water has not degraded further in recent years, it has not improved and still remains unacceptable. As the population and industrialization of the area increase, the condition of the lake is going to get worse, when it actually needs to improve. Although the efforts to date by government and industry have been good, they have not been adequate. The nearshore areas of the East Basin are, by their very nature, sensitive to nutrient pollution, and great care will be needed to prevent massive *Cladophora* growths. Strict agricultural practices must be followed to prevent leakage of phosphorus to the lake. All sewage wastes from the municipalities will have to be low in phosphorus, so the total amount of bioavailable phosphorus released to the basin decreases to less than 500 tons per year. Perhaps the most important requirement of all is that there be offshore disposal of these effluents—probably a minimum of 5 km from the shore. If the northshore waters of the East Basin can be kept clean and its biota relatively free from toxic metals and organics while a large industrial development is being built, the people of Ontario, Canada, will have produced a remarkable achievement.

The Peninsulas

The two peninsulas of the East Basin, Presque Isle and Long Point, are sandspits comprising long curving ridges with sloughs between the ridges. The ridges of Presque Isle are somewhat smaller than those of Long Point. Presque Isle is about 9 km long and has been made into a high-use state park with about 4,000,000 visitors annually. Almost the entire lake side of the park consists of sandy beaches; a paved road running most of the length of the spit provides easy access to the water. On a sunny summer Sunday, nearly all these beaches are packed, while many other people use the hiking trails at the wider east end of the spit. A small pleasure-boat harbor and marina in a little bay within the spit is well used; the main harbor formed by the curving landform is large enough to be used for sailboat races. Erie, the port city of Presque Isle Bay, has a history of

Figure 10.10 Port Maitland on the Grand River, Ontario, illustrating the normal mix of industrial and recreational uses of Great Lakes waters.

shipbuilding from the time five ships were built there in 1813. These ships were part of Perry's fleet when he defeated the British in 1814 in the battle fought among the Lake Erie islands. Continuing the shipbuilding tradition, the "Stewart J. Cort" was completed in Erie in 1972. Shown in Figure 10.11 this cargo ship is 305m long and 32m in the beam, with a carrying capacity of 45,000 metric tons of iron ore—a massive ship by any standards. At present there is little shipbuilding activity at Erie.

Long Point is about 33 km long, and the extreme 20 km is in a natural state and has few visitors. The history of the area begins with the wreck of the "Annette" in 1789 off Long Point (Barrett 1977), the first of a total of about 200 ships to be lost on sand bars off Long Point. When four American ships were lost in a November storm in 1827, the American government demanded that the British Parliament build a lighthouse on the point. When construction was completed in 1830, the lighthouse keeper became one of the earliest residents of the point. After the first "cut" was made through the peninsula in 1833, many ships used this route instead of going around the end of the point. This was, nevertheless, a dangerous procedure at night in the early years, because salvagers moved the lights around on shore and lured ships onto the sand banks. Few men from these wrecks survived. This stopped with the establishment of a lightship a little distance offshore in 1840, followed by the construction of "Old Cut Lighthouse" in 1879.

Many early activities on Long Point were illegal and stopped after most of Long Point and Inner Bay were bought by the Long Point Company in 1866:

> Activities there were many and varied but the greatest impact on the bay and ridges of the point itself was due to uncontrolled and illegal lumbering. This was carried on from as early as 1830 by both Canadians and Americans. Wherever they made a cut, wind and water combined to destroy the thin topsoil, create blowouts, and in many cases, wash the fragile exposed ridges into the surrounding water. Large parts of Long Point were lost wherever lumbering was carried out.
>
> By the 1840s and '50s the poachers were beginning to take their toll as well. Muskrat were taken at all seasons of the year and often put on the market in very poor condition. The normal payment was whiskey.
>
> By the late 1850s the market hunter had moved in from both sides of the lake, taking a tremendous toll each spring and fall as migrating red head, canvasback, blacks, and mallards attempted to settle in to rest and feed. Nor did summer bring much respite for them or for the young muskrat and deer that also lived and thrived in the long protected marshes.
>
> In no time Long Point developed an unenviable reputation as a "no-man's land" of drunkenness, murder, and debauchery of every kind. So-called hotels appeared. Steamboats and sailing schooners could readily be hired from Buffalo or Erie by those gamblers and others wishing to indulge in activities now being regulated or made illegal by the laws of both the American and Canadian governments. Complaints reaching the government finally became

Figure 10.11 The "Stewart J. Cort," the first 1000-footer on the Great Lakes, undergoing completion at Erie, Pennsylvania, in 1972. (Photo by J.P. Barry.)

so embarrassing that they were forced to take some form of action. Attempts to police it were fruitless. The simplest solution appeared to be to sell it, and the Crown Land Department was instructed to offer it for sale at public auction.

In the meantime a few people had become sufficiently concerned with the now obvious degradation and destruction of the area to attempt to do something about it. About 1860, a few of them asked the advice of a local lawyer, Col. D. Tisdale of Simcoe, and he was more than willing to work with them to try and bring some kind of sensible discipline to the big marsh. The group was made of several Scottish merchants of Hamilton: William Hunter, a Canadian tea merchant living in New York; and Samuel D. Woodruff, of St. Catharines.

On May 4th, 1866, Col. Tisdale and his group purchased Long Point under the name of the Long Point Company. They immediately petitioned the government for a Charter of Incorporation of those lands on Long Point which they now owned and "are desireous of promoting for fishing and hunting and otherwise to manage and make the land available for the purposes of the Company incorporated by this Act." This was assented to by the Legislative Assembly on the 15th of August 1866.

The members of the newly incorporated "Long Point Company" reacted with alacrity as their first meeting was held in Hamilton on August 16th, 1866 (ref: Minutes of Long Point Company).

At this initial meeting they began to lay down rules of good management which to this day have given the company a good name in the eyes of conservationists and wildlife management people. From that time on no spring duck hunting would be allowed and fall hunting would not commence before September 1st. No trapping would be allowed in the fall [Barrett 1981].

Under the policies and custody of the Long Point Company most of the ravages of the last century have repaired themselves so that Long Point is now in a comparatively natural state.

The area of Long Point and Inner Bay is quite large, being about 40 km long and about 7 km wide at the widest point. It starts in the west with the Big Creek Marsh, so-named because Big Creek once flowed through the marsh into the lake. It was diverted during the last century into Inner Bay to develop the small harbor of Port Royal, which has long since silted up. The Big Creek Marsh was used for waterfowl hunting and muskrat farming and even now is very close to its natural condition (Hardy 1980). In the early 1970s most of the privately owned parts of the marsh were bought up by public or government bodies. Some of the area is today classified as sanctuary, but muskrat trapping, spear fishing, waterfowl hunting, and canoeing are presently allowed on a limited basis while an overall management strategy for the marsh is being developed by the Canadian Wildlife Service.

Farther to the east, the Ontario Ministry of Natural Resources permits controlled hunting in their section of the marsh. Most of the higher land just south of this marsh is now privately owned or is part of the Long

Point Provincial Park. The remainder of Long Point used to belong to the Long Point Company, except for a few small parts close to the tip of the point. Management of this large area became increasingly arduous to the company because of greater pressure by the public to use this area, higher levies, and the possibility of fire. In 1978 and 1979 the Long Point Company donated 3239 ha to the Canadian Wildlife Service under a number of restrictive covenants that dictated which type of activity may occur. For instance, camping and road building are prohibited, while hiking trails for nature appreciation are allowed. The company has retained ownership of the adjacent marsh for the use of its members, who are mostly interested in duck hunting and fishing. A village of cottages in the marsh, connected to each other and to the main dining hall by boardwalks, forms the retreat built up by the club over the years. Bradstreet (1981) recounts the following thought he had on the recent changes of ownership while he was walking Long Point one night:

> On this cold November night I ponder a new stewardship for one of Ontario's most precious natural jewels, and I pause and privately thank the Long Point Company members and keepers for having kept this jewel safe for over a hundred years. For let's make no mistake about it. If it hadn't been for the powers of private ownership there would be little worthwhile left here today. Exceeding wealth and private opulence are frequently disdained by naturalists. At least this one time, personal wealth and personal conscience have resulted in a great gift.

Long Point is a jewel indeed, to be all the more valued because it is both fragile and close to the habitat of many people.

Toward the end of the point the dry land increases with the more northerly part being older and higher from blown sand that has settled out. There are eleven different types of environments, as shown in Figure 10.12. Not all the ponds are beach pools close to the south shore; some of them run right across the spit where water has flowed into former blow-outs. These ponds are sometimes closed off from the lake and sometimes open. When the barriers separating the ponds from the lake are beached, the ponds are invaded by fish from the lake (Mahon 1979) and become rich spawning grounds. On occasion many fish are trapped in these ponds when there are water-level changes, and sometimes when the shallower ponds dry out, the fish in them are eaten by the many piscivores and scavengers on the point. Schueler (1981) has described the vitality of the pond system (Figs. 10.12, 10.13) as follows:

> Ponds at Long Point on summer nights are full of large animals and unsettling sounds. The swell raised by a distant storm crashes on the beach, while huge snapping turtles and heavy-bodied water snakes loom up in the shallows. Deer snort and crash through the buttonbush swamp, carp churn

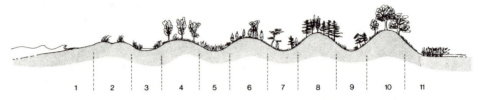

1 BEACH STRAND
2 BEACH GRASS
3 BEACH POOL
4 COTTONWOOD
5 SEDGE – RUSH SWALE
6 JUNIPER SAVANNA
7 TAMARACK – CEDAR SLOUGH
8 PINE – CEDAR FOREST
9 SEDGE – TAMARACK POND
10 OAK – MAPLE FOREST
11 CATTAIL MARSH

1   2   3   4   5   6   7   8   9   10   11

Figure 10.12 A schematic cross-section of Long Point, showing the eleven different environments encountered in the natural parts of the peninsula. (After Catling and Reznicek 1981.)

away close to shore, and mobs of ducks burst into flight or flail across the dark water with wings and feet. Bullfrogs are the most alarming of all. They float at the surface of the water, pale green in the darkness, waiting for prey. They are big and strong, almost more than a handful. When caught, some of them open their mouths to full gape and scream incessantly like a terrified baby until they are released.

Long Point has been dealt with in some detail because it provides an unusual example of the preservation of a natural environment in a developed area. Perhaps it will inspire other authorities to follow this example to preserve areas under their control, particularly in the western part of the lake basin.

Summary

The quality of the nearshore waters of the East Basin needs improvement, and care must be taken to control the inputs to the lake from the continuing industrial development at Nanticoke. The offshore waters are of good quality, but the fisheries for some species have been damaged by siltation of spawning streams and overfishing. The East Basin, though damaged, is not a badly degraded habitat and is indeed very different from the image of Lake Erie that many people have. The beaches of the East Basin are often free of *Cladophora*, and some of them are lovely. These beaches and the clear offshore waters, together with the treasures of Long Point, provide unknown and unexpected aspects of beauty in Lake Erie.

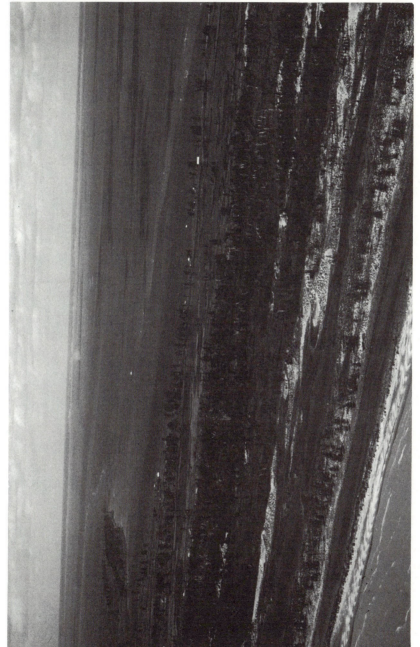

Figure 10.13 A view across Long Point, showing the open lake in the foreground, Long Point Bay in the background, and the intervening ponds and ridges.

IV

ALTERNATIVES
AND DECISIONS

This book is about the survival of the Lake Erie ecosystem and its good health in the future. Many of the ills of this system have been diagnosed, but decisions for its recovery must still be made. This final part outlines the problems examined in detail in the other parts of the book and evaluates the possible remedial measures, in terms of both cost and effectiveness. This clarification of alternatives is the first step to ensure that the best decisions for the future of Lake Erie will be made.

11

Measuring Change in a Lake

This short chapter has been written for those who wish to make assessments of environmental change. These assessments are difficult when changes have been small, but investigations must be able to detect small changes or degradations in an environment so they can be reversed before major damage ensues.

We know that Lake Erie has deteriorated badly during the past century. Yet we hope that we will reverse this trend and begin to rehabilitate the lake and restore some of its best features. To do this we need to be able to measure how degraded the system has become and the response of the system to our efforts at improvement. The rehabilitation of a lake the size of Erie has never before been attempted, and although we are sure it can be done, we cannot anticipate the speed of recovery. We know which rehabilitative measures must be carried out, but are not sure of the efficacy of each and the degree of implementation to be applied in each case. Thus an early knowledge of the response of the lake to the different measures would help the clean-up of Lake Erie immensely.

Quantifying the change in state of a lake turns out to be a far more difficult task than anticipated, especially if one wants to know about changes that have occurred over the period of a few years. Over a longer period the changes can be quite obvious, especially in the nearshore region. A once-clean beach is now covered with plastic debris or by rotting *Cladophora*. Thick weedbeds can be seen where once was open water. Water that was once clear and safe now appears turbid, and can infect children swimming in it. Nevertheless, even while conditions are getting worse there will sometimes be a year when there is little *Cladophora* on the beaches or the water is unexpectedly clear. While judgments based over a long period of time can be straightforward, the assessment of change over short periods can be difficult.

A lake, like all natural systems, is much affected by the weather and other event-type processes. For example, unexpectedly clean beaches may be the result of a late spring storm that broke the *Cladophora* from its holdfasts before it reached maturity, and thus stunted its growth. Events increase the difficulty of assessing environmental change particularly in the offshore regions where the main response to pollution is a change in the number and species of phytoplankton. Even under stable conditions, the dominant species at one time of the year can be very different from that at the same time of the previous year. Also, for reasons not yet known, the succession of algal species can be quite different from one year to the next.

How, then, can one determine whether a lake is changing over the short term, or make the even more difficult assessment that the lake is in a stable condition, neither deteriorating further nor improving? The surest way is to monitor all the important variables regularly. The ability to perceive change depends on both the magnitude of the change and the precision with which the system is monitored. This precision will depend on the number of variables sampled, as well as the frequency and accuracy of measurements. The greater the amount of careful work, the shorter will be the time required for a definitive answer about a change in trophic state in a body of water. The following sections describe the variables that are useful indicators of change, together with the complications to be considered when making interpretations.

Nutrients

The first variable to be carefully monitored is the external loading of pollutant substances into the lake from the atmosphere, rivers and direct discharges to the lake. This must be done whether the material is sediment, toxic chemicals, bacteria, or nutrients. (In the case of Lake Erie it is all of these.) Because of variability in rainfall, episodic dumping of materials, and variable river flows, this can be a very difficult assessment to make. Nevertheless, it is the first clue to change because if the load of damaging materials is definitely increasing, the lake will probably continue to deteriorate. If the loadings are decreasing, the lake will probably not get any worse but it may also not improve immediately. A lake that has been receiving heavy loads of chemicals or nutrients for a long while will undoubtedly have high concentrations of nondegradable chemicals and nutrients in the sediments. Because of the nature of chemical equilibria, some of these materials will desorb from the sediments and return to the overlying water. This return of materials from the sediments to the water, termed "internal loading," may compensate for the decrease in external loading so that no change in the lake is discernible for a number of years.

This process will continue until much of the labile material has been desorbed from the sediment, the rate of internal loading will finally drop, and improvements will be noted. Another situation that will show little immediate response to reduced loadings occurs with a substance that has been loaded in excess of its usage in the lake. In this case, the loading of the nutrient will have to be decreased to the point where it becomes limiting to growth, on occasion, by virtue of its scarcity before any effect resulting from the decreased loading will be observed.

As mentioned earlier, the soluble nutrients that will support organic growth in the lake to the greatest extent are phosphate (PO_4), nitrate (NO_3), ammonia (NH_3) and silica (SiO_2). Unfortunately, the relationship between concentrations of these nutrients and phytoplankton is indirect. If large quantities of nutrients are loaded into the lake, the concentrations of these materials in the water will be high preceding a growth pulse and low during the pulse or immediately following it. These nutrients are changed from the soluble form into the particulate organic form by growth and are thus poor indicators of the fertility of the water, unless they are monitored before the growth pulse. The first pulse often occurs early in the spring, usually before the survey ships can even get through the ice in Lake Erie, and is seldom observed. Other pulses occur at different times during the year, and if the lake is monitored frequently, periods of high nutrient concentrations between growth pulses will occasionally be encountered and can be used in assessment of the trends. Thus the maximum and minimum nutrient concentrations measured can be at least as informative as the average value.

If the soluble forms of phosphorus and nitrogen are not reliable indicators because of interconversion with the particulate form, then one might expect the total quantity of the element in the water to give unequivocal evidence of increasing concentration. In this measurement, both the soluble and particulate forms are assayed, and thus the quantity of the element measured should be greater if it has been increasingly available. This is often the case: total phosphorus, total nitrogen, and particulate organic carbon are variables that give much information about increasing concentrations of nutrients and organic matter in the water. These variables, however, are also subject to difficulties, some analytical and some interpretive. Many laboratories experience problems analyzing concentrations of these elements, and reported differences can often be a function of the different analytical laboratories, rather than of actual concentration changes in the lake water.

The values of total phosphorus, total nitrogen, and particulate organic carbon, even when analyzed correctly, are much affected by processes within the lake. If a calm period follows an algal bloom, much of the particulate material settles out of the water column onto the bottom of the lake, substantially lowering the values observed for total phosphorus or nitrogen. This is particularly the case in Lake Erie, because it is shallow and the settling material soon reaches the sediments. Conversely, if the weather is stormy, a considerable quantity of sediment can be resuspended from the bottom, increasing the concentration of these materials, particularly phosphorus, in the water column. A stormy November in 1970 caused the amount of phosphorus in Lake Erie waters to increase from 8,761 tons on 26 October to 14,190 tons on 30 November (Burns 1976b). Thus the total quantities of the indicator elements in lakewater are not only a function of loading but of physical and biological processes, so that limnological knowledge must be used when interpreting these values.

Algae

Since weeds and phytoplankton increase in quantity with the increased nutrient supply, they might seem to be a most-informative parameter to measure. This is often the case, but once again the matter is not straightforward. The growth of these aquatic flora is very dependent on weather and other limnological variables. A stormy spring with heavy erosional loads and turbulent water would result in highly turbid water in the lake, and this would drastically affect the growth of macrophytes and attached plants. The production of *Cladophora* is normally difficult to estimate because it grows on rough, rocky areas or bottoms strewn with boulders, so the measurement of the appropriate unit area is troublesome. Phytoplankton can also be difficult to sample correctly because they can collect in layers in the thermocline or just above it and sometimes close to the surface. Under these circumstances the calculation of the mean water column content of phytoplankton is troublesome or impossible. Sometimes a pulse of zooplankton growth will occur, and these creatures will graze the phytoplankton down to well below their normal concentrations. Perhaps the most-difficult part of phytoplankton density estimation is the actual sample counting. Not only must each cell be identified as to species, but the major dimensions of the cells must be measured so their volume or biomass can be estimated. (This is not done for every cell, but for a number of cells representative of a species.) This microscope work can be tedious, and the comparability of identical samples counted by different analysts is notoriously poor. The counting rate of these samples is one to three a day per person, which compares with the chemical analysis rate for total phosphorus of about 200 samples per person per day.

The plant pigment chlorophyll *a* controls photosynthesis and is present in all aquatic plants. This pigment can be chemically assayed and provides an alternative method for estimating algal abundance. About 50 more samples a day can be analyzed by this method than by counting with a microscope. Measurements of chlorophyll *a* concentration, however, can only partially substitute for algal counting because the chemical analysis does not give any information as to the species present. Since some species grow well in oligotrophic conditions while others do far better under eutrophic conditions, the decline or increase of appropriate indicator species provides additional insight into trends.

Oxygen

The increased production of organic material resulting from increased phytoplankton growth causes greater amounts of oxygen to be taken up by respiration and decay processes in the lake. The oxygen taken up by decay of organic material settling through the thermocline into the bottom waters cannot be replenished during the summer in lakes that stratify. The rate of disappearance of oxygen from bottom waters, the oxygen depletion rate, provides an indicator of changes in the trophic state of a lake. Of course, the interpretation of this parameter is complicated by variable hypolimnion thicknesses that alter the oxygen supply, or by hypolimnion temperatures that affect the rates of the decomposition of the organic material.

Oxygen uptake also occurs in shallow water systems subject to temporary stratification. In these waters the organic detritus settles to the bottom and lies there during calm weather. Temporary stratification can also occur with calm weather, and the colder water near the bottom loses oxygen because of the decay of the material lying on the sediment. The drop in oxygen concentration below saturation depends on the duration of the stratification, prevailing temperature, and the accumulation of organic matter on the sediments. As the lake becomes more eutrophic, the spells of calm weather begin to induce lower and lower concentrations in the near-bottom waters. The intermittent nature of these low concentrations makes them difficult to measure, but in these shallow water systems certain benthic organisms can also provide very solid information about the changing state of the water. Tubificid worms are very tolerant of eutrophic conditions, whereas mayflies can survive only in well-oxygenated mesotrophic water. If mayfly populations give way to tubificid worms, it is probable that conditions are degrading; the reverse will be the case if the mayfly populations are increasing. Populations of organisms in sediments can be quite patchy, and careful sampling and statistical evaluation of data is required before population trends can be established. Since many of the benthic indicator-organisms of trophic state are aquatic insects, a serious complication arises from the use of the insecticides DDT and DDE in the lake catchment. Since the aquatic insects are susceptible to these pesticides just as terrestial insects are, the sudden disappearance of benthic insects from lake sediments may not be related to increasing eutrophication, but be due to increased loading of insecticides to the sediments. These materials have been used widely in the Great Lakes Basin, and all these sediments contain some pesticide residues that unfortunately remain potent for many years and can confuse the meaning of trends in benthic population.

Toxic Materials

The question of whether toxic materials are increasing in concentration in a lake and thus damaging the biota of a lake is a fairly new study. Most research in lakes on the behavior of low concentrations of man-made organics and many of the trace metals is new. Often the problems in this field of research are methodological, with adequate analytical and sample handling techniques still being developed.

Fish are at the top of the foodchain in the lake and thus serve as indicator organisms. Since humans eat them, fish are often analyzed to determine their body accumulation of trace metals, such as mercury, and toxic organics, such as PCB. Providing that the sampling program is good and the chemical methods adequate, trends of increasing or decreasing concentration of contaminant can be established. Seagulls, as well as man, are a final element in the Great Lakes foodchain, and often seagull eggs are analyzed to check on changes in concentrations of bioaccumulating organic materials. A current major problem in toxic material evaluation is that many short-lived compounds in the lake environment are carcinogenic. They do not readily enter the food web of the lake, but can enter water intake pipes of large cities, pipes which are often fairly close to river mouths and other sources of chemical wastes. The concentrations of these chemicals in the lake are low, and their cause-effect relationships are usually very subtle, with the results often showing up only after years of exposure. The assessment of this type of problem is very difficult.

Conclusions

Finally, in trying to assess change in a lake as large as Lake Erie or even the West Basin, the differences in concentration associated with location in the lake and with time of year must be taken into account. This means that in assessing change in a large lake, a basic decision has to be made between sampling a few sites in the lake frequently (e.g., on a weekly basis), or many sites across the lake every month or two. These decisions will be based not only on information requirements, but also on resource availability. A complete surveillance plan of Lake Erie would call for a lakewide survey of about 40 offshore stations and the same number of inshore stations near the major rivers and cities. A sample of such a sampling station pattern is shown in Figure 11.1; the ship that carried out the program is shown in Figure 11.2. It deployed a launch for sampling the shallow water stations.

The samples taken should be analyzed for the concentration of major nutrient forms, benthic organisms, phytoplankton, chlorophyll *a*, and toxic materials in fish. There should be ten nearshore stations to check on *Cladophora* growth. Also, many temperature profiles must be taken so the thermal structure of the lake at the time of survey is known. The cost of

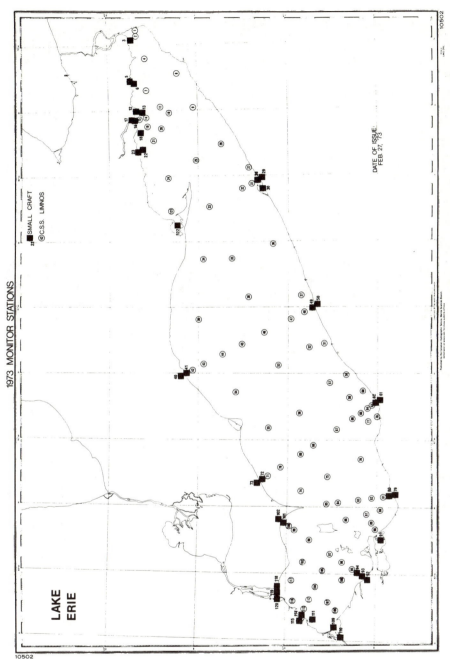

LAKE
ERIE

22 ■ SMALL CRAFT
⊙ C.S.S. LIMNOS

DATE OF ISSUE
FEB. 27, '73

10502

Figure 11.1 The pattern of sampling stations used in the 1973 monitoring of the nutrient and biological concentrations in Lake Erie.

Figure 11.2 The "C.S.S. Limnos," a vessel operated by the Canada Centre for Inland Waters, carries out both surveillance and research tasks. The boom of her crane, used for lifting small vessels from her deck and deploying heavy equipment, is extended. (Photo by W. Booth.)

this work would be between $150,000 to $200,000 ($ 1980 U.S.) per survey of Lake Erie. If six surveys a year were carried out the cost would be approximately $1,000,000. Alternatively, if six mid-basin sites and ten nearshore sites were sampled weekly for the same variables, the cost would be less but still very high. If these large data-gathering programs were run every alternate year, a careful analysis of the data would reveal changes in the lake. The high costs of such programs means, however, that ideal data sets are seldom collected and judgments must usually be made using whatever information is available. This consists of data collected during the course of individual research projects that are not extensive in time or space, together with other data from the limited number of lakewide survey investigations. With care and effort, the changing trends in large lakes can be discerned from such information. The poorer the data base, however, the longer the period of time or the greater the magnitude of the change must be before the changes can be ascertained and described.

When the change in the state of lake is small, the estimate of change in each parameter will often be statistically uncertain. Thus, a decision about change usually cannot be made on the basis of one or two variables but requires a number of variables to be assessed. If some of the changes indicate increased eutrophication while others indicate a decrease, the probability is that no significant change has occurred. If, on the other hand, all the variables indicate a similar change of state, however uncertain it may be in each case, and if the processes that cause these changes are in accordance with known principles of limnology, then it is almost certain that a change of state has occurred. Scientists can then make a definite statement. Science is considered to be precise, but this is not always the case. In environmental science, personal judgment is used continually because the available data base is usually inadequate to demonstrate the cause of a change in an unequivocal manner. The situations where cause and effect are conclusively shown are usually found only in laboratories where carefully controlled experiments can be arranged.

This discussion demonstrates that limnology, like most science, is not simple, and that all aspects of a lake must be studied and taken into account when making judgments. Environmental scientists must often make decisions using the best available knowledge, even when this does not provide certainty. The undesirable situation of requiring best-judgment decisions arises because of the additional damage that can occur while one waits for additional data to provide the security of certainty. If a scientist delays in making a judgment on an environmental issue, a government official or local politician with far less knowledge of the situation may make the required decision, sometimes with disastrous results. The following chapter and appendix demonstrate the process of making decisions on environmental matters using data collected in the manner described in this and earlier chapters. The topics discussed in the following chapter and appendix are not only examples; their main purpose is to clarify the issues on Lake Erie so that good decisions can be made.

12

Lake Erie—Past, Present, and Future

Today's Problems

Many changes have occurred in the Lake Erie ecosystem since the first settlers arrived almost 200 years ago. Some of the major changes and their causes have been described in the earlier chapters, together with the work of the scientists involved in understanding these changes. Although some aspects of the lake are not yet understood, we now are aware of the worst problems of the lake. Further, the causes of most of these problems are known as well as an idea of how to minimize or solve them. Seven problems resulting from past actions have been identified as requiring serious attention, and this chapter focuses on these problems and their solutions.

1. The first problem is the soil loss from the land, which leads to the siltation of streams, harbors, marshes, and spawning reefs. Soil erosion is a result of clearing nearly all forest cover from the land and, after the annual harvest, leaving it bare during the winter and the following spring. The land that yields the largest quantity of soil once constituted the bottom of the former Lake Maumee and is very erodible (Fig. 3.7). It is now valuable agricultural land and is intensely cultivated, but present agricultural practice is not good enough to prevent much of the springtime erosion.

2. The loss of shoreline marshes is another serious problem. Some of these marshes, such as those in Maumee Bay, were lost because the sediment carried down from a river silted up the shallower parts of the marsh and destroyed the aquatic plants in the deeper parts of the marsh. This also happened in Sandusky Bay, the size of which permits the wind to mix the

waters vigorously and keep them muddy. As the plants begin to die, each windstorm lifts and disperses the bottom sediments to a greater extent and thus kills more plants. Shoreline marshes are also being lost as they are filled in to make new land for industrial enterprises or lakeshore cottages.

3. The third problem is the destruction of the fisheries of certain species. The herring and lake trout were basically eliminated by overfishing. The sturgeon, whitefish, sauger, and blue walleye were also overfished and struggled with the additional problem of their spawning habitats being badly damaged by siltation. Still other fish species have suffered from these two stresses, as well as having to compete for food against increasing numbers of fish of undesired species.

4. Pathogenic bacteria and refuse entering into the lake is a long-standing problem. The pathogens are coliforms and viruses in human and animal waste, while the refuse is largely made up of oil and other floating debris such as bottles, rotting wood, paper, and plastics. Initially, when populations were small, these loadings were not unduly harmful, but with time an increased amount of garbage and bacteria have been dumped into the lakes, while an increasing number of people use the lake as a source of water and recreation. Prime examples of this state of affairs are the Cleveland lakeshore and the Cuyahoga River, which was so bespoiled that it caught fire in the 1960s because of the oil scum on its surface.

5. Excessive loading of phophorus to the lake is causing severe eutrophication, the harmful effects of which were realized during the 1960s. Initially, the loading of phosphorus to the lake increased with the population living around the lake, because of the bioavailable phosphorus in human waste. The phosphorus load was further increased with the extensive use of chemical fertilizers, which enriched the water draining from agricultural land. But perhaps the largest increase in the load to the lake came from the phosphorus added to detergents after World War II, when the cleaning ability of phosphate was first utilized. It is pure coincidence that this compound, which is so useful as a cleanser, is also the one usually in shortest supply in freshwater biological systems, but it has, nevertheless, caused severe perturbation of ecosystems.

6. The loading of a vast array of toxic materials into Lake Erie, which will perhaps prove to be the most difficult problem of all to solve, has continued for a long time, but its existence has only recently been realized. The 1969 Report to the International Joint Commission (IJC) by the International Lake Erie Water Pollution Board did not mention any specific toxic materials in Lake Erie. Nevertheless, the problem was thrust on the public and the scientific community simultaneously in 1970 with the discovery of high concentrations of mercury in fish from Lakes St. Clair and Erie. Since then the magnitude of the problem of toxic contaminants has become increasingly understood.

7. The killing and removal of a large amount of fish from the lake ecosystem as water passes through electrical generating stations, industrial

intakes, and municipal water works is a seldom-stressed problem. Although the loss of fish at the moment is severe, the intake problem is going to become far more serious because of the planned increase in the number of nuclear generating stations and cities to be sited along or near the shore of Lake Erie.

The first task at present is to diminish the seven problems just described. Recent research has led us to an understanding of the processes causing many of the undesired results and also to the means of abating some of the problems. Other problems, however, are still not understood sufficiently to provide effective guidelines for management, and research must continue on them. In addition, the population living around the lake will undoubtedly cause future stress in ways we are not yet aware of. Surveillance and research must continue so these problems can be readily identified, investigated and remedied.

In the interim, common sense provides good guidelines for alleviating the stresses. We know that most of the problems were caused by either loading too much extraneous material into the lake, filling in shorelines, or plundering fish stocks. Thus, while precise guidelines are being developed we can immediately alleviate the situation by decreasing the loads of all unnatural materials to the lake, by ceasing to restructure shorelines, and by ceasing the overfishing that further weakens fish stocks.

Senior government officials in both the United States and Canada felt sufficient confidence in this commonsense assessment of the situation that they, much to their credit, developed the first Great Lakes Water Quality Agreement to implement the obvious remedial programs.

The Great Lakes Water Quality Agreement

The Great Lakes Water Quality Agreement was signed on 15 April 1972 by Prime Minister Pierre Trudeau and President Richard Nixon. At the signing of the Agreement Mr. Trudeau said,

> The importance of what we have done this morning cannot be described or measured by conventional means, for this agreement does not fall within the normal categories of international activity. It will not contribute materially to the economics of either of our countries; it makes neither of us more secure in our relations with one another or in the world beyond; it does little to diminish or remove any of the social problems which worry Americans and Canadians alike.
>
> Yet while doing none of these things it accomplishes much more. For it marks our recognition of the fragility of our planet and the delicacy of the biosphere on which all life is dependent. This agreement deals with the most vital of all issues—the process of life itself. And in doing so it contributes to the well-being of millions of North Americans, for it promises to restore to a

wholesome condition an immense area which, through greed and indifference, has been permitted to deteriorate disgracefully.

The Great Lakes Water Quality Agreement of 1972, although not perfect, is a great achievement both in terms of the aims of the agreement and the degree to which the United States and Canada committed themselves to the stated objectives. The Agreement did not call for further studies before making decisions on critical issues, but instead established guidelines on the important issues using the best knowledge available at the time. It then stated that these guidelines could be changed by the two Parties in light of new information that would become available later. The clear-cut, decisive nature of the Agreement has had much to do with its success. For example, the objectives for the maximum quantities of phosphorus to be loaded into Lake Erie were stated as follows: 1972, 24,200 tons yr^{-1}; 1973, 20,200 tons yr^{-1}; 1974, 15,400 tons yr^{-1}; 1975, 15,200 tons yr^{-1}; and 1976, 14,600 tons yr^{-1}.

Programs for the abatement of pollution from municipal, industrial, agricultural, forestry, shipping, and dredging sources were outlined. Further, the Agreement stated that the lakes should be free of mercury and other toxic metals, persistent organic contaminants, oil, and other floating debris. In particular, the two countries committed themselves to providing the funds to build the required sewage and pollution abatement facilities and to police the activities of industry to see that they were obeying regulations. Further, the Agreement provided funds to the International Joint Commission (IJC) to oversee the implementation of the Agreement and to report on all aspects, including non-compliance by one of the Parties. In this regard, Article VI states, "The Commission may in its discretion publish any report, statement or other document prepared by it in the discharge of its functions under this Agreement."

Great progress has been made in improving the quality of the water in the Great Lakes because of the 1972 Great Lakes Water Quality Agreement, and it has resulted in the "survival" of Lake Erie. But this Agreement made no statements on a number of matters, such as shoreline restructuring or overfishing. Water quality matters that affect the state of the lake have been addressed by the IJC, but other serious problems have not yet been attended to because fisheries problems are usually considered by an entirely separate body, the Great Lakes Fishery Commission (GLFC). These two organizations, the IJC and GLFC, have only recently begun to address Great Lakes problems jointly (Johnson 1980).

Much requires to be done to manage the air, water, and land resources of the Great Lakes ecosystem on a holistic basis for the benefit of the humans, wildlife, and fish living in the basin. The nature of this approach and its importance to environmental management of the Great Lakes was emphasized by J.R. Vallentye in a report on the ecosystem approach (Great Lakes Science Advisory Board 1980b). Because of this type of work by committed people, this shortcoming in earlier management practice is more widely realized. As a result, an objective for the 1978 Great Lakes Water Quality Agreement was stated thus:

> The purpose of the Parties is to restore and maintain the chemical, physical, and biological integrity of the waters of the Great Lakes Basin Ecosystem. In order to achieve this purpose, the Parties agree to make a maximum effort to develop programs, practices and technology necessary for a better understanding of the Great Lakes Basin Ecosystem and to eliminate or reduce to the maximum extent practicable the discharge of pollutants into the Great Lakes System.

It is relatively straightforward to state an objective, but the real achievement lies in attaining it. The International Joint Commission is now taking appropriate action.

The 1981 report of the Great Lakes Water Quality Board (GLWQB) of the IJC provides one of the first concrete examples of the application of the ecosystem approach. Previously, problem areas were simply cited for exceeding a microbiological, nutrient, or toxic chemical concentration objective. For example, the Ashtabula Sewage Treatment Plant was mentioned for having too high a concentration of metals in its effluent (GLWQB 1980). Now a description is given of all the problems in an area, and the area is classified as to its degree of general perturbation. This new system is outlined as follows:

> The description and evaluation of an area of concern provides a more complete perspective on the issue. Available environmental data—fish, sediment, and water—are used to provide as complete a description as possible for each area. The 1978 Agreement objective, along with jurisdictional standards, criteria, and guidelines, provides the basis for review and evaluation of these data. To the extent possible, the Board has established the human health and environmental cause-effect relationship between these conditions and the sources of environmental insult. This leads to a description of regulatory and remedial measures required to restore ecosystem integrity [GLWQB 1981b].

The Great Lakes Water Quality Agreements of 1972 and 1978 represent a high level of political achievement and have resulted in a great change for the better in the Great Lakes Basin. No temporarily elected political authority should be permitted to unilaterally weaken the present Agreement. Changes to the Agreement should be made only under consensus of both governments party to the Agreement.

A number of challenges to be faced regarding the future of the great Lakes Basin and solutions to the problems mentioned earlier are a direct result of the fact that the Lake Erie and Ontario basins are now fairly crowded environments. The population of the Great Lakes Basin is predicted to increase steadily in the future, so efforts must be made to understand the ecosystem and to plan its well-being. As the population grows, so must our wisdom.

Requirements for the Solution of Present Problems

Although planning intelligently for the future is complex and difficult, even the management of the present in a rational and realistic manner is not easy. The seven problems outlined above must be solved so that we can achieve three simple objectives. (a) We should ensure that the water and the fish in Lake Erie are safe to consume. (b) All the water in the lake and the beaches around it should be clean enough for enjoyable swimming (not because swimming is all-important, but because we are the best test-organisms available). (c) We should increase the restoration of some of the fish stocks and the natural resources around the lake. Commercial development of presently available natural areas should proceed only after a broad understanding of the needs of the inhabitants has been reached. By trying to alleviate the problems discussed below we will be both improving the present situation and working for the future.

The identification of the seven major problem areas is somewhat artificial because many of these problems have common elements. For example, 65 percent of the phosphorus entering Lake Erie is from agricultural sources (PLUARG 1978), with the majority of the phosphorus associated with clay particles; thus if sediment loading is diminished so also will be the phosphorus loading to the lake. If efforts are made to reduce the magnitude of all seven problems simultaneously, the effect will be a considerable overall improvement in the state of the lake.

1. SOIL EROSION

Soil erosion rates in the Maumee River basin can vary between 0.5 and 5.6 tons ha^{-1} yr^{-1} (PLUARG 1978) and are typical for the agricultural soils surrounding the West Basin. The high rates of loss are caused mostly by sheet erosion from fields with little or no cover, when the soils are saturated during the spring or any time during the year when there has been a lengthy wet spell. Gully erosion can be severe if the drainage streams and ditches have unprotected banks.

Soil erosion can be minimized by strip cropping, contour terracing, maintaining grassed waterways for drainage from fields, and maintaining a strip of unfarmed land along the banks of streams. Conservation tillage is now being tried as a means of diminishing soil loss. In this system, a strip only 2″ (5 cm) wide is cultivated for each row of a crop and then seeded while the rest of the area remains covered with the residue of the previous crop. This system cannot be applied on all soils, but when used on suitable soils can result in slightly higher crop yields at reduced cost, with a considerable reduction in soil loss (U.S. Army Corps Eng. 1982). It is strange that the most-severe erosion rates can be encountered in urban areas where construction is in progress, where soil losses of 27.5 tons ha^{-1} yr^{-1} have been measured (PLUARG 1978). Obviously, these losses should be curtailed. Alleviating sediment loads would decrease phosphorus loading to the lake as well as stream-bed siltation. It would also decrease harbor dredging and the suffocation of fish eggs in spawning streams and reefs, while permitting greater macrophyte growth in protected bays.

2. SHORELINE CHANGE

Most modern shoreline change has resulted from the filling in of marshland for industrial and urban use. Only recently has the public begun to realize the ecological value of marshes and that land "reclaimed" for the building of one more factory is actually land "lost" from the shrinking area of natural habitat. As mentioned in Chapter 8, only 12,000 of the original 40,000 ha of Ohio Lake Erie marshes now exist, and about 57 percent of these remaining wetlands are privately owned (GLBC, App. 17, 1975). Some of the wetlands have been filled in by power companies, who sited their plants close to the lake for easy access to the required cooling water. Unfortunately, these utilities have also sequestered large areas of marshland to dump their waste ash on, as is the case in Maumee Bay. Another example is the Plum Creek Bay Wildlife Area south of the Raisin River, which the Michigan Department of Natural Resources was forced to abandon when it was unable to prevent the construction of a huge land disposal site (Jaworski and Raphael 1976). The Great Lakes Basin Commission (App. 17, 1975) described the situation as follows:

> Losses have been significant in many parts of the Basin. The western Lake Erie marshes of Ohio and Michigan and the connecting waterway and associated shoals and marshes between Lake Erie and Lake Huron have been especially hard-hit in recent years. Within the last ten years thousands of acres of prime wetlands in the northern part of Lake St. Clair have been lost to a Venetian-type housing development. Further south in the vicinity of Monroe, Michigan, hundreds of acres of prime wetlands have been used as sanitary fill areas by the city of Detroit and are slated for industrial development.

Along parts of the West Basin shoreline, sandy barrier beaches would sometimes develop and enclose a pond behind them. Some of these beaches have later been stabilized and cottages built on them. This is unfortunate because, if left alone, a storm at some time would have broken though the beach and connected the pond with the lake; this would then have provided a good nursery area for fish from the lake (Fig. 12.1). At present, storms at high water cause flooding and destruction of these cottages, often without breaking the stabilized beach. This does not help the fish, but merely leads to insurance claims from individuals who built on what was essentially a flood plain. Also, the shooting clubs build dikes around areas where they

Figure 12.1 A barrier beach at Magee Marsh. A strong onshore wind blowing during a period of high water level inundates the beach, indicated here by the trees. (Photo by J.P. Barry.)

wish to entice ducks. These areas represent a loss to the total ecology of the system, for they are no longer open to fish for spawning and exchange with surrounding waters.

The solution to these problems requires responsible public or government bodies to purchase the undeveloped shoreline areas. The Ohio Division of Wildlife, for example, hopes to purchase the 6,000 ha of marshes along Lake Erie that are privately owned (GLBC, App. 17, 1975). Another possibility is to develop new wetlands at appropriate sites by using dikes and material dredged from harbors and channels. Whenever shoreline structures are to be built, the changes that will occur in the area from changes in littoral drift and fish movement patterns should be first investigated. The Stelco, Inc., dock, built in the East Basin with the nearshore segment consisting of a bridge structure to permit normal water and fish movement, is a good example of this type of forethought.

If presently existing wildlife shoreline areas are purchased and managed well, the first result would be to stabilize or increase resident and migrating bird populations. And the number of fur-bearing animals, such as muskrat and mink, would increase, as would the number of racoons and weasels. There would be a substantial increase in areas suitable for fish breeding. Also, marshes dominated by emergent plants are known to cause settling out of suspended sediments and to absorb nutrients from water, thus acting as natural purification systems for turbid, enriched river water (Mudroch 1980). Since many of the marshes do exist at the mouths of streams, their purification function can be considerable.

3. OVERFISHING AND UNDERFISHING

The fish of Lake Erie have endured many stresses, and many populations have disappeared under the pressure, but their most severe stress has probably been overfishing. The species that were fished heavily during the last century and in the early years of this century were affected adversely while environmental conditions in the lake were still fairly good. The yellow perch, a favored commercial species is now showing definite signs of stress (Leach and Nepszy 1976) related to commercial fishing pressure. The walleye population, severely reduced by overfishing, surged when fishing was banned in 1970. At the opposite extreme is an overabundance of unwanted fish species such as carp, gizzard shad, and freshwater drum (sheepshead). Carp uproot and destroy submerged aquatic vegetation that is essential for survival of native species (Scott and Crossman 1973); hence, control of their numbers is desirable. While gizzard shad and yellow perch occupy similar ecological niches, the perch are valuable as food for humans and for larger fish. The shad, however, quickly grow past the size when they can be eaten by other fish and are not eaten by man. Drum compete with yellow perch for food since they both favor similar invertebrates and forage fish. If carp, shad, and drum were harvested in amounts similar to walleye and yellow perch, it might be possible to produce more of the favored native species such as bass, pike, walleye, and yellow perch because of reduced competition for food. If the favored species are to be fished, their ecological competitors need to be fished also to maintain balance in the system. For example, pressure from the rapidly increasing smelt population in the 1950s probably reduced larval walleye numbers through predation and competition (Regier, Applegate, and Ryder 1969). No doubt this species interaction is still occurring, but the successful fishery for smelt, together with predation on smelt by walleye in the western part of the Central Basin, has allowed the populations to coexist successfully.

The problem of underfishing coarse fish could be mitigated if a sizable market existed for them, because they would then be removed by commercial fishermen. The mink-food market once consumed large quantities of coarse fish but is now depressed, partly because of a suggestion that pesticide concentrations in Great Lakes fish might be partially responsible for the failure of the mink to reproduce satisfactorily (GLBC, App. 8, 1975). The coarse-fish situation would be improved if their harvesting were subsidized until markets were found. The overfishing of desired species could be better controlled by placing quotas on both sport and commercial fishermen. This type of management has been successful with the West Basin walleye fishery, and the case for good fisheries management has been stressed by Leach & Nepszy (1976).

4. REFUSE AND PATHOGENS

In the 1950s and 1960s the limnologists studying the system were perturbed by many changes in the lake, such as the extensive anoxia in the Central Basin and the extirpation of the mayflies in the West Basin, but these concerns did not evoke a strong response in the public. However, the unsightly and stinking rivers, the beaches closed because of bacterial contamination or polluted with decaying algae and fish, together with the infections contracted by people using the lake, finally caused a strong public outcry and generated momentum for the movement to clean up the lakes.

Much has been achieved since. The rivers, if not inviting, are nevertheless no longer repulsive; most of the beaches are open and many of them are clean; and people swim and fish without fear of infection. The effort to clean up the appearance of the environment has been markedly successful, but further efforts in this regard are still necessary. In July 1980, the author swam at a public beach in Ashtabula, where the water was delightfully clear and the sand was clean and free from washed-up algae. Nevertheless, farther down the beach was a large refuse pile of discarded cans and bottles, many of which were broken and partly hidden in the sand. The average man has much to learn about appreciating the environment, especially the public areas. A public area belongs to everyone, and all who use it must care for it.

Since the signing of the 1972 Agreement, a vigorous program of sewage treatment plant construction has been in progress in the Great Lakes Basin.

Figure 12.2 Fishing trawlers at Wheatley, Ontario, unloading their catches. The design of the vessels, whose fine bows cut into the choppy waves characteristic of Lake Erie, has evolved over the years. The covered-in deck enables the boat to go out in −10°C weather. (Photo by J.P. Barry.)

Most of the treatment plants in the Lake Erie Basin have been completed, except for a few in the Cleveland area. It has been an expensive program: more than $7.25 billion was spent or committed in the Great Lakes Basin, and the Cleveland and Detroit treatment plant upgrading programs have cost more than $400 million each (GLWQB 1981b). The benefits from this program are many, but one of importance is that the water in Lake Erie is now considered safe for body contact except in the Detroit River and Cleveland Harbor. In 1967, in contrast, the water at 24 beaches and almost every southshore river mouth was bacterially contaminated (USFWPCA 1968).

The present-day discharges of bacteria to the lake result largely from combined stormwater and sewage systems. When storms occur, the large volume of water in these combined systems forces the release of raw wastes into the rivers and lake. Unfortunately, this problem is difficult to solve, and the cost of upgrading this type of system in the Great Lakes Basin is estimated at $6100 million (GLWQB 1981c), almost as much as it has cost to implement the treatment plant program. This problem will have to be tackled, especially in the Detroit area, because 17 percent of the water samples from the river during 1980 were badly contaminated with fecal coliforms. The most worrisome aspect of the combined sewer problem is that the governments of Canada and United States seem much less prepared to spend money on correcting the faults in the sewer systems than they were in voting funds for the waste treatment plants. Although the combined sewer problem is less pressing, it is nevertheless a serious problem in the long term.

5. THE PHOSPHORUS OVERLOAD

The 1972 Great Lakes Water Quality Agreement called for a review of its effectiveness before the formulation of objectives for the 1978 Agreement. Thus, Task Group III was commissioned to determine the load of phosphorus that should be considered as the permissible maximum for Lake Erie. They recommended that the load be limited to 10,900 ton of phosphorus yr^{-1} to eliminate 90 percent of the anoxia in the Central Basin (Task Group III 1978). But two other suitable objectives are also possible, to maintain an annual average phosphorus concentration in the Central Basin of 10 mg P m^{-3} or less, and to eliminate almost completely the anoxia in the Central Basin. A serious consideration of four different models (see Appendix) led to load limit of 9000 tons P yr^{-1} to the whole lake, based on the 10 mg P m^{-3} objective. This quantity also happens to be close to the task group other recommendation of 9,500 tons P yr^{-1} load limit based on the other objective of eliminating anoxia. These arguments and considerations lead to the conclusion that the optimum phosphorus load limit for the lake lies in the close range of 9000 to 9500 tons P yr^{-1}. As mentioned earlier, this load does not include phosphorus from shoreline erosion.

The maintainance of good nearshore conditions would require much care to be taken with the release of the phosphorus to the lake, even if the amount were within the recommended load limits. The rivers should not be permitted to enter the lake with concentrations of phosphorus greater than 150 mg P m^{-3}. The highly concentrated effluents from city waste treatment plants (800 mg m^{-3} of bioavailable phosphorus) should be piped as far offshore as expense will allow and then exited through diffusers to cause immediate maximum dilution. The zone where the offshore waters do not mix readily with the nearshore waters commences in many cases at about 8 km from shore (Boyce 1974). Thus, the city outfalls should be located this distance offshore, although, in reality, each case would require special study and many outfalls could be located closer to shore. Advances in phosphorus removal from waste waters have been substantial, and city wastes can be treated to contain as little as 300 mg P m^{-3}. In these cases, the outfalls could be located much closer to shore than would be required when disposing of more concentrated wastes. The higher costs of treatment could be offset by lower disposal costs.

The phosphorus-loading objective should really be stated in terms of the load of bioavailable phosphorus, because this is the actual active nutrient. The unavailable apatite phosphorus, included in the total phosphorus loads from rivers, tends to confuse the issue and should be eliminated from the discussion. For example, a municipal source producing 1000 tons of total phosphorus (TP) adds approximately 800 tons of bioavailable phosphorus (BP) to the lake, but an agricultural source of 1000 tons TP adds only about 500 tons of BP. It is obviously more effective to diminish the municipal source when possible.

The models of phosphorus processes occurring within Lake Erie (see Appendix) have provided good estimates of appropriate levels of phosphorus loading to the lake. The next step is the selection of the best method to achieve these loads. This has been initiated by Johnson et al. (1980), who have devised a model to estimate phosphorus loads from the different societal components of the Lake Erie Basin for the present and for the near future. The phosphorus load to the lake was estimated by summing up the contributions from all the different components of the Lake Erie Basin. A schematic of the different sources of phosphorus supply is shown in Figure 12.3. The model calculated that the load to the lake in 1975 was 17,812 tons, while the monitored load to the lake in 1976 was estimated to be 17,362 tons, indicating that the model was realistic. Since the magnitude of each source in the model is known, it is possible to estimate the individual source loads and thus the total loads to the lake under different management plans. One of the controlling factors in the calculation is that the amount of urban land in the basin is predicted to increase in the future, with a corresponding decrease in the amount of rural land. The TP loadings shown can be converted to BP loadings by using appropriate conversion factors, which are taken as being 0.8 for municipal wastewater at 1 g P m^{-3};

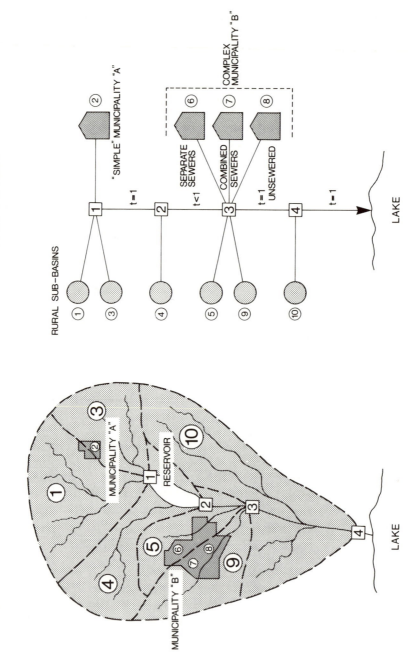

Figure 12.3 A schematic diagram of the watershed pollutant output model, illustrating relationships between geographic and model units. (Johnson et al. 1980.)

Table 12.1   Possible Strategies to Maintain Phosphorus Loads at Different Levels of Treatment to Lake Erie in the Year 2000

MP1 — Continue to operate treatment systems in existence in 1975.
MP2 — Maintain all effluents at 1 g P m^{-3}.
MP3 — Maintain all effluents at 0.5 g P m^{-3}.
MP4 — Maintain all effluents at 0.3 g P m^{-3}.
UD1 — No remedial storm sewer program.
UD2 — Reduction of pollutants and stormwater at source, including development of controls, use of natural storage capacities, street-cleaning.
UD3 — Artificial detention and sedimentation of stormwater runoff plus provisions under UD2.
RD1 — No rural source remedial program.
RD2 — Sound management practices such as proper nutrient application, minimum tillage, mulching, avoiding slopes near streams.
RD3 — Conservation tillage, contour strip cropping, use of cover crops, plus provisions under RD2.
RD4 — Implementation of RD3 to a greater extent.

Note: Symbols above are also used in Table 12.2.
Source: After Johnson, Corneau, Heidtke, Sonzogni, and Stahlbaum 1980.

0.65 for municipal wastewater at 0.5 g P m^{-3}; 0.5 for municipal wastewater at 0.3 g P m^{-3}; (preliminary tests of bioavailability of waste treatment waters indicate decreasing P availability with decreasing P concentration to the levels listed, E. Shannon, personal communication); and 0.5 for urban diffuse loads and 0.5 for rural diffuse loads in accordance with the factors listed in Appendix Table A.1.

The availability of this large quantity of data on phosphorus sources makes it possible to consider the costs of the different possible strategies and select the best plan to implement. Of course, all this information is based on currently available knowledge and costs, so some of the estimates will be erroneous; but many of the mistakes will be compensated for by advances in technology, which will permit achievement of the desired goals at lower costs. The information is organized in Tables 12.1 and 12.2 to make the selection of the best option as straightforward as possible. The data for the year 2000 are used because the phosphorus loading problem is a dynamic one, changing with population and land use patterns, so present plans should make provision for future growth.

The data in Table 12.2 show two important points. First, the necessary phosphorus objective of a total loading of 9,000 to 9,500 or a bioavailable loading of 5000 tons yr^{-1} can be achieved and maintained. Second, it can be achieved at moderate cost and without disrupting the present-day pattern of living. The MP1, UDI and RDI loads are totally unacceptable because of the excessive loads of soil, bacteria, and phosphorus resulting from these procedures. Thus the cheapest possible option is #2, which will cause an overload of 1865 tons yr^{-1} of bioavailable phosphorus (BP), or an overload of about 37 percent. Option #2 requires that the MP2 strategy would have

Table 12.2　Estimated Annual Costs Necessary to Maintain Phosphorus Loads at Different Levels of Treatment to Lake Erie in the Year 2000

Option number	Strategy level	Total phosphorus (tons yr⁻¹)	Bioavailability factor	Bioavailable phosphorus (tons yr⁻¹)	Cost ($ million) (1980 $)
1	MP1	10,570	0.8	8,456	11.0
	UD1	3,325	0.5	1,663	0
	RD1	5,575	0.5	2,787	0
	Total	19,470		12,906	11.0
2	MP2	3,635	0.8	2,908	24.0
	UD2	2,750	0.5	1,375	36.5
	RD2	5,165	0.5	2,582	0.0
	Total	11,550		6,865	60.5
3	MP3	2,000	0.65	1,300	34.5
	UD3	2,125	0.5	1,062	133.0
	RD3	4,850	0.5	2,425	22.5
	Total	8,975		4,787	190.0
4	MP4	1,205	0.5	603	95.0
	UD3	2,125	0.5	1,063	133.0
	RD4	4,570	0.5	2,285	75.5
	Total	7,900		3,951	303.5
5	MP3	2,000	0.65	1,300	34.5
	UD2	2,750	0.5	1,375	36.5
	RD2	5,165	0.5	2,582	0.0
	Total	9,915		5,257	71.0
6	MP3	2,000	0.65	1,300	34.5
	UD2	2,750	0.5	1,375	36.5
	RD3	4,850	0.5	2,425	22.5
	Total	9,600		5,100	93.5

Note: See Table 12.1 for explanation of symbols used. Costs estimated on the basis of 1980 dollars and are for implementing specified strategies in 1980. Estimate of costs in year 2000 is not realistically possible.
Source: After Johnson et al. 1980.

have to be set in place; the UD2 strategy of storm sewer management would have to be implemented to control bacterial contamination, and the RD2 strategy of erosion control would have to be in place to decrease sediment transport to the lake. The most-reasonable option is #5, which has an overload of only 257 tons BP yr⁻¹, about 5 percent, and yet this costs only about $10 million a year more to implement. This cost can be stated differently by saying that for less than a $1 per year per inhabitant of the Lake Erie Basin over the minimum expenditure, Lake Erie can be kept close to its optimum trophic state. The cost-effectiveness of this option makes it an outstanding bargain.

The International Joint Commission (IJC 1981), after considering the inputs of the different phosphorus Task Forces, has recommended that the phosphorus control program for Lake Erie should be the one shown as Option #3 in Table 12.2. This option happens to estimate the load for the year 2000 at 8975 tons TP or 4787 BP yr^{-1}, almost exactly the limit to phosphorus loading recommended above. This is more costly than Option #5 but undoubtedly is the best option because it ensures a safe level of phosphorus loading to the lake, together with minimum pollution from urban and diffuse sources. It also ensures extensive conservation of soil, which means a minimum loading of sediment into the lake. If this option were implemented with the provision that the municipal effluents generated under this program were piped 4 to 5 km offshore, Lake Erie would remain a clean and productive ecosystem indefinitely. Options #5 and #6 do not provide this longterm guarantee.

6. TOXIC MATERIALS

The problem of toxic materials in the Great Lakes Basin is viewed very seriously. The aim of the 1978 Great Lakes Water Quality Agreement in this regard is stated quite explicitly: "The philosophy adopted for control of inputs of persistent toxic substances shall be zero discharge." Achieving proper control of toxic materials discharge is going to be more difficult than proper control of nutrients, partly because we know far less about the behavior of toxins in the environment than we do about nutrients. Also, the control and elimination of inputs of toxic materials requires far more change in present industrial and municipal procedures than does the control of phosphorus. Phosphorus inputs can be minimized simply by adding on to present municipal treatment facilities, but toxins can be controlled only by major modification of many different industrial processes and use patterns.

Regarding toxins in the Great Lakes Basin, the Great Lakes Water Quality Board (1981b) made the following statement:

> While declines in the concentrations of some toxic chemicals in the sediment and biota have been observed in most lakes, the general level of contamination remains constant because, as a result of improved analytical capability, new contaminants are identified. Clearly, the lakes suffer from widespread contamination and continue to be a major sink for toxic substances.

The persistence of some of the major toxins in this ecosystem is given in Table 7.4 in the form of the half-lives of contaminants in gulls eggs. All the severely impacted areas in Lake Erie (i.e., Water Quality Board Class A concerns for 1981) carry heavy burdens of toxic materials. They are described as follows (GLWQB 1981b):

Detroit River: "Sediments remain polluted as a result of past discharges, necessitating confined disposal of dredged materials."

Rouge River: "While significant control measures have been implemented, the river remains severely impacted by combined sewer overflows and industrial waste discharges."

Raisin River: "Sediments are heavily enriched and polluted with metals. Fish are contaminated with PCBs and other organic compounds, and substantial violations of water quality objectives exist."

Maumee River: "The fishery in the lower Maumee River is impaired because of elevated levels of PCB."

Black River: "The sediments of the lower Black River are heavily polluted. Area fish are contaminated with complex organic substances. Consequently, the area fishing industry is impaired."

Ashtabula River: "Fish from the lower Ashtabula River, the harbor area, and inflowing tributaries are contaminated with complex organic substances; for several of these compounds, the human health effects are not known. Heavy sediment contamination requires more costly confined disposal for dredged materials. Restrictions on dredging have also resulted in navigational problems in the area."

Many industries were once permitted to pass their wastes into the municipal sewer systems, on the theory that most of the toxic contaminants would be removed in the wastewater treatment plant after incorporation into the sewage sludge. This procedure is no longer acceptable, because disposal of contaminated sludges has itself become a serious problem. In addition, considerable interest has developed in using sewage sludge as fertilizer on agricultural land. This practice is frequently the least-expensive disposal alternative (Webber 1982) and is now extensive, accounting for 34 percent and 31 percent of the sludge disposed of in Ontario and the United States, respectively (Bridle 1982). This method of disposal is a form of recycling and does not depend on the existence of suitable landfill sites. Further, the sludge will become more valuable as fertilizer resources become depleted.

Contaminated sludge poses a problem when the toxic organics and metals leach out into the drainage water when it is used for landfill purposes. In addition, contaminated sludge cannot be used on agricultural land because the metal and organic contaminants in the sludge enter the food or grass once the absorptive capacity of the land is exceeded. Definite guidelines for the use of sludge on land have been issued in Ontario (Ministries of Agriculture and Food and of the Environment 1981). Because of the problems with contaminated sludge, every effort must be made to prevent the entry of toxic materials into sewer systems; and these materials must be the responsibility of the industries producing them.

The industries of our chemically oriented society produce vast quantities of wastes and need assistance in disposing of them. Waste disposal facilities operated by or supervised by government personnel are needed for the prevention of illicit disposal of chemical wastes. Unfortunately, the authorities find siting and construction of these facilities difficult, because the residents in the locality of a proposed waste disposal plant usually protest the construction of the plant. Nevertheless, numerous waste disposal facilities will have to be established. Another approach, a partial solution to the problem, is the establishment of waste exchanges. Evidently the wastes from some industries can act as raw materials for others, and this type of recycling should be greatly assisted. The problem of toxic materials in the Great Lakes will persist, and more research on the cycling of toxic materials in the aquatic ecosystem is required.

7. ELECTRICAL POWER GENERATION

The synopsis of a recent study on electrical power requirements in the Great Lakes Basin concluded with the statement that "The reconciliation of ecological and environmental values with the growing demands for electrical power presents a challenge to the power industry which must be met if the Great Lakes Basin is to maintain its national position and retain its quality of life" (GLBC, App. 10, 1975). Although the generation of hydro-electric power causes relatively little stress on the environment, the generation of elecrical power by fossil or nuclear fuels does affect the environment in a number of different ways.

The huge volumes of water withdrawn from Lake Erie for cooling leads to a massive loss of fish from the system. In addition, the water returned to the lake is from 6° to 8°C higher than at intake. Temperatures in excess of 30°C have been observed in the West Basin near power plant effluent sites (Fay, personal communication), and 30°C is a temperature warm enough to stress a number of warm-water fish species. A different perturbation occurs in winter when fish concentrate in the warm effluent waters. In addition, the fossil-fuel plants emit large quantities of sulfurous and nitrous gases to the atmosphere to produce acid rain. Some of the nuclear plants emit H_2S gas, while all of them release some radioactive material to the atmosphere. As a result of a number of accidents in nuclear generating stations, such as occurred at Three Mile Island, Harrisburg, Pennsylvania, there is now a genuine element of fear in the minds of people living near these plants. Another problem is related to spent-fuel disposal. Most spent fuel is now held at the generating stations while governments attempt to find a safe mechanism for permanent disposal. The fly ash from coal-fired plants also creates problems. Finally, a considerable amount of land is taken out of use by high-voltage transmission lines.

All these difficulties and perturbations associated with the generation of electricity will be vastly increased in future by growth in usage of electricity. For example, the estimated generating capacity in the American part of the Lake Erie Basin, including Lake St. Clair and the St. Clair River, was 19,880 megawatts in 1980, but this is expected to triple to

58,430 megawatts in twenty years (GLBC, App. 10, 1975). The cooling water requirement would increase as well, from 14.2 km^3 yr^{-1} in 1980 to 47.7 km^3 yr^{-1} by 2000. If we add the water taken in for municipal use to this amount for the year 2000, 2.9km^3 (GLBC, App. 6, 1975) and take 10 percent of the American value as being the Canadian usage, then the total amount of water passing through intake pipes in the year 2000 will be approximately 55.7 km^3. The total volume of water in the Lake Erie–St. Clair system is about 475 km^3. Unless development plans change considerably from those predicted, approximately 12 percent of the water within the Lake St. Clair–Lake Erie system will be cycled through a power plant or municipality each year by the turn of the century. The problem of water withdrawals from the lake must be considered seriously and requires imaginative research because no good solutions to the problem are known at present.

Lake Erie and the Future

The first step to correct Lake Erie's difficulties is to solve the seven problems described in the previous section. If these problems were solved overnight, the lake would be in a fit state for the present inhabitants of the basin. But would this situation continue to be satisfactory into the future? It would not, because the population living around the lake in A.D. 2000 will be larger and will enjoy a different lifestyle. We must therefore begin to make provision for the future. Only with forethought can we improve on the present style of "crisis management" of environmental problems.

The population of the Lake Erie Basin in 1970 was about 11.6 million and is growing at the rate of about 1.1 percent per year (GLBC, App. 19, 1975), so by A.D. 2000 the population could reach a total of 16 million people. The largest proportion of the workforce in the Great Lakes region are construction, factory and office workers whose recreation time will increase. The average workweek decreased from 70 hours in 1820, to 39 hours in 1960, and to about 36 hours in 1976 and is expected to decline to 32 hours by the year 2000 (GLBC, App. 21, 1975). These changes mean that in little more than a decade from now, people living around Lake Erie will be more crowded and will have more free time. Since most people will be tied to indoor occupations, many will wish to spend some of their recreational time in natural settings. The irony of the situation is that as the need for access to lakes, beaches, wetlands, and parklands increases, the accessibility of these areas will probably diminish.

The administrative authorities are aware that there will be increasing numbers of people wishing to swim, fish, boat, and sail on the lake. Many others will want to hunt, trap, bird-watch, hike, cycle, and observe nature in various areas in the Lake Erie Basin. The authorities should act on the knowledge of this forthcoming increase in the need for contact with nature by ensuring that the required lands, and the access to them, are available.

The need for more wildlife areas, parks, beaches, and harbors around the lake is becoming increasingly obvious. In 1975 approximately 83 percent of the American Great Lakes mainland shore was privately owned (GLBC, App. 12, 1975). Luckily, much of this private land has not been heavily developed. The various Departments of Natural Resources and Recreation in the jurisdictions within the Lake Erie Basin should buy up areas suitable for public use before they become developed or prohibitive in price. A similar policy of forethought should apply in regard to the fisheries because pressure from anglers and commerical interests will become increasingly intense. Licences and quota systems will be needed for both commercial and recreational fishing. Most anglers prefer to stay in sight of land, which on small boats around Lake Erie is usually no more than 5 km offshore, except on exceedingly clear days. Unpredictable storms make it unsafe to be too far from a harbor of refuge. This means that the 90 km-wide Central Basin and 50 km-wide East Basin are the large offshore areas best suited to commercial fishermen. In addition, a subsidized commercial fishery can be used to crop off some of the unwanted species and keep the fishing pressure on all species balanced.

Other problems deriving from an increased population in the basin will be an increased amount of waste heat and volumes of waste treatment effluent. These so-called "waste" products can actually become valuable resources if the necessary research on finding out how to recycle and utilize them is done. More work on the use of the heat and nutrients for greenhouse production of vegetables or aquaculture of fish should be carried out. Also, cooling ponds should be used to cool water from generating stations instead of using the once-through system of cooling with lakewater. With appropriate research and development of techniques, these cooling ponds could become small warm-water ecosystems. The application of sewage sludges to the land is an obvious move but has been found to be problematical. This type of research is expensive and should be carried out by the various governments in the Great Lakes Basin.

Conclusion

The Lake Erie Basin was initially one of the richer ecosystems on this earth. The clear waters of the lake, the prodigious number of fish of many species, the peninsulas and islands with millions of permanent and migrant birds, the wetlands full of marsh creatures, the forests and meadows populated with deer, bears, and small animals all made the area appear to be an earthly paradise to the first visitors from Europe. After discovery of the lake, the explorers were followed by increasing numbers of European settlers. The white man, first in his need, later in his ignorance, and finally in his greed, damaged and annihilated many parts of this fragile system.

Fortunately, the more thoughtful among us have begun to point out the nature of our behavior, and our concern has taken us forward to examine this ecosystem in its present state. We find that some of the treasures of nature have been lost, some have survived and can be retained, while others can be revived with care and knowledge. But we now know that we can never take Lake Erie and its hinterland back to its original untouched state. Nor would we wish to do so, for civilized man would then have to leave the environs of this lake. We would rather live beside Lake Erie, which, by the health of its ecology and the treasures that will have been preserved, shall magnify the spirit of the humans who live on its shores.

Appendix:
Models of Lake Erie
Processes

The models described in this appendix are not physical models, such as scale models of river systems in which liquids of different colors are released to indicate the probable flow patterns of water in the real systems, but are intellectual constructs of processes and events occurring in environmental systems. If these mental reconstructions or intellectual models of reality simulate the real world accurately, they can be extremely useful in predicting the probable results of specific management actions, for they present a manager with an array of the consequences that will follow from different decisions. With a wide range of possible actions and consequences before him, a manager is able to make wise decisions.

Ever since the decision to improve the state of Lake Erie was taken in 1972, government administrations have asked scientists what remedial actions are needed. Many of the responses have been based on information gained from models of processes in Lake Erie. Some of the early models were simple, but those developed recently are among the most complex and advanced environmental systems models in the world today. Yet the danger exists that those people who are most concerned with models may begin to believe that the outputs of the models depict reality. This is not so; the natural world is the reality, and the relationships and predictions of the models are only relatively crude simulations of what happens in nature. Nevertheless, honest modeling produces simplifications necessary for decision-making in complex environmental issues.

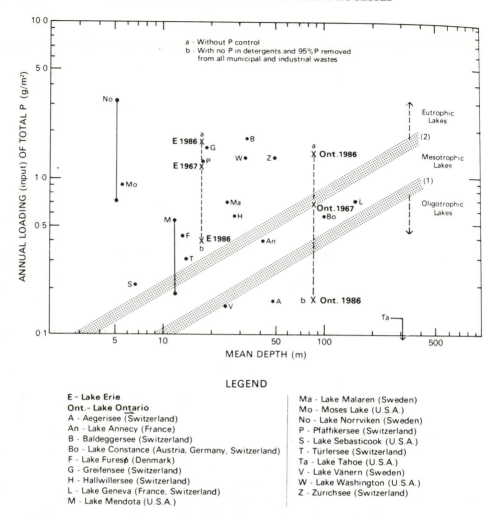

Figure A.1 State of eutrophication for a number of lakes in Europe and North America. (International Lake Erie Water Pollution Board 1969.)

Empirical and Systems Models

The first model used on Lake Erie was a loading model developed by R. A. Vollenweider (1968) and shown in Figure A.1. This is an empirical model, which means that a relationship between certain variables was noted in a limited number of circumstances, without elucidating the cause-and-effect relationships between the variables; these relationships were then assumed to hold more widely and applied to new situations to give information on managing them. By plotting the phosphorus load per unit surface area against the mean depths of many lakes, Vollenweider found he was able to classify the lakes of the temperate zones of the world into meaningful groups. The group of lakes above the upper reference line in Figure A.1 were eutrophic, while the lakes under the lower reference line were oligotrophic. This simple model depicted the probable trophic states of Lakes Erie and Ontario in 1986 with and without implementation of phosphorus loading controls. If no controls were implemented, both lakes would become very eutrophic and unsatisfactory, as judged by their estimated positions in Figure A.1. If controls were implemented, however, Erie would become a mildly eutrophic lake and Ontario would become oligotrophic. This model gave strong evidence for the need of phosphorus control on Lake Erie, but gave no further information about the lake. It could give no indication, for example, of the phosphorus concentrations likely to be encountered in the different basins of the lake, corresponding to different phosphorus loads to the lake. Information of this kind can be generated only by using an appropriate systems model, one that postulates the form of the relationships between the sets of dependent and independent variables. The empirical model was later investigated to establish the relationships between the dependent and independent variables, and the results were published by Vollenweider (1975).

A systems model relates cause and effect in a quantitative way by means of a series of mathematical equations. Often a systems model will be a combination of several submodels. For example, Simons (1976) developed a hydrodynamic model for movements in the waters of Lake Erie, and the outputs from this model were used as inputs to chemical models. The quantitative nature of the information from these models permits the output from one model to be used as the input to another.

HYDRODYNAMIC MODELS

In the present context, the principles on which these computations for hydrodynamic models are based are more relevant than the mathematical formulations. The basic conceptual models or laws underlying the numerical hydrodynamic model are the law of conservation of mass and the law of conservation of momentum. The first law, applied to continuous deformable fluids, states that the fluid particles, being in intimate contact with one another, do not move independently. The law of conservation of momentum means that a fluid particle accelerates at a rate proportional to the vector sum of all the forces acting on it and in the direction of the resultant force. In the language of mathematics these concepts can be expressed rigorously as partial differential equations. In an application, however, the modeler has to divide the lake into a finite number of elements or cells, which he then treats as an interacting set of finite-sized masses of fluid. Much of the success of these models depends on the choice of the element dimensions. The state of motion is described as a sequence of instants, much the same as a movie film is a sequence of still photographs. In the case of most models, a computer is used to do the repetitive calculations.

More specifically, in formulating the differential equations based on the above two laws, the following effects must be taken into account:

1. the pressure gradient experienced by water masses below a sloping water surface;
2. the tendency of currents to deviate to the right in the Northern Hemisphere, under influence of the earth's rotation;
3. the force exerted by the wind at the water surface;
4. the bottom stress opposing the movement of bottom water;
5. the mixing of water masses with different momentum; and
6. the pressure gradients in the water resulting from internal temperature gradients and the associated density gradients.

Simons's (1976) model incorporated these effects, and the lake was divided into grid cells 6.67 km long on each side. Current flows for each cell for all of 1970 were then calculated by inserting the necessary weather data into the equations and using a computer.

The modeler's task is not an easy one because, in the absence of required information, he is forced to make assumptions or use his own judgment about the value of certain constants, such as the coefficients of bottom friction. Nevertheless, Simons's model was able to predict accurately the water-level changes in the lake caused by wind. Circulation patterns were also predicted for different wind conditions during stratified and unstratified conditions, in far more detail than could ever have been measured with current meters.

Figure A.2 illustrates the information about currents in the lake that can be generated by the model. The surface currents in the middle of the Central and East Basins were probably as strong as, or stronger than, the nearshore currents, although Figure A.2 shows weaker currents in the center of the basins. The currents shown are the average of all the currents in the vertical segment below the arrow. There were probably mid-basin return currents, so that the integrated deep water column current velocity was less than that shown for the nearshore areas where there was no return flow. Thus, it is important to understand the nature and limitations of data generated by models.

This model predicts fairly strong flow in the West Basin south of Pelee Island, which is not in agreement with the flows shown in Fig. 5.7(a). This limitation of the model in the West Basin occurs because the 44.5 km² grid cells are large when compared with the small size of the Bass Islands and nearby reefs. Thus a cell in part of the lake could contain a significant amount of land or very shallow water while having a mean depth of greater than 2 m, and the model would have predicted a small flow where land actually blocked it. Nevertheless, the computer model was particularly

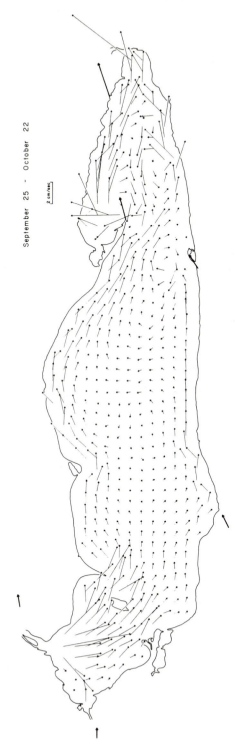

September 25 - October 22

2 cm/sec

Figure A.2 Depth-averaged Lake Erie water circulation patterns computed by a homogenous model for the interval indicated. Heavy arrows indicate directions and relative magnitude of wind stresses. (Simons 1976.)

powerful when dealing with the lake under stratified conditions. Figure A.3 shows the complexity of flow and the increased mean speeds that probably exist under stratified conditions in each layer. This illustration also shows the good agreement achieved between computed and measured currents.

DISPERSION MODELS

The use of the output of one model as the input of another model to generate new information was demonstrated by Lam and Simons (1976). They calculated chloride concentrations in Lake Erie in 1970 by using the flow data computed by Simons's model, together with actual river loads of chloride, to predict distributions in the lake. In their study, Lam and Simons started with a chloride distribution in the lake, as observed during a 1970 ship survey, and computed the probable distribution of chloride at the time of the next survey a month later. A comparison of the predicted and actual distribution patterns showed that best agreement was achieved when the value for the horizontal diffusion coefficient was set at 2.5×10^5 cm^2 sec^{-1}. This value is smaller than that proposed by Boyce and Hamblin (1975), 15×10^5 cm^2 sec^{-1}, because Lam and Simons used a 6-hr time step, whereas Boyce and Hamblin used a period of months. Since transports that were considered as diffusional by Boyce and Hamblin (1975) were considered advective in the time scale of Lam and Simons (1976), they had to use a smaller horizontal diffusion coefficient. This was the only adjustable variable in the computation, and after the first comparison trial it was kept constant.

There were seven more ship surveys of chloride concentrations in 1970, spaced one month apart, making possible seven more comparisons between predicted and observed distribution patterns. Two comparisons of estimated and observed distributions are shown in Figure A.4. The agreement in each case was good, demonstrating that the hydrodynamic model and the estimated horizontal diffusion coefficients were basically correct. In the West Basin, however, because of the built-in bias, the computer model displaced Detroit River concentrations slightly to the southeast of where they were actually observed.

The models of Simons (1976) and Lam and Simons (1976) are important in that they are basic to the development of any ecosystem model of Lake Erie, since these models can show the movement of contaminants and nutrients within the lake. These models can also be useful in a more-direct sense, in that the hydrodynamic model can predict storm surges at harbors and water-level changes around the lake. The transport of sediment in the lake can also be predicted. Of further importance is the capability of these models to predict various distribution patterns of toxic materials in the

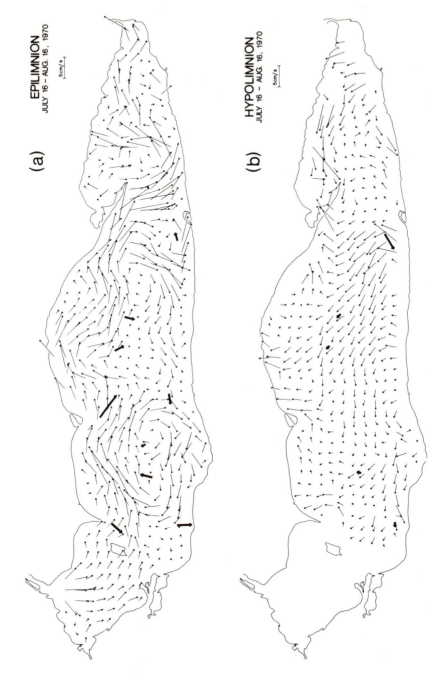

Figure A.3 Current computed for the epilimnion and hypolimnion water masses for the period 16 July to 16 August 1970. The heavy arrows represent currents observed with meters. (Simons 1976.)

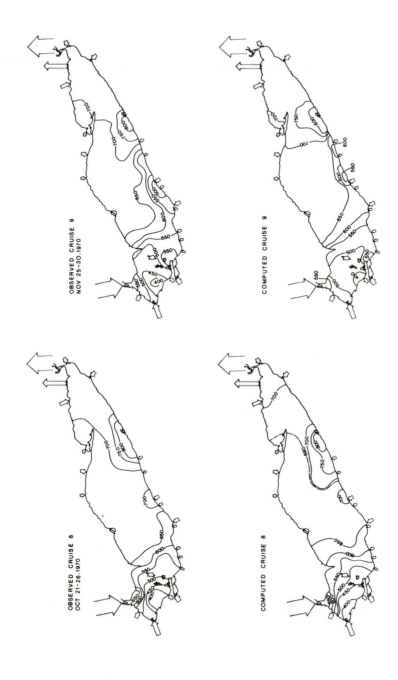

CHLORIDE CONC. (µ moles/l)

Figure A.4 Chloride concentration patterns in 1970 computed with the use of Simon's model, showing good agreement with observed concentrations. (Lam and Simons 1976.)

lake for different weather conditions, should there be a spill of material into a tributary river or from a vessel in the lake.

Interacting Models

The extent of modern chemical, physical, and biological knowledge of limnological systems has led to the development of mathematical models for many aspects of lakes. These models of different segments of the environment can be linked in a dynamic manner to determine the effect of change in each of the numerous components. These ecosystem response models are large, such as the conceptual model of the Lake Erie aquatic system shown in Figure A.5, which has nineteen submodels. If this model were expanded to be a total ecosystem model, including land management practices and economic factors prevailing in the drainage basin, it would contain many more submodels.

Each of the submodels in an ecosystem model handles a fraction of the ecosystem under consideration, and each is required to detail the response of that particular part of the environment to the factors affecting it. Since a model can describe the states of all the component parts, the model can be interrogated for computed values for the variables of interest, for specific times and places. If accurate in their predictions, these models can provide very valuable information to decision-makers. Except for the hydrodynamic models that use complex mathematics, most of the submodels are not difficult to understand. Yet the number of parts or submodels comprising environmental models makes them very complex and difficult to manage, with the result that a group of specialists in this field is developing. These modelers are now very much a part of all environmental institutes; their craft or science is becoming as well known and as separately identifiable as physics or biology.

Lam and Jaquet (1976) combined a number of submodels and, using certain observed data, were able to calculate the amount of phosphorus regenerated from the sediments to the waters of Lake Erie during the stormy month of November 1970. Regeneration from sediments is a process of fundamental importance in a lake, but one that is almost impossible to measure in a lake the size of Erie. The workings of their model can be understood by referring to Figure A.5, where they initially used the output of the hydrodynamic model with the sediment-water interaction model and known sedimentation patterns to estimate the total phosphorus regeneration. They then used these results to calculate the soluble and particulate concentrations observed in the lake at the end of November 1978. The predicted concentrations of phosphorus compared most favorably with those observed. Since phosphorus availability controls growth, the outputs of a model similar to Lam and Jaquet's (1976) can be linked with other submodels, as shown in Figure A.5, to predict values of biological variables in Lake Erie, but these developments have not yet occurred.

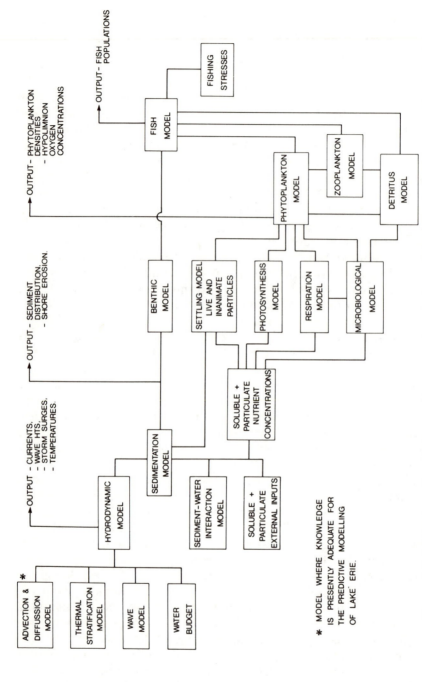

Figure A.5 Schematic outline of the more important data inputs, submodels, and links between the submodels necessary for the formulation of a predictive model for a lake system. Many minor linkages between submodels have been omitted for the sake of simplicity. (Burns et al. 1976b.)

Models of Phosphorus Concentration

Mean concentrations of phosphorus in the different basins of the lake can be predicted from the loadings of phosphorus to the lake by the use of numerical models. If a model is good, the predictions it produces will be reasonably accurate. Unfortunately, scientists and modelers differ as to what elements must be included in good models, with the result that many different models have been created. Some are complex; some are simple. One might think that a complex model accounting for many different processes would be the more correct model, but the state of environmental modeling is such that complex models can introduce more errors into the calculations than they avoid, and thus can have a low predictive capability. Whether a model is good or not still remains a somewhat subjective judgment. Thus, both simple and complex models can be used when evaluating alternative strategies to achieve a required condition in a lake.

Average phosphorus concentrations are often used to categorize the condition of a lake. A suitable phosphorus management objective for Lake Erie is to achieve a mean annual concentration of 15 mg P m^{-3} in the West Basin and 10 mg P m^{-3} in the Central and East basins, as suggested in a review of managment objectives for the lake by Thomas, Robertson and Sonzogni (1980). This is in accordance with another suggestion (Vollenweider, Rast and Kerekes 1980) that the boundary between oligotrophic and mesotrophic lake conditions be considered as a mean concentration of 10 mg P m^{-3}, while the boundary between mesotrophic and eutrophic conditions be 20 mg P m^{-3}, at spring overturn. The waters of the Central and East Basins can be very clear and should be managed to be oligotrophic, while those of West Basin are naturally more enriched and could be considered acceptable at concentrations of 15 mg P m^{-3} as recommended by the Phosphorus Management Strategies Task Force (1980).

Three models of lake response to phosphorus loads, developed for consideration by Task Group III and the Phosphorus Management Strategies Task Force in 1980, permit calculation of the loads likely to result in a mean concentration of 10 mg P m^{-3} in the Central Basin. Two additional models exist that also permit calculation of the phosphorus loads that will achieve this objective. These five models will be considered below, starting with the simplest.

Figure A.1 is an illustration of the first model suggested by R. A. Vollenweider in 1968. The desired mean phosphorus concentration for Lake Erie was taken to be 10 mg P m^{-3}; by using the mean depth of Lake Erie at 18.6 m, the desired annual phosphorus loading to the lake was determined to be 0.14 gm P m^{-2} yr^{-1}, or 3,600 tons per year for the whole lake. Further research, however, revealed that the residence time of water in a lake is an important feature controlling trophic state. Lakes with short residence times require relatively more phosphorus to achieve a specified concentration than do lakes having long residence times. By

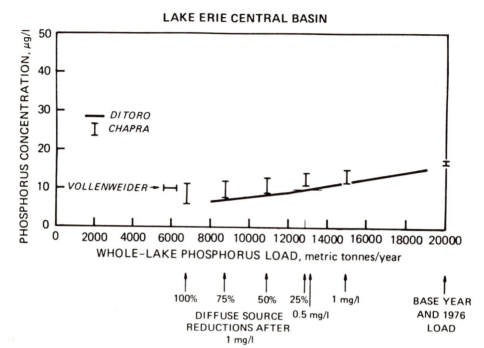

Figure A.6 Relationship between phosphorus concentration in the Central Basin and whole-lake phosphorus load to Lake Erie for the models of the Vollenweider (1977), DiToro and Matystik (1978), and Chapra (1978) models. (Task Group III 1978.)

including this feature into updated models (Vollenweider, Rast, and Kerekes 1980; Vollenweider 1975) increased his original estimate of the phosphorus load that would give the desired phosphorus concentration in the lake up to 6,000 tons per year. This result is shown in Figure A.6.

Chapra's (1978, 1980) model is considerably more complex than the two foregoing models. It considers flow through the lake, diffusion within the lake, settling velocity of phosphorus from the lake waters, and two different sediment feedback situations. These situations are (a) no feedback of phosphorus from sediments to the lake water and (b) maximum feedback at specified rates. These situations create a range of possible loads varying from 7,000 to 11,000 tons, with a mean value of 9,000 tons phosphorus per annum, which will give the Central Basin a mean concentration of 10 mg P m^{-3} (Fig. A.6).

A MODEL FOR BIOAVAILABLE PHOSPHORUS IN LAKE ERIE

The author has developed a model estimating the mean phosphorus concentrations of waters within the basins, together with the average inflow and outflow concentrations. It is similar to Chapra's (1980) model, but with some significant differences. The biggest difference is that this model considers input of only bioavailable phosphorus, not total phosphorus, as in the case of all the other Lake Erie models. Also, Lake Erie is modeled here as a slowly flowing river with continuous inputs and losses from each basin. The object of this model is to estimate the external loadings of phosphorus that will result in the desired mean concentration of 15 mg P m^{-3} in the West Basin and 10 mg P m^{-3} for total phosphorus concentrations in the Central and East Basins.

The basic components of the model are:

1. The flow of water through all the basins is taken as the hydraulic flow of 520 × 10^6 m^3 day^{-1}, giving residence times for water in the West, Central, and East Basins as being 54, 529, and 320 days respectively. The lake is treated as a broad, slow-flowing river.

2. The external load to the West Basin is considered to be contained in the inflowing water with no further phosphorus additions once the water is in the basin. The external phosphorus load to the Central Basin is considered to be added to the water coming from the West Basin and then to diffuse through the basin at a constant rate, thus increasing concentrations daily throughout the basin at a rate dependent on the external load (Boyce and Hamblin 1975). The external load to the East Basin similarly increases the concentration of phosphorus in the water coming from the Central Basin.

3. The phosphorus which is not bioavailable settles out of the water soon after entering the lake and remains in the sediments. Only bioavailable phosphorus enters into the phosphorus metabolism of the lake and requires modeling. Resuspension of apatite phosphorus, however, causes an increase of about 2 mg P m^{-3} in the mean concentration of the West Basin above that computed on the basis of bioavailable phosphorus.

4. The total phosphorus is eliminated downward at the rate of 40 m yr^{-1}, or 11 cm day^{-1}. This concept is artificial because only particulate phosphorous can settle, but since there is a rapid interconversion of particulate and soluble phosphorus, this simplification can be used. The downward flux and concentration change resulting from this process is calculated as follows:

$$\text{Flux (mg P m}^{-2}\text{ yr}^{-1}) = \text{settling velocity (m yr}^{-1}) \qquad \text{(A.1)}$$
$$\times \text{ concentration (mg P m}^{-3})$$

and

$$\text{Concentration change} = \frac{\text{flux}}{\text{mean basin depth}} \text{ (mg P m}^{-3}\text{ yr}^{-1}) \qquad \text{(A.2)}$$

The phosphorus lost to the sediments is replaced by the external load to the lake or internal regeneration from the sediments. Thus, in a 10m water column remaining at constant concentration, the phosphorus is effectively settled out and renewed four times a year. The settling and regenerative processes occur simultaneously.

5. The mean annual regeneration rate of phosphorus for the West and Central Basins is a composite of oxic and anoxic regeneration rates. The East Basin rate is the oxic regeneration rate of 0.7 mg P m^{-2} day^{-1} (Burns and Ross 1972a). The Central Basin rate for 1970 is 1.0 mg m^{-2} day^{-1} and is based on the duration of both oxic and anoxic conditions during 1970, with the anoxic regeneration rate being 7.6 mg P m^{-2} day^{-1} (Burns and Ross 1973a). The duration of anoxic conditions in 1980 was short, and the 1980 Central Basin phosphorus regeneration rate is taken as the oxic rate, 0.7 mg P m^{-2} day^{-1}. Interface anoxia occurs in the West Basin (Burns 1976b) and so does extensive physical disturbance of the sediments. Thus, the West Basin regeneration rate is taken as 1.5 mg P m^{-2} day.

The basic equation for determining changes in concentration in a cubic meter of water in the lake arising from these initial conditions is

$$\frac{dC}{dt} = \frac{L}{V} + \frac{R}{D} - \frac{S}{D} \cdot C \quad (\text{mg P m}^{-3}\text{ day}^{-1}) \tag{A.3}$$

where C = concentration (mg P m^{-3}),
    L = external loading to a basin (mg day^{-1}),
    V = volume of the basin (m^{-3}),
    R = regeneration rate as defined above (mg m^{-2} day^{-1}),
    D = mean basin depth (m),
    S = settling rate,
      = 40 m yr^{-1} or .11 m day^{-1}.

If I = L/V + R/D and E = S/D, then equation A.3 simplifies to

$$\frac{dC}{dt} = I - E.C \quad (\text{mg P m}^{-3}\text{ day}^{-1}) \tag{A.4}$$

with I being the loading term and E.C being the elimination term.

If T is the residence time of water in a basin in days, then the concentration of phosphorus in water leaving the basin, C_2, is given by

$$C_2 = \frac{I}{E} - \left[\frac{I}{E} - C_1\right] e^{-ET} \quad (\text{mg P m}^{-3}) \tag{A.5}$$

where C_1 is the incoming concentration. If the water takes n days to pass through the basin, then the average concentration, C_{av}, will be given by summing the daily concentrations of a unit volume of water flowing through the basin and dividing by the number of days the water is in the basin:

Table A.1 Loadings of Total and Bioavailable Phosphorus to Lake Erie (in metric tons)

	1970 TP	Bioav. factor (average)	1970 BP	1980 TP	Bioav. factor (average)	1980 BP
West Basin						
Detroit River	15421	0.50	7710	4745	0.50	2372
Tributaries	2656	0.50	1328	3772	0.50	1886
Municipal	120	0.80	96	482	0.80	386
Industrial	15	0.80	12	50	0.80	40
Atmospheric	128	0.50	64	128	0.50	64
Erosional	115	0.023	3	115	0.023	3
West Basin total	18455		9213	9292		4751
Non-erosional total	18340	0.50	9210	9177	0.52	4748
Central Basin						
U.S. tributaries	1269	0.50	635	2196	0.50	1098
Can. tributaries	120	0.50	60	410	0.50	205
Municipal	1482	0.80	1185	669	0.80	535
Industrial	29	0.80	24	20	0.80	16
Atmospheric	387	0.50	194	387	0.50	194
Erosional	4032	0.023	93	4032	0.023	93
Central Basin total	7319		2191	7714		2141
Non-erosional total	3287	0.64	2098	3682	0.56	2048
East Basin						
Grand River	1306	0.80	1044	698	0.80	551
Tributaries	135	0.35	47	124	0.35	44
Municipal	69	0.80	55	181	0.80	145
Industrial	73	0.80	58	11	0.80	19
Atmospheric	259	0.50	129	259	0.50	129
Erosional	403	0.023	10	403	0.023	10
East Basin total	2245		1343	1676		898
Non-erosional total	1842	0.72	1333	1273	0.69	888
Lake total	28019		12747	18682		7790
Erosional total	4550		106	4450		106
Non-erosional total	23469		12641	14132		7684

Note: Values for bioavailability factors are detailed in section on Phosphorus Loading, Chapter 6.
Source: 1970 data, Frazer and Wilson (1981). 1980 data, John Clark (personal communication). Erosion, Kemp, McInnes and Harper (1977).

$$C_{av} = \frac{\sum\limits_{i=1}^{n} C_i}{n} = \frac{1}{T}\left[\frac{I}{E}\cdot T + \left(\frac{C_1}{E} - \frac{I}{E^2}\right)(1 - e^{-ET})\right] \qquad (A.6)$$

The concentrations computed on the basis of the 1970 and 1980 phosphorus loads (Table A.1) are shown in Figure A.7. The observed West

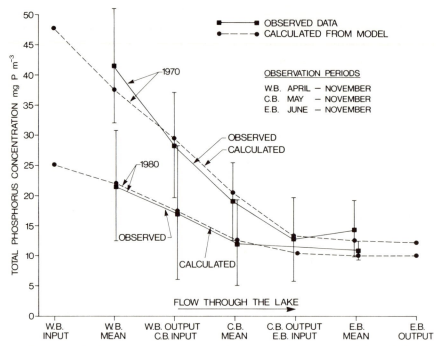

Figure A.7 Average concentrations of total phosphorus observed in 1970 and 1980 for the three basins of Lake Erie and their boundary zones. The corresponding concentrations predicted by the model described in this appendix are also shown.

Basin mean concentrations were decreased by 2.0 mg P m^{-3} to account for resuspended apatite. The observed data covered only part of each year (Fig. A.7) because observations in 1980 were somewhat limited and the same data period was used for both 1970 and 1980.

The agreement between the observed concentrations and those computed on the basis of the model is reasonably good, especially since the external loads in 1970 were quite different from those in 1980 (Table A.1). This means that the model appears to simulate the processes controlling total phosphorus concentration reasonably well and can thus be used tentatively to predict concentrations that are likely to result with different loading programs.

The data in Figure A.7 show a number of things. The first is that the mean concentration of phosphorus observed in the West Basin is approximately equal to that calculated by dividing the annual loading of bioavailable phosphorus (BP) to that basin by the annual flow of water to the basin. This would not be the case if the values for total phosphorus were used instead. Another is that the concentration of phosphorus drops as the water passes down the lake, with the decrease in concentration being largest when the concentration is the highest, as in the West Basin in 1970. It seems that once the concentrations drop below 10 mg P m^{-3}, they tend to remain fairly stable because, by the assumptions made in setting up this model, the regeneration processes at these concentrations are roughly equal to the elimination processes. These processes can be illustrated by the following set of calculations: Suppose that the loading to the West Basin were 2641 m ton BP per year and that there were no other loadings of phosphorus to the lake; the incoming concentration would be 13.9 mg P m^{-3}. At this concentration the elimination and regeneration processes in the West Basin would be equal and the water would leave the basin at the incoming concentration. If there were no further loading to the Central Basin the concentration would decline to 6.6 mg P m^{-3} for the water leaving this basin, while the basin average concentration would be 8.6 mg P m^{-3}. The water leaving the Central Basin at 6.6 mg P m^{-3} would hardly change in concentration with time. Average concentrations for the East Basin would be 6.4 mg P m^{-3}, with the water leaving this basin at 6.3 mg P m^{-3}, if no further phosphorus were added.

The above model also permits an estimate of phosphorus loadings required to achieve the Phosphorus Management Strategies Task Force (1980) objective concentrations of 15, 10, and 10 mg P m^{-3} for the West, Central, and East Basins, respectively. The loadings of bioavailable phosphorus and total phosphorus (TP) to these basins to achieve these required concentrations are calculated using the model and the conversion factors listed in Table A.1 below.

	BP	TP	(not including P from shoreline erosion)
West	2942	5657	t yr^{-1}
Central	1090	1946	t yr^{-1}
East	515	746	t yr^{-1}
Total	4547	8349	t yr^{-1}

With these loads, the mean concentration of the Central Basin would be 10 mg P m^{-3} with an exit concentration from the Central Basin to the East of 8.4 mg P m^{-3}. The desired mean for the East Basin is 10 mg P m^{-3}, and this can be achieved only by increasing the concentration in this basin by loading 1434 tons BP yr^{-1} to the basin. This is an excessive amount of phosphorus and derives only from the need to raise the exit concentration from the East Basin to 11.0 mg P m^{-3} to achieve a 10 mg P m^{-3} average concentration for the basin. A far more reasonable East Basin load is 515 tons BP yr^{-1}, which would maintain the incoming concentration at 8.4 mg P m^{-3} in the water moving through the basin and give mean and exit concentrations of the same value.

To summarize, the author's model predicts the following approximate results:

	Max. BP load	Max. TP load	Resultant Mean Conc.
West	3000t yr^{-1}	5750t yr^{-1}	15 mg P m^{-3}
Central	1000	2000	10
East	500	750	8.4
Total	4500	8500	

The fifth model to give information on the question of the appropriate loading of phosphorus to Lake Erie is that of DiToro and Connolly (1980). This is a very complex model that considers the kinetic interconversion of fifteen different variables, such as concentrations of phytoplankton, zooplankton, forms of phosphorus, nitrogen, silica, carbon, and dissolved oxygen. Processes such as the transport of water, heat, and materials by means of advection, dispersion, and vertical diffusion were considered. The effects of thermal stratification, air-water interchange, sediment-water interchange, and external nutrient loading were also taken into account. A complex model of this kind should be tested for sensitivity of the output to changing model parameters. This step will reveal where the modeler must be especially careful in choosing parameter values.

Since all the variables in this type of model are interconnected with each other by means of a series of equations containing kinetic coefficients, the final values of the variables are determined by the initial data inputs and the chosen coefficients. Thus, if any of the important kinetic coefficients were given values that are very different from the real ones, many of the computed values of the state variables would probably be different from those actually observed in the lake. Therefore, one significant error in these complex, deterministic models can ruin their predictive capability. This likelihood was overcome, in this case, by calibrating all the values of the variables calculated by the model against those observed in 1970. After this was done, the calibrated model was rerun for the year 1975, changing only the weather, flow, and nutrient input data to those of 1975. The values computed by the model for the state variables in 1975 were compared against those observed. The 1975 predictions of the model were found to be good in a majority of the comparisons, and thus DiToro and Connolly (1980) felt that their model made good predictions and simulated many processes in the lake correctly. Indeed, the model produced a wealth of information on concentration changes in the biological and chemical variables, both in the three different basins of the lake and in the upper and lower layers in these basins during thermal stratification. Their model predicts that a loading of about 13,000 tons of phosphorus per year to the whole lake would produce a mean phosphorus concentration of 10 mg P m^{-3} in the Central Basin (Fig. A.6).

The loading estimate based on the 1968 Vollenweider model has been superceded by the value derived from his 1975 model. This means there are four estimates of the loading to the whole lake that will achieve the Central Basin concentration of 10 mg P m^{-3}. These are

Vollenweider	6,000	m tons yr.$^{-1}$
Chapra	7,000 to 11,000	"
Burns	8,500	"
DiToro & Connolly	13,000	"

The difference between the estimates is not extreme, and thus their average is meaningful. The average is 9,125 m tons yr^{-1}, and therefore a carefully considered estimate of the maximum loading for acceptable conditions in Lake Erie would be 9,000 tons of phosphorus per year.

Models Estimating Anoxia in the Central Basin

The estimate of an optimum phosphorus loading, calculated on the basis of a phosphorus concentration objective, has been confirmed by using a quite different management objective. This objective is based on the elimination of anoxia from the Central Basin hypolimnion. Task Group III (1978) stated that their objective for the water quality of Lake Erie was "the reduction of approximately 90% in the area of anoxia in the Central Basin and prevention of any substantial phosphorus release from the sediments." Task Group III received submissions on this topic from Vollenweider (1977), Chapra (1978) and DiToro and Matystik (1978), based on their respective models. These linked oxygen conditions in the Central Basin hypolimnion to phosphorus loads to the lake. After considering these reports, Task Group III concluded that

> It is recommended that a phosphorus loading of 10,900 mta (metric tons per annum) be established for Lake Erie to eliminate 90 per cent of the anoxic area in the Central Basin. The ideal phosphorus loading objective for Lake Erie would be 9,500 mta to ensure optimum conditions for fish in the Central Basin hypolimnion.

The last part of this recommendation basically confirms the loading recommendation of 9,000 tons yr^{-1} based on phosphorus concentrations that was made in the last paragraph.

As the phosphorus loads are reduced to this level, there will be a marked improvement in the oxygen conditions of the Central Basin. The progress toward improved conditions, however, will be erratic, largely because of the weather factors causing variable hypolimnion conditions, as mentioned in Chapter 9. The weather effects on the Central Basin thermal structure have recently been simulated by Lam, Schertzer, and Fraser (1983a) as part of their model of the changes in Lake Erie water quality resulting from weather and loading variations. Their data (Fig. A.8) shows just how

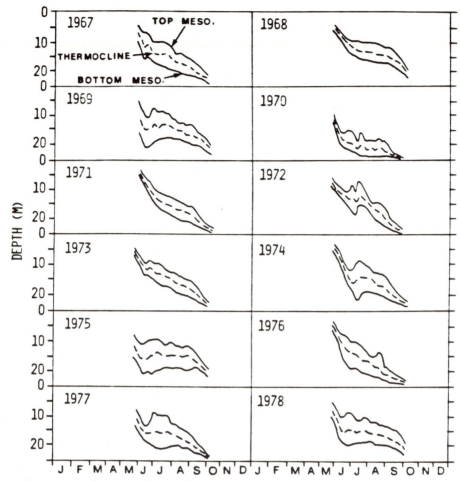

Figure A.8 The variability of the Central Basin thermocline position and meso-limnion thickness caused by the different weather conditions prevailing between 1967 and 1968. (Lam, Schertzer, and Fraser 1983a.)

variable the thermocline dynamics can be. They describe the years 1967, 1968, 1971, 1973 and 1976 as normal with a monotonic downward movement of the thermocline. The years 1970, 1975, 1977, and 1978 are stable and show very little change in the thickness of the hypolimnion over the season, with 1970 for example, having a thin hypolimnion and 1975 having a thick one. Finally, the years 1969, 1972 and 1974 show definite thickening of the hypolimnion after its initial formation.

The information on the manner in which weather affects the thermocline makes it possible to understand the pattern of Central Basin hypolimnion improvement, following the substantial phosphorus loading reductions that have occurred (Table A.1). As the phosphorus loads begin to drop in an orderly fashion and the corrected and standarized oxygen depletion rates do the same, it does not mean that there will be a similar orderly improvement in the oxygen conditions observed in the basin. The small annual improvement will frequently be overshadowed by effects caused by large-scale weather fluctuations. Nevertheless, as the basic condition of the lake improves, the probability and hence the frequency of occurrence of periods of intensive anoxia will diminish, until conditions similar to those prevailing in 1929 may be reestablished, if the phosphorus loads are maintained at the 1929 levels. It is quite probable that year-round aerobic conditions will return permanently to the central area of the Central Basin, if the requirements of the Water Quality Agreement are implemented. It is unlikely, however, that this condition will ever prevail in the Sandusky subbasin at the southwest corner of the Central Basin. This area is highly enriched and traditionally has a warm, thin hypolimnion. Although the extent and duration of anoxic conditions in this area may be diminished, it is unlikely that anoxic conditions will ever be entirely eliminated from the Sandusky subbasin.

Cladophora Growth

Research on *Cladophora* growth and metabolism has been carried out by Auer and Canale (1982), who organized some of their results into a form of a model of *Cladophora* growth. They showed the dependence of the two major dependent variables, standing crop and internal phosphorus content, on the independent variable, soluble reactive phosphorus (SRP). These relationships are shown in Figure A.9. Other variables controlling *Cladophora* growth are the presence of a suitable substrate (rock), light, and temperature. Light and temperature seldom limit growth along the shorelines of the Great Lakes in the summer, but availability of a suitably rocky bottom and adequate SRP concentration can do so.

In the West Basin, there is nearly always adequate SRP, so there are large growths of *Cladophora* wherever there are reef areas. The Central Basin does not have rocky shorelines, so *Cladophora* is not a big problem there. The East Basin does have large areas of suitable rocky bottom, and *Cladophora* growth is controlled by nutrient availability along the shorelines in this basin.

Auer and Canale (1982) found that *Cladophora* could not live if it did not have a phosphorus tissue content of more than 0.05 percent of dry weight (Fig. A.10). Their research and model indicate that if concentrations of SRP in the water are as low as 2.0 mg P m^{-3}, *Cladophora* becomes sensitive to further reductions in the availability of phosphorus. The 2 mg P m^{-3} SRP limit seems extremely low, but is attainable in reality because SRP is the form of phosphorus most readily taken up by phytoplankton and bacteria in the water. If its availability is restricted, concentrations of this nutrient are usually very low. Concentrations of SRP have

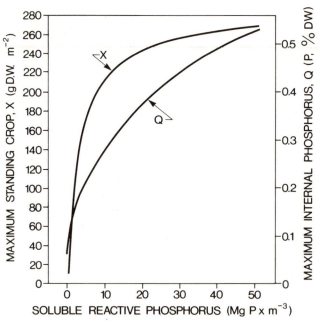

Figure A.9 Estimates of the maximum standing crop of Cladophora *as a function of average soluble reactive phosphorus concentrations in the surrounding water. Also shown is the phosphorus within the plant as a function of the phosphorus concentration in the surrounding water. (M.T. Auer, personal communication.)*

been measured along a 14 km stretch of the East Basin shoreline near Nanticoke (Heathcote 1979) between the depths of 1 and 10 m and are shown in Figure A.10. The late spring and summer concentrations in these waters were below 2 mg P m^{-3}. The early spring inshore values of SRP, however, are too high, indicating that phosphorus availability at this time is the probable source of the *Cladophora* problem. The late spring and summer values are within the safe limit and cause the growth of *Cladophora* to be slower in the late summer. Thus, a careful program of phosphorus control, resulting in diminished loadings of phosphorus, would lead to a considerable reduction in the *Cladophora* problem in the East Basin. The required low phosphorus concentrations could be attained if the wastewaters were pumped well offshore, away from the critical nearshore zone.

Conclusions

The use of models in defining management alternatives has been illustrated in this appendix. Despite some present limitations, models will become an increasingly important part of environmental science as their predictive capability grows. This will happen as the dominant processes in natural

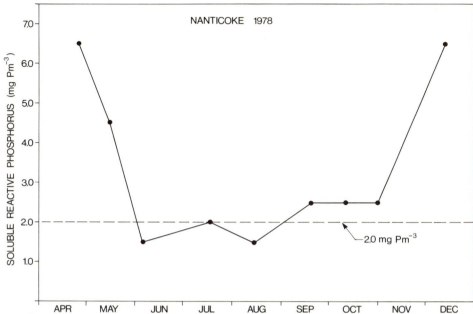

Figure A.10 Average concentrations of soluble reactive phosphorus (SRP) found at depths less then 10 m along a 14 km segment of shoreline near Nanticoke in the East Basin. This diagram shows that during the summer the SRP concentrations are below or close to the critical level for **Cladophora** *growth.*

environments are discovered or identified. Important variables must be selected so that models can reproduce and predict the main pattern of events. Models inevitably become inaccurate if they try to reproduce a large number of details. The fine points of nature are not likely to be reproduced by models and will forever be the preserve of the field scientist. Yet the simplifications and basically accurate predictions produced by good models will be increasingly valuable in a world where humans are struggling with the complexity of the decisions they must make.

References

Allen, R.T. 1970. *The Great Lakes*. Vol. 3 of the Illustrated Natural History of Canada. Toronto: Natural Science of Canada Ltd.

Apmann, R.P. 1975. Historical trends in pollutant loadings to Lake Erie. U.S. Army Corps of Engineers, Buffalo, N.Y. 14207.

Atkins, W.R.G. 1932. The copper content of sea water. *J. Mar. Biol. Assn.* (U.K.) 18:193–98.

Auer, M.T. Personal communication, Michigan Technical University, Houghton, Mich. 49931.

Auer, M.T., and R.P. Canale. 1982. Ecological studies and mathematical modelling of *Cladophora* in Lake Huron: 7. Model verification and system response. *J. Great Lakes Res.* 8:134–43.

Baker, D.P. 1980. Fluvial transport and processing of sediments and nutrients in large agricultural river basins. Environmental Research Lab., U.S. Environmental Protection Agency, Athens, Georgia 30605.

Baldwin, N.S., and R.W. Saalfeld. 1962. Commercial fish production in the Great Lakes 1867–1960. (Supplement 1961–68). Great Lakes Fish. Comm. Tech Rept 3. 166 pp. Supplement in 1970.

Barica, J. 1982. Lake Erie Oxygen Depletion Controversy. *J. Great Lakes Res.* 8:719–22.

Barrett, H.B. 1977. *The Lore and Legends of Long Point*. Toronto: Burns & MacEachern. 239 pp.

_____. 1981. History of human use impacts on Long Point Bay. *J. Great Lakes Res.* 7:81–88.

Barry J.P. 1973. *Ships of the Great Lakes: 300 Years of Navigation*. Berkeley, Calif.: Howell-North. 250 pp.

Beeton, A.M. 1961. Environmental changes in Lake Erie. *Trans. Amer. Fish. Soc.* 90(2):153–59.

————. 1965. Eutrophication of the St. Lawrence Great Lakes. *Limnol. and Oceanogr.* 10:240–54.

Beeton, A.M., and W.T. Edmondson. 1972. The eutrophication problem. *J. Fish. Res. Board Can.* 29:673–82.

Beier, K., and A. Jernelov. 1979. Methylation of mercury in aquatic environments. In *The Biogeochemistry of Mercury in the Environment*, ed. J.O. Nriagu. Amsterdam: Elsevier, North Holland.

Bellrose, F.C. 1968. Waterfowl migration corridors east of the Rocky Mountains in the United States. Biological Notes #61. Urbana, Ill., Illinois Natural History Survey.

Bennet, E.B. 1976. Effect of flowthrough on the chloride content of Lake Erie, 1964–1974. Canada Centre for Inland Waters, Burlington, Ontario L7R 4A6 (unpublished).

Berkes, F., and D. Pocock. 1980. Issues and conflicts in fisheries management in Lake Erie. Inst. of Urban and Environmental Studies, Brock University, St. Catharines, Ontario. 99 pp.

Blanton, J.O., and R.A. Winklhofer. 1972. Physical processes affecting the hypolimnion of the Central Basin of Lake Erie. In "Project Hypo" and Canada Centre for Inland Waters, Burlington, Ontario, Paper #6; U.S. EPA Rept. TS-05-71-208-24 (1972). Also in *Proc. 14th Conf. Great Lakes Res.* (1971), pp. 788–98.

Boulden, R.S., ed. 1975. Canada/Ontario Great Lakes shore damage survey. Technical Rept. of Environment Canada and Ontario Min. of Nat. Res. 96 pp.

Boyce, F.M. 1974. Some aspects of Great Lakes physics of importance to biological and chemical processes. *J. Fish. Res. Board Can.* 31:689–730.

————. Personal Communication—Canada Center for Inland Waters, Burlington, Ontario L7R 4A6.

Boyce, F.M., F. Chiocchio, B. Eid, F. Penicka, and F. Rosa. 1980. Hypolimnion flow between the Central and Eastern Basins of Lake Erie during 1977. *J. Great Lakes Res.* 6:290–306.

Boyce, F.M., and P.F. Hamblin. 1975. A simple diffusion model of the mean field distribution of soluble materials in the Great Lakes. *Limnol. and Oceanogr.* 20:511–17.

Boyd, J.D. 1980. Metalimnetic oxygen minima in Lake Ontario, 1972. *J. Great Lakes Res.* 6:95–100.

Boyko, M. 1973. European impact on the vegetation around Crawford Lake in southern Ontario. M.Sc. thesis, Univ. of Toronto, Toronto, Ontario.

Bradshaw, A.S. 1964. The crustacean zooplankton picture: Lake Erie 1939–49–59; Cayuga 1910–51–61. *Verh. Internat. Verein. Limnol.* 15:700–708.

Bradstreet, M.S.W. 1981. Here about the beach I wander. *Seasons* 21:14–17.

Braidech, T., P. Gehring, and C. Kleveno. 1972. Biological processes related to oxygen depletion and nutrient regeneration processes in the Lake Erie Central Basin. *Proc. 14th Conf. Great Lakes Res.* (1971), pp. 805–17. Internat. Assoc. Great Lakes Res. In "Project Hypo" and Canada Centre for Inland Waters, Burlington, Ontario, Paper #6; U.S. EPA Rept. TS-05-71-208-24 (1972).

Bridle, T.R. 1982. The impact of toxic organics on residue management. Wastewater Technology Centre, Environmental Protection Service, Burlington, Ontario. L7R 4A6 (unpublished).

Brinkhurst, R.O. 1969. Changes in the benthos of Lakes Erie and Ontario. In *Proc. Conf. on Changes in the Biota of Lakes Erie and Ontario. Bull Buffalo Soc. Nat. Sci.* 25:45–71.

Britt, N.W. Personal communication. Ohio State University, Columbus, Ohio 43210.

———. 1955a. Stratification in western Lake Erie in summer of 1953: Effects on the *Hexagenia (ephemeroptera). Ecology* 36:239–44.

———. 1955b. *Hexagenia (ephemeroptera)* recovery in Western Lake Erie following the 1953 catastrophe. *Ecology* 36:520–22.

Britt, N.W., A.J., Pliodzinskas, and E.M. Hair. 1980. Benthic macroinvertebrate distributions in the Central and Western Basins of Lake Erie. In Lake Erie Nutrient Control Program—An Assessment of Its Effectiveness in Controlling Lake Eutrophication. U.S. EPA Rept. EPA-600/3-80-062.

Britt, N.W., E.J. Skoch, and K.R. Smith. 1968. Record low dissolved oxygen in the island area of Lake Erie. *Ohio J. of Sci.* 68:175–79.

Brown, S.R. 1815. *An Authentic History of the Second War for Independence.* Auburn, N.Y.: J.G. Hathaway, Kellogg and Beardslee. 715 pp.

Bryson, R.A. 1966. Air masses, streamlines and the Boreal Forest. Dept. of Energy, Mines and Resources, Ottawa, Canada. *Geogr. Bull.* 8:228–69.

Bukata, R.P., W.S. Haras, and J.E. Bruton. 1975. The application of ERTS -1 digital data to water transport phenomena in the Point Pelee–Rondeau area. *Verh. Internat. Verein. Limnol.* 19:168–78.

Burns, N.M. 1976a. Oxygen depletion in the Central and Eastern Basins of Lake Erie, 1970. *J. Fish. Res. Board Can.* 33:512–19.

———. 1976b. Nutrient budgets for Lake Erie, 1970. *J. Fish. Res. Board Can.* 33:520–36.

———. 1976c. Temperature oxygen and nutrient distribution patterns in Lake Erie, 1970. *J. Fish. Res. Board Can.* 33:485–511.

Burns, N.M., J.-M. Jaquet, A.L.W. Kemp, D.C.L. Lam, J.H. Leach, M. Munawar, T.J. Simons, P.G. Sly, R.L. Thomas, N.H.F. Watson, and J.D.H. Williams. 1976. Processes within Lake Erie. *J. Fish. Res. Board Can.* 33:639–43.

Burns, N.M., and F. Rosa. 1980. In situ measurement of settling velocity of organic carbon particles and 10 species of phytoplankton. *Limnol. and Oceanogr.* 25:855–64.

Burns, N.M., F. Rosa, and C.H. Chan. 1976. Lake Erie water chemistry data 1970–71. Canada Centre for Inland Waters, Burlington, Ontario, Paper #16.

Burns, N.M., F. Rosa, and A. Gedeon. 1978. Lake Erie in mid-winter. *J. Great Lakes Res.* 4:134–41.

Burns, N.M., and C. Ross. 1972a. Oxygen-nutrient relationships within the Central Basin of Lake Erie. In "Project Hypo" and Canada Centre for Inland Waters, Burlington, Ontario, Paper #6, and U.S. EPA Rept. TS-05 in *Nutrients in Natural Waters*, ed. H.E. Allen and J.R. Kramer. New York: Wiley-Interscience (1972). 457 pp.

———. 1972b. Project Hypo—An introduction. *Proc. 14th Conf. Great Lakes Res.* (1971), pp. 740–42. Also in "Project Hypo" and Canada Centre for Inland Waters, Burlington, Ontario, Paper #6; U.S. EPA Rept. TS-05-71-208-24.

———. 1972c. Project Hypo—Discussion of findings. *Proc. 14th Conf. Great Lakes Res.* pp. 761–67. Internat. Assoc. Great Lakes Res. In "Project Hypo" and Canada Centre for Inland Waters, Burlington, Ontario, Paper #6; U.S. EPA Rept. TS-05-71-208-24.

Burns, N.M., J.D.H. Williams, J.-M. Jaquet, A.L.W. Kemp, and D.C.L. Lam. 1976b. A phosphorus budget for Lake Erie. *J. Fish. Res. Board Can.* 33:564–73.

Carignan, R., and R.J. Flett. 1981. Postdepositional mobility of phosphorus in lake sediments. *Limnol. and Oceanogr.* 26:361–66.

Carr, J.F. 1962. Dissolved oxygen in Lake Erie, past and present. *Proc. 5th Conf. on Great Lakes Res.* 9:1–14. Univ. Mich. Great Lakes Div. Pub.

Carr, J.F., V.C. Applegate, and M. Keller. 1965. A recent occurrence of thermal stratification of low dissolved oxygen in western Lake Erie. *Ohio J. Sci.* 65:319–27.

Carr, J.F., and J.K. Hiltunen. 1965. Changes in the bottom fauna of western Lake Erie from 1930 to 1961. *Limnol. and Oceanogr.* 10:551–69.

Carter, C.H., D.J. Benson, and D.E. Guy. 1976. Shoreline and bathymetric changes in and around Sandusky Bay since 1848. *Proc. of Sandusky River Symp.* International Joint Commission, Windsor, Ontario, N9A 6T3. 475 pp.

Catling, P.M., and A.A. Reznicek. 1981. Flora of Long Point. *Seasons* 21:34–39.

Chandler, D.C. 1940. Limnological studies of western Lake Erie. I. Plankton and certain physical-chemical data of the Bass Islands region from September 1938 to November 1939. *Ohio. J. of Sci.* 40(6):291–326.

———. 1942a. Limnological studies of western Lake Erie. II. Light penetration and its relation to turbidity. *Ecology* 23(1):41–52.

———. 1942b. Limnological studies of western Lake Erie. III. Phytoplankton and physical-chemical data from November 1939 to November 1940. *Ohio J. of Sci.* 42(1):24–44.

———. 1944. Limnological studies of Lake Erie. IV. Relation of limnological and climatic factors to the plankton of 1941. *Trans / Amer. Micro. Soc.* 63(3):203–6.

Chandler, D.C., and O.D. Weeks. 1945. Limnological studies of western Lake Erie. V. Relations of limnological and meteorological conditions to the production of plankton in 1942. *Ecol. Monogr.* 15:435–57.

Chapman, L.J., and D.F. Putnam. 1966. *The Physiography of Southern Ontario.* 2nd ed. Toronto, Ontario: Univ. of Toronto Press. 386 pp.

Chapra, S.C. 1978. The effect of phosphorus load reductions in the Great Lakes, Jan. 10, 1978. Rept. for the Large Lakes Research Station. U.S. Environmental Protection Agency, Grosse Isle, Mich. See also Chapra, S.C. 1977. Total phosphorus models for the Great Lakes. *J. Environ. Eng.* (ASCE) 103(EE2):147–61.

———. 1980. Application of the phosphorus loading concept to the Great Lakes. In *Phosphorus Management Strategies for Lakes*, ed. R.C. Loehr, C.S. Martin, and W. Rast. Ann Arbor, Mich.: Ann Arbor Science.

Charlton, M.N. 1979. Hypolimnetic oxygen depletion in Central Lake Erie: Has there been any change? Inland Waters Directorate Scientific Series 110, Ottawa, Ontario.

———. 1980. Oxygen depletion in Lake Erie: Has there been any change? *Can. J. Fish. Aquatic Sci.* 37:72–81.

Chau, Y.K., and P.T.S. Wong. 1978. Occurrence of biological methylation of elements in the environment. In *Organometal and Organometalloid Occurrence and Fate in the Environment*, ed. F.E. Brindman and J.M. Bellama. *Amer. Chem. Soc. Sym.* 82:39–51.

Clark, J. Personal communication. International Joint Commission, Windsor, Ontario N9A 6T3.

Clayton, G.D., and F.E. Clayton. 1981. *Patty's Industrial Hygiene and Toxicology.* 3rd rev. ed. Vol. 2a, Toxicology. New York: Wiley-Interscience.

Coakley, J.P. 1976. The formation and evolution of Point Pelee, western Lake Erie. *Can. J. Earth Sciences* 13:136–44.

Coakley, J.P., W. Haras, and N. Freeman. 1973. The effect of storm surge on beach erosion, Point Pelee. *Proc. 16th Conf. Great Lakes Res.*, pp. 377–89.

Cole, C. 1820. History of dysentry, flux and fever sometimes accompanied with black vomit as they occurred among the inhabitants of Sandusky, in the Ohio State, near Lake Erie. *Medical Repository* (New York) 20:134–38.

Committee on the Assessment of Human Health Effects of Great Lakes Water Quality. 1981. Workshop on the compatibility of Great Lakes Basin Cancer Registries. International Joint Commission, Windsor, Ontario, N9A 6T3.

Cooper, J. 1980. Planning and management of Long Point and Turkey Point Provincial Parks. *Contact* 12:31–48.

Coyne, J.H., trans. and ed. 1903. *Exploration of the Great Lakes 1669–1670 by Dollier de Casson, De Bréhant and De Gallinée. Gallinée's narrative and map.* Ontario Historical Soc. 89 pp.

Dambach, C.A. 1969. Changes in the biology of the Lower Great Lakes. *Proc. Conf. on Changes in the Biota of Lakes Erie and Ontario. Bull. Buffalo Soc. Nat. Sci.* 25:1–17.

Davis, C.C. 1964. Evidence for the eutrophication of Lake Erie from phytoplankton records. *Limnol. and Oceanogr.* 3:275–83.

————. 1966. Biological research on the Central Basin of Lake Erie. Univ. Mich. Great Lakes Res. Div., *Proc. 9th Conf. Great Lakes Res.* 15:18–26.

DeLong, B. 1981. Map illustration in *Seasons* 21:30–31.

Delorme, L.D. 1978. Distribution of freshwater ostracodes in Lake Erie. *J. Great Lakes Res.* 4:216–20.

De Pinto, J.V., M.S. Switzenbaum, T.C. Young, and J.K. Edzwald. 1980. Phosphorus removal in lower Great Lakes municipal treatment plants. U.S. EPA Municipal Environmental Research Lab., Cincinnati, Ohio, 45268. International Seminar on Control of Nutrients in Municipal Wastewater Effluents.

De Pinto, J.V., T.C. Young, and S.C. Martin. 1981. Algal-available phosphorus in suspended sediments from lower Great Lakes tributaries. *J. Great Lakes Res.* 7:311–25.

D'Itri, P.A., and F.M. D'Itri. 1977. *Mercury Contamination, a Human Tragedy.* New York: Wiley-Interscience. 300 pp.

DiToro, D.M. 1980. The effect of phosphorus loadings on dissolved oxygen in Lake Erie. In *Phosphorus Management Strategies for Lakes*, ed. R.C. Loehr, C.S. Martin, and W. Prast. Ann Arbor, Mich.: Ann Arbor Science. 485 pp.

DiToro, D.M., and J.P. Connolly. 1980. Mathematical models of water quality in large lakes. Part 2, Lake Erie. U.S. EPA Rept. #600/3-80-065.

DiToro, D.M., and W.F. Matystik, Jr. 1978. Report on Lake Erie mathematical model. U.S. Environmental Protection Agency Ecological Research Services (in preparation). See also DiToro (1980).

Dobson, H.H. Personal communication. Canada Centre for Inland Waters, Burlington, Ontario L7R 4A6.

Dobson, H.H., and M. Gilbertson. 1972. *Proc. 14th Conf. Great Lakes Res.* (1971), pp. 743–48. Also in "Project Hypo" and Canada Centre for Inland Waters, Burlington, Ontario, Paper #6; U.S. EPA Rept. TS-05-71-208-24 (1972).

Donelan, M. 1980. Similarity theory applied to the forecasting of wave heights, periods and directions. *Proc. Canadian Coastal Conf.*, Burlington, Ontario, pp. 47–61.

Dorich, R.A., D.W. Nelson, and L.E. Sommers. 1980. Algal availability of sediment phosphorus in drainage water of the Black Creek watershed. *J. Environ. Qual.* 9:557–63.

Ekert, D.J., and W.H. Schmidt. 1981. Using conservation tillage in north central Ohio. Bulletin FAC-10, Coop. Extension Service, Ohio State University, Columbus, 24 pp.

Evans, R.J., J.D. Bails, and F.M. D'Itri. 1972. Mercury levels in muscle tissues of preserved museum fish. *Environ. Sci. Tech.* 6:901–5.

Fay, L.A. Personal communication. Center for Lake Erie Area Research, Ohio State University, Columbus, Ohio 433210.

Fay, L.A., and C.E. Herdendorf. 1981. Lake Erie water quality assessment of 1980 open lake conditions and trends for the preceding decade. Tech. Rept. #219. Ohio State Univ. Center for Lake Erie Area Res.

Federal-Provincial Working Group on Drinking Water. 1978. Guidelines for Canadian Drinking Water Quality. Ottawa: Information Canada.

Fee, E.J. 1979. A relation between lake morphometry and primary productivity and its use in interpreting whole-lake eutrophication experiments. *Limnol. and Oceanogr.* 24:401–16.

———. 1980. Reply to comments by Patalas & Schindler. *Limnol. and Oceanogr.* 25:1152–53.

Fetteroff, C.M., Jr. 1975. The Introduction in *Cladophora in the Great Lakes*, ed. H. Shear and D.E. Konasewich. International Joint Commission Regional Office, Windsor, Ontario N9A 6T3.

Fish. C.J., and Associates. 1960. Limnological survey of eastern and central Lake Erie 1928–29. U.S. Fish. and Wildlife Service, Special Scientific Rept. Fisheries #334.

Foster, J.R., and T.J. Wheaton. 1981. Losses of juvenile and adult fishes at the Nanticoke Thermal Generating Station due to entrapment, impingement and entrainment. *J. Great Lakes Res.* 7:162–70.

Frank, R., M. Holdrinet, H.E. Braun, R.L. Thomas, and A.L.W. Kemp. 1977. Organochlorine insecticides and PCB's in sediments of Lake St. Clair (1970 and 1974) and Lake Erie (1971). *Science of the Total Environment* 8:205–27.

Fraser, A. Personal communication. Canada Centre for Inland Waters, Burlington L7R 4A6, Canada.

Fraser, A.S., and K.E. Wilson, 1981. Loading estimates to Lake Erie (1967–1976). Inland Waters Directorate, Scientific Series #120, Canada Centre for Inland Waters, Burlington, Ontario L7R 4A6.

Gächter, R., and Associates (1979). Melimex, an experimental heavy metal pollution study. *Schweiz. Z. Hydrol.* 41:165–314.

Gächter, R., K. Lum-Shue-Chan, and Y.K. Chau. 1973. Complexing capacity of the nutrient medium and its relation to inhibition of algal photosynthesis by copper. *Schwiez. Z. Hydrol.* 35:252–61.

Gelinas, P.J., and R.M. Quigley 1973. The influence of geology on recession rates along the north shore of Lake Erie. *Proc. 16th Conf. Great Lakes Res.*, pp. 421–30.

Gilbertson, M. 1974. Pollutants in breeding herring gulls in the lower Great Lakes. *Can. Field-Naturalist* 88:273–80.

Gilbertson, M., H.H. Dobson, and T.R. Lee. 1972. Phosphorus and hypolimnial dissolved oxygen in Lake Erie. In "Project Hypo" and Canada Centre for Inland Waters, Burlington, Ontario, Paper #6; U.S. EPA Rept. TS-05-71-208-24.

Giussani, G., I. Borroni, and E. Grimaldi. 1976. Role of un-ionized ammonia in pre-disposing gill apparatus of *Alburnus alburnus alborella* to fungal and bacterial diseases. *Mem. Inst. Ital. Idrobiol.* 33:161–75.

Glooshenko, W.A., J.E. Moore, and R.A., Vollenweider. 1974. Spatial and temporal distribution of chlorophyll *a* and pheopigments in surface waters of Lake Erie. *J. Fish. Res. Board Can.* 31:265–74.

Golterman, H.L. 1975. *Physical limnology.* Amsterdam: Elsevier, North Holland. 489 pp.

Great Lakes Basin Commission (GLBC). 1975. Great Lakes Basin framework study. Appendix 6: Water Supply—Municipal, Industrial, and Rural. App. 8: Fish. App. C 9: Commercial Navigation. App. 10: Power. App. 12: Shore Use and Erosion. App. 17: Wildlife. App. 19: Economic Demographic Studies. App. 21: Outdoor Recreation. Great Lakes Basin Comm., Ann Arbor, Mich.

Great Lakes Institute, University of Toronto. 1964. Great Lakes Institute Data Record, 1962 Surveys. Part I: Lake Ontario, Lake Erie and Lake St. Clair Prelim. Rept. 16. 97 pp.

———. 1965. Great Lakes Institute Data Record, 1963 Surveys. Part I: Lake Ontario, Lake Erie and Lake St. Clair Report Prelim. Rept. 23. 195 pp.

Great Lakes Science Advisory Board. 1980a. Report of the Aquatic Ecosystem Objectives Committee. International Joint Commission, Windsor, Ontario N9A 6T3.

———. 1980b. *The Ecosystem Approach.* International Joint Commission, Windsor, Ontario N9A 6T3.

Great Lakes Water Quality Agreement with annexes and texts of reference between the United States of America and Canada. Signed at Ottawa 15 April 1972. Copies available from the International Joint Commission, Windsor, Ontario N9A 6T3.

Great Lakes Water Quality Agreement of 1978. With annexes and terms of reference between the United States of America and Canada. Signed at Ottawa 22 November 1978. Copies available from the International Joint Commission, Windsor, Ontario N9A 6T3.

Great Lakes Water Quality Board (GLWQB). 1978a. Report on Great Lakes water quality 1977. International Joint Commission, Windsor, Ontario N9A 6T3.

———. 1978b. 1977 Report on Great Lakes water quality. Appendix B. Surveillance Subcommittee Rept, International Joint Commission. 116 pp.

———. 1978c. Report on Great Lakes water quality, 1977. Status report on organic and heavy metal contaminants in Lakes Erie, Michigan, Huron and Superior Basins. International Joint Commission. 372 pp.

———. 1980. 1980 Report on Great Lakes water quality. Appendix. International Joint Commission. 82 pp.

———. 1981a. 1981 Report on Great Lakes water quality. International Joint Commission. 74 pp.

———. 1981b. Appendix for 1981 Report on Great Lakes Water Quality, International Joint Commission. 174 pp.

———. 1981c. Report on Great Lakes Water Quality Appendices. International Joint Commission. 140 pp.

———. 1981d. Report of the Committee on the Assessment of Human Health Effects of Great Lakes Water Quality. International Joint Commission.

Hamblin, P.F. 1969. Hydraulic wind-induced circulation in a model of a Great Lake. *Proc. 12th Conf. Gt. Lakes Res.*, pp. 567–882.

_____ . 1971. Circulation and water movement in Lake Erie. Scientific Series #7. Dept. Energy, Mines and Resources, Ottawa, Ontario. 50 pp.

Hamley, J.M., and N.G. MacLean. 1979. Impacts of Nanticoke Industrial Development. *Contact* 11:81–116.

Hardy, P.A. 1980. Land use history and management of Big Creek Marsh. Contact 12:1–12.

Harris, C.R., and J.R.W. Miles. 1974. Unpublished Rept., Agriculture Canada, London, Ontario.

Harris, G.P., and R.A. Vollenweider. 1982. Paleolimnological evidence of early eutrophication of Lake Erie. *Can. J. Fish. Aquat. Sci.* 39:618–26.

Harris, R.C., and J. Warkentin. 1974. *Canada before Confederation*. New York: Oxford Univ. Press. 338 pp.

Hartley, R. P., 1968. Bottom currents in Lake Erie. *Proc. 11th Conf. Great Lakes Res.*, pp. 398–405.

Hartman, W.L. 1972. Lake Erie: Effects of exploitation, environmental changes and new species on the fishery resources. *J. Fish. Res. Board Can.* 29:899–912.

Hatcher, H. 1944. *The Great Lakes*. New York: Oxford Univ. Press. 374 pp.

_____ . 1945. *Lake Erie*. New York: Bobbs-Merrill. 416 pp.

Heathcote, I.W. 1979. Nanticoke water chemistry. Report by Ministry of the Environment, Queen's Park, Toronto, Ontario.

Heathcote, I.W., R.R. Weiler, and J.W. Tanner. 1981. Lake Erie nearshore water chemistry at Nanticoke, Ontario, 1969–1978. *J. Great Lakes Res.* 7:130–35.

Hefferman, S., and J.G. Nelson. 1979. Land use history, vegetation and planning for Long Point, Rondeau, and Point Pelee peninsulas, Lake Erie. *Contact* 11:53–80.

Herberger, R.F., and J.B. Reynolds. 1977. Abundance, composition and distribution of crustacean zooplankton in relation to hypolimnetic oxygen depletion in west-central Lake Erie. U.S. Fish. Wildlife Service Tech. Paper #93. 17 pp.

Herdendorf, C.E. 1975. Shoreline changes in Lakes Erie and Ontario. *Proc. Conf. on Changes in Physical Aspects of Lakes Erie and Ontario. Bull. Buffalo Soc. of Nat. Sci.* 25(3):43–76.

_____ . 1980. Lake Erie nutrient control program—an assessment of its effectiveness in controlling lake eutrophication. U.S. Environmental Protection Agency Rept. #600/2-80-062. 354 pp.

Herdendorf, C.E., and S.M. Hartley. 1980. Fish and wildlife resources of the Great Lakes coastal wetlands within the United States. CLEAR Tech. Rept. #170. Vol. 1., 471 pp. Vol. 3, 505 pp. Columbus: Ohio State University.

Herdendorf, C.E., D.E. Rathke, D.D. Larson, and L.A. Fay. 1977. Suspended sediment and plankton relationships in Maumee River and Maumee Bay of Lake Erie. In *Geobotany*, ed. R.C. Romans. New York: Plenum Pub. Co., pp. 247–82.

Higgins, E. 1928. Cooperative fishery investigations in Lake Erie. *Sci. Monthly* 27:306.

Hopkins, G.T. 1862. A mission to the Indians, from the Indian Committee of the Baltimore yearly meeting, to Fort Wayne in 1804. Philadelphia: T.E. Zell. 198 pp.

Hough, J.L. 1958. *Geology of the Great Lakes*. Urbana, Ill.: Univ. of Illinois Press. 313 pp.

Howe, H. 1900. *Historical Collections of Ohio*. Cincinnati: C.J. Krehbiel & Co., Vol. 1:1–9111.

Huckabee, J.W., J.W. Elwood, and S.G. Hildebrand. 1979. Accumulation of mercury in freshwater biota. In *The Biogeochemistry of Mercury in the Environment*, ed. J.O. Nriagu. Amsterdam: Elsevier.

Inland Water Directorate. 1973. Population estimates for the Great Lakes. Social Science Series #1, Canada Centre for Inland Waters, Burlington, Ontario L7R 4A6.

International Joint Commission. 1981. Supplemental report under the reference on pollution in the Great Lakes system from land use activities on phosphorus management strategies. International Joint Commission, Windsor, Ontario N9A 6T3.

International Lake Erie Water Pollution Board and International Lake Ontario–St. Lawrence River Water Pollution Board. 1969. Report to the International Joint Commission on the Pollution of Lake Erie, Lake Ontario and the International Section of the St. Lawrence River. Vol. 2: *Lake Erie*.

Ivey, G.N., and F.M. Boyce. 1982. Entrainment by bottom currents in Lake Erie. *Limnol. and Oceanogr.* 27 1029–38.

Jaworski, E., and C.N. Raphael. 1976. Modification of coastal wetlands in southeastern Michigan and management alternatives. *Mich. Acad.* 8(3):303–17.

Jeffs, D.N. 1981. Introduction to Long Point Bay study. *J. Great lakes Res.* 7:77–80.

Jennings, D.E. 1930. Peregrinating Presque Isle. *Carnegie Mag.* 4(6):171–75.

Jerome, John. Personal communication. Canada Centre for Inland Waters, Burlington, Ont. L7R 4A6.

Johnson, M.G. 1980. Great Lakes environmental protection policies from a fisheries perspective. *Can. J. Fish. Aquat. Sci.* 37:1106–1204.

Johnson, M.G., J.C. Corneau, T.M. Heidtke, W.C. Sonzogni, and B.W. Stahlbaum. 1980. Modelling effects of remedial programs to aid Great Lakes environmental management. *J. Great Lakes Res.* 6:8–21.

Kaatz, M.R. 1952, 1953. The settlement of the Black Swamp of northwestern Ohio. Parts I, II and III. *Northwest Quarterly* 25. Library of the Ohio Historical Society, Columbus, Pt. I:23–36; Pt. II:134–56; Pt. III:201–17.

Kaiser, K.E.L., and I. Valdmanis. 1979. Volatile chloro- and chlorofluoro-carbons in Lake Erie 1977 and 1978. *J. Great Lakes Res.* 5:150–69.

Keeler, L.E. 1904. The Sandusky River. *Ohio Archaeol. and Hist. Pub.* 13:190–247.

Kelso, J.R.M., and G.S. Milburn. 1979. Entrainment and impingement of fish by power plants in the Great Lakes which use the once through cooling process. *J. Great Lakes Res.* 5:182–94.

Kemp, A.L.W., C.B.J Gray, and A. Mudrochova. 1972. Changes in C, N, P and S in the last 140 years in three cores from Lakes Ontario, Erie and Huron. In *Nutrients in Natural Water*, ed. H.E. Allen and R.J. Kramer. New York: Wiley-Interscience.

Kemp, A.L.W., G.A. McInnes, and N.S. Harper. 1977. Sedimentation rates and a revised sediment budget for Lake Erie. *J. Great Lakes Res.* 3:221–33.

Kemp, A.L.W, R.L. Thomas, C.I. Dell, and J.-M. Jaquet. 1976. Cultural impact on the geochemistry of sediments in Lake Erie., *J. Fish. Res. Board Can.* 33:440–62.

Kinkaid, J.D., and Y. Hamdy. 1978. Trends in the mercury content of western Lake Erie fish and sediment. Ontario Ministry of the Environment. 19 pp.

Kirby, M.K., and W.E. Dunford. 1981. Attached algae of the Lake Erie shoreline near Nanticoke generating station. *J. Great Lakes Res.* 7:249–57.

Kirsch P.H. 1895. A report upon investigation in the Maumee River Basin during the summer of 1893. *U.S. Fish. Commission Bull. 14* (1894):315–37.

Lam, D.C.L., and J.-M. Jaquet. 1976. Computations of physical transport and regeneration of phosphorus in Lake Erie, fall 1970. *J. Fish. Res. Board Can.* 33:550–63.

Lam, D.C.L., and C.R. Murthy. 1978. Outfall diffusion models for the coastal zone. *Proc. 16th Coastal Engineering Conf.* (ASCE), pp. 2584–97.

Lam, D.C.L., W.M. Schertzer, and A.S. Fraser. 1983a. Simulation of Lake Erie water quality responses to loading and weather variations. Inland Waters Directorate Scientific Series# 134. Canada Centre for Inland Waters, Burlington, Ont. L7R 4A6.

————. 1983b. Modelling the effects of sediment oxygen demand on Lake Erie water quality conditions under the influence of pollution control and weather variations. Symposium on Sediment Oxygen Demand, Athens, Ga.

Lam, D.C.L., and T.J. Simons. 1976. Numerical computations of advective and diffusive transports of chloride, 1970. *J. Fish. Res. Board Can.* 33:537–49.

Langlois, T.H. 1954. *The Western End of Lake Erie and Its Ecology.* Ann Arbor, Mich.: J.W. Edwards Pub.

Larson, D.D., and D.E. Rathke. 1980. Zooplankton distributions in the Central and Western Basins of Lake Erie. In *Lake Erie Nutrient Control Program—An Assessment of Its Effectiveness in Controlling Lake Eutrophication.* U.S. EPA Rept. EPA-600/3-80-062.

Leach, J.H. 1981. Comparative limnology of Inner Long Point Bay, Lake Erie, and adjacent waters of the Outer Bay. *J. Great Lakes Res.* 7:123–29.

————. Personal communication. Lake Erie Fisheries Research Station, Wheatley, Ontario.

Leach, J.H., and S.J. Nepszy. 1976. The fish community in Lake Erie. *J. Fish. Res. Board Can.* 33:622–38.

Lean, D.R.S., A.P. Abbott, M.N. Charlton, and S.S. Rao. 1983. Seasonal phosphate demand for Lake Erie plankton. *J. Great Lakes Res.* 9:83–91.

Lean, D.R.S., and F. Pick. 1981. Photosynthetic response of lake plankton to nutrient enrichment: A test for nutrient limitation. *Limnol. and Oceanogr.* 26:1011–19.

Leckie, J.O., and J.A. Davis. 1979. Aqueous environmental chemistry of copper. In *Copper in the Environment - Part I,* ed. J.O. Nriagu. New York: Wiley-Interscience.

Legge, R.F., and D. Dingeldein. 1970. We hung the phosphates without a fair trial. *Can. Res. Dev.* 3:19–42.

Leslie, J.K., and K. Lum-Shue-Chan. 1982. Dissolved and particulate trace metals in Lake Erie. Manuscript Report, Canada Centre for Inland Waters, Burlington, Ontario L7R 4A6.

Letterhos, J. Personal communication. CLEAR, Ohio State University, 484 W. 12th Ave., Columbus, Ohio, 43210.

Logan, T.J., T.O. Aloya, and S.M. Yaksich. 1979. Phosphate characteristics and bioavailability of suspended sediments from streams draining into Lake Erie. *J. Great Lakes Res.* 5:112–23.

Lowden, R.M. 1967. A vascular flora of Winous Point, Ottawa, and Sandusky Counties, Ohio. M.Sc. thesis, Ohio State Univ., Columbus. 109 pp.

————. 1969. A vascular flora of Winous Point, Ottawa, and Sandusky Counties, Ohio. *Ohio J. of Sci.* 69:257–84.

Lucas, A.M., and N.A. Thomas. 1972. Sediment oxygen demand in Lake Erie's Central Basin, 1970. *Proc. 14th Conf. Great Lakes Res.* (1971), pp. 781–87. In "Project Hypo" and Canada Centre for Inland Waters, Burlington, Ontario Paper #6; U.S. EPA Rept. TS-05-71-208-24 (1972).

McAndrews, J.H. 1976. Fossil history of man's impact on the Canadian flora: An example from southern Ontario. *Can. Bot. Assoc. Bull. Suppl.* 9:1–6.

MacCallum, W.R., and H.A. Regier. 1970. Distribution of smelt, *Osmerus mordax*, and the smelt fishery in Lake Erie in the early 1960's. *J. Fish. Res. Board Can.* 27:1823–46.

MacCrimmon, H.R., and D.J. Gordon. 1981. Salmonid spawning runs and estimated ova production in Normandale Creek of Lake Erie. *J. Great Lakes Res.* 7:155–61.

McCullough, G.B. 1981. Migrant waterfowl utilization of the Lake Erie shore, Ontario, near the Nanticoke industrial development. *J. Great Lakes Res.* 7:117–22.

Mahon, R. 1979. The structure of fish communities in lakeshore lagoons and their significance. *Contact* 11:19–36.

Mathias, J.A., and J. Barica. 1980. Factors controlling oxygen depletion in ice-covered lakes. *Can. J. Fish. Aquatic Sci.* 37:185–94.

Menon, A.S., C.V. Marion, and A.N. Miller. 1972. Microbiological studies related to oxygen depletion and nutrient regeneration processes in the Lake Erie Central Basin. *Proc. 14th Conf. Great Lakes Res.* (1971), pp. 768–80. Internat. Assoc. Great Lakes Res. Also in "Project Hypo" and Canada Centre for Inland Waters Paper, Burlington, Ontario, #6; U.S. EPA Rept. TS-05-71-208-24 (1972).

Middleton, J.E., and F. Landon. 1927. *The Province of Ontario History 1615–1927.* Toronto: Univ. of Toronto Press.

Mineau, P., G.A. Fox, R.J. Norstrom, D.V. Weseloh, D.J. Hallett and J.A. Ellenton. 1984. Using the Herring Gull to monitor levels and effects of organochlorine contamination in the Canadian Great Lakes. In *Toxic Contaminants in the Great Lakes,* ed. J.O. Nriagu and M.S. Simmons. New York: J. Wiley & Sons.

Ministries of Agriculture and Food and of the Environment. 1981. Guidelines for sewage sludge utilization on agricultural lands. Province of Ontario, Queen's Park, Toronto, Ontario.

Mormon, R.H., D.W. Cuddy, and P.C. Rugen. 1980. Factors influencing the distribution of the sea lamprey (*Petromyzon marineas*) in the Great Lakes. *Can. J. Fish. Aquat. Sci.* 37: 1811–26.

Mortimer, C.H. 1961. Motion in thermoclines. *Verh. Internat. Verein. Limnol.* 14:79–83.
_____. 1971. Chemical exchanges between sediments and water in the Great Lakes; speculations on probable regulatory mechanisms. *Limnol. and Oceanogr.* 16:387–404.

Mosely, E.L. 1899. Sandusky flora: A catalogue of the flowering plants and ferns growing without cultivation in Erie Country, Ohio, and the peninsula and islands of Ottawa County. Ohio State Acad. Sci. Special Papers #1. 167 pp.

Mudroch, A. 1980. Biogeochemical investigation of Big Creek Marsh, Lake Erie, Ontario. *J. Great Lakes Res.* 6:338–47.

Munawar, M., and N.M. Burns. 1976. Relationships of phytoplankton biomass with soluble nutrients, primary production and chlorophyll 'a' in Lake Erie. 1970. *J. Fish. Res. Board Can.* 33:601–11.

Munawar, M., and I.F. Munawar. 1975. Some observations on the growth of diatoms in Lake Ontario with emphasis on *Melosira binderana kutz* during thermal bar conditions. *Arch. Hydrobiol.* 75:490–99.

———. 1976. A lakewide study of phytoplankton biomass and its species composition in Lake Erie, April-December, 1970. *J. Fish. Res. Board Can.* 33:581–600.

———. 1980. The importance of using standard techniques in the surveillance of phytoplankton indicator species for the establishment of long range trends in the Great Lakes: A preliminary example, Lake Erie. *Proc. 1st Biological Surveillance Symp., 22nd Conf. on Great Lakes Res.*, Rochester, N.Y. 1979. *Can. Tech. Rep. Fish. Aquat. Sci.* 976:59–87.

Murphy, T.J., and P.V. Doskey. 1976. Inputs of phosphorus from precipitation to Lake Michigan. *J. Great Lakes Res.* 2:60–70.

Murphy, T.P., K.J. Hall, and I. Yesaki. 1983. Coprecipitation of phosphate with calcite in a naturally eutrophic lake. *Limnol. and Oceanogr.* 28:58–69.

Murthy, C.R. 1972. An investigation of diffusion characteristics of the hypolimnion of Lake Erie. *Proc. 14th Conf. Great Lakes Res.* (1971), pp. 799–804. Internat. Assoc. Great Lakes Res. In "Project Hypo" and Canada Centre for Inland Waters, Burlington, Ontario, Paper #6; U.S. EPA Rept. TS-05-71-208-24 (1972).

Murty, T.S., and R.J. Palovarapu. 1975. Reconstruction of some early storm surges on the Great Lakes. *J. Great Lakes Res.* 1:116–29.

National Academy of Sciences. 1980. Lead in the human environment. A Report Prepared by the Committee on Lead in the Human Environment.

National Academy of Sciences, National Academy of Engineers. 1974. Research needs in water quality criteria (1972). Water Quality Criteria Comm. Environmental Studies Board, Washington, D.C.

Neil, J.H., and G.E. Owen. 1964. Distribution, environmental requirements and significance of *Cladophora* in the Great Lakes. Pub. #11, Great Lakes Res. Div., Univ. of Michigan, pp. 113–21.

Nepszy, S.J. 1977. Changes in percid populations and species interaction in Lake Erie. *J. Fish. Res. Board Can.* 34:1861–1868.

Newberry, J.S. 1874a. On the structure and origin of the Great Lakes. *New York Lyceum Nat. History Proc.* 2:136–38.

———. 1874b. Geology of Ohio. Ohio Geol. Survey Rept. Part 1, 2:1–80.

Nicholls, K.H., D.S. Standen, and G.J. Hopkins. 1980. Recent changes in the near-shore phytoplankton of Lake Erie's Western Basin at Kingsville, Ontario. *J. Great Lakes Res.* 6:146–53.

Noble, W.C. 1978. The Neutral Indians. In *Essays in Northeastern Anthropology*, ed. W.E. Engelbrecht and D.G. Grayson. Occ. Pub. in Northeastern Anthropology. #5.

Nriagu, J.O. 1978. Dissolved silica in pore waters of Lakes Ontario, Erie and Superior sediments. *Limnol. and Oceanogr.* 23:53–67.

Nriagu, J.O., and C.J. Dell. 1974. Diagenetic formation of iron phosphates in recent lake sediments. *Am. Mineralogist* 59:934–46.

Nriagu, J.O., A.L.W. Kemp, H.K.T. Wong, and N. Harper. 1979. Sedimentary record of heavy metal pollution in Lake Erie. *Geochim. et Cosmochim. Acta.* 43:247–58.

Nriagu, J.O., H.K.T. Wong, and R.D. Coker. 1981. Particulate and dissolved trace metals in Lake Ontario. *Water Research* 15:91–96.

Ongley, E.D. 1976. Sediment yields and nutrient loading from Canadian watersheds tributary to Lake Erie: An overview. *J. Fish. Res. Board Can.* 33:471–84.

Parks Canada. 1980. Investigating . . . Canada's Deep South. Point Pelee National Park, Parks Canada, Leamington, Ontario.

Parmenter, R. 1929. Hydrology of Lake Erie. In *Preliminary Report on the Cooperative Survey of Lake Erie. Bull. Buffalo Soc. Nat. Sci.* 14(3):25–50.

Patalas, K. 1972. Crustacean plankton and the eutrophication of St. Lawrence Great Lakes. *J. Fish. Res. Board Can.* 29:1451–62.

Pennak, R.W. 1953. *Fresh-water Invertebrates of the United States.* New York: Ronald Press. 769 pp.

Philips, D.W., and J.A.W. McCulloch. 1972. The climate of the Great Lakes Basin. Climatological Studies #20. Environment Canada, Toronto, Ontario. 93 pp.

Phosphorus Management Strategies Task Force. 1980. Phosphorus management for the Great Lakes. International Joint Commission, Windsor, Ontario N9A 6T3.

Pieters, A.J. 1901. The plants of western Lake Erie with observations on their distribution. *Bull. U.S. Fish. Comm.*, 47–79 and 11–20.

Platzman, W.G. 1963. The dynamical prediction of wind tides on Lake Erie. *Metorol. Monogra.* 4. 44 pp.

PLUARG (International Reference Group on Great Lakes Pollution from Land Use Activities). 1978. Environmental management strategy for the Great Lakes System. International Joint Commission, Windsor, Ontario, N9A 6T3. 115 pp.

Potos, C. 1968. A study of taste and odor in the municipal water supply at Clevelend, Ohio. *Proc. 11th Conf. Great Lakes Res.* (1968), pp. 571–84.

Powers, C.F., D.L. Jones, P.C. Mundinger, and J.C. Ayers. 1960. Applications of data collected along shore conditions in Lake Erie. Univ. Mich. Great Lakes Res. Div. Pub. #5. 78 pp.

Rathke, D.E., J. Bloesch, N.M. Burns, and F. Rosa. 1981. Settling fluxes in Lake Erie (Canada) measured by traps and settling chambers. *Verh. Internat. Verlih. Limnol.* 21:383–88.

Rattigan, W. 1960. *Great Lakes Shipwrecks and Survivals.* New York: Galahad Books. 333 pp.

Regier, H.A., V.C. Applegate, and R.A. Ryder. 1969. The ecology and management of the walleye in western Lake Erie. Great Lakes Fish. Comm. Tech. Rept. #15. 101 pp.

Regier, H.A., and W.L. Hartman. 1973. Lake Erie's fish community: 150 years of cultural stress. *Science* 180:1248–55.

Reinert, R.E. 1970. Pesticide concentrations in Great Lakes fish. *Pesticides Monitoring J.* 3:233–40.

Reuter, J.M. 1981. Gill nets and their use. *Ohio Sea Grant Twine Line* 3:8–11.

Rickard, D.T., and J.O. Nriagu. 1978. Aqueous environmental chemistry of lead. In *Biogeochemistry of Lead in the Environment* (Part A), ed. J.O. Nriagu. Pp. 219–84. Amsterdam: Elsevier.

Ridgley, J.I. 1976. Ontario commercial fish industry: Statistics on landings 1971–1975. Ministry of Natural Resources, Toronto, Ontario.

Robbins, J.A. 1978. Geochemical and geochemical applications of radioactive lead isotopes. In *Biogeochemistry of Lead*, ed. J.O. Nriagu, pp. 285–393. Amsterdam: Elsevier.

Robbins, J.A., D.N. Edgington, and A.L.W. Kemp. 1978. Comparative ^{210}Pb, ^{137}Cs and pollen geochronologies of sediments from Lakes Ontario and Erie. *Quarternary Research* 10:256–78.

Rodgers, G.K. 1962. Lake Erie Data Report, 1961. Great Lakes Institute, Univ. of Toronto, Ontario, Prelim. Rept. No. 3. 141 pp.

———. 1963. Lake Erie Data Report, 1960. Great Lakes Institute, Univ. of Toronto, Ontario, Prelim. Rept. No. 11. 138 pp.

Rosa, F., and N.M. Burns. 1982. Oxygen depletion rates in the hypolimnion of central and eastern Lake Erie—A new approach indicates change. Manuscript Report Canada Centre for Inland Waters, Burlington, Ontario L7R 4A6.

Schelske, C.L., and E.F. Stoermer. 1972. Phosphorus, silica and eutrophication of Lake Michigan. Nutrients and Eutrophication. *Am. Soc. Limnol. Oceanogr.* Special Symposia VI: 157–71.

Schienberg, I.H. 1979. Human health effects of copper. In *Copper in the Environment*, ed. J.O. Nriagu. New York: Wiley-Interscience.

Schindler, D.W. 1980. The effect of fertilization with phosphorus and nitrogen versus phosphorus alone on eutrophication of experimental lakes. *Limnol. and Oceanogr.* 25:1149–52.

Schneider, J.C., and J.H. Leach. 1977. Walleye (*Stizostedion vitreum vitreum*) fluctuations in the Great Lakes and possible causes, 1800–1975. *J. Fish. Res. Board Can.* 34:1878–89.

Schueler, F.W. 1981. A herpetologist's Long Point notebook. *Seasons* 21:40–43.

Schuldt, A.A. 1980. Commentary on air quality research and management in the Long-Point, Haldimand-Norfolk area by M. Lusis. *Contact* 12:80–84.

Scott, W.B., and E.J. Crossman. 1973. *Freshwater Fishes of Canada.* Fish. Res. Board of Canada Bull. #184, Ottawa, Ontario. 965 pp.

Shannon, E. Personal communication. Canviro consultants Ltd., 178 Louisa Street, Kitchener, Ontario N2H 5M5.

Simons, T.J. 1973. Development of three-dimensional numerical models of the Great Lakes. Canada Centre for Inland Waters, Burlington, Ontario, Scientific Series #12. 26 pp.

———. 1976. Continuous dynamical computations of water transports in Lake Erie for 1970. *J. Fish. Res. Board Can.* 33:371–84.

Sly, P.G. 1976. Lake Erie and its Basin. *J. Fish. Res. Board Can.* 33:355–70.

Sly, P.G., and C.F.M. Lewis. 1972. *The Great Lakes of Canada—Quarternary Geology and Limnology.* Int. Geol. Cong., Montreal, Quebec, Guidebook Trip, A43. 92 pp.

Smith, J. 1799. An account of the remarkable occurrences in the life and travels of Col. James Smith. In Henry Howe, *Historical Collections of Ohio* VII. Norwalk: Laning Printing Co. for State of Ohio.

Smith, S.H. 1972. The future of salmonid communities in the Laurentian Great Lakes. *J. Fish. Res. Board Can.* 29:951–57.

Sonzogni, W.C., S.C. Chapra, D.E. Armstrong, and T.J. Logan. 1981. Bioavailability of phosphorus inputs to lakes: Significance to management. Great Lakes Basin Commission, Ann Arbor, Michigan 48104, Contrib. #40.

Spectator, The. 1980. Nanticoke Souvenir section, September 16. Hamilton, Ontario.

Standke, S.J., and B.P. Monroe. 1981. Forms of physical damage and related effects to zooplankton as a result of entrainment of Nanticoke G.S., 1976. *J. Great Lakes Res.* 7:136–43.

Stewart, D., with contributions from D. Ross. 1977. Point Pelee, Canada's Deep South. Don Mills, Ont.: Burns and MacEachern Ltd.

Stewart, K.M. 1973. Winter conditions in Lake Erie with reference to ice and thermal structure and comparison to Lakes Winnebago (Wisconsin) and Mille Lacs (Minnesota). *Proc. 16th Conf. Great Lakes Res.*, pp. 845–57.

Strothers, D.M., and R.A. Yarnell. 1976. An agricultural revolution in the lower lakes. In *Geobotany*, ed. R.C. Romans. New York: Plenum Press.

Stuckey, R.L. 1971. Changes of vascular aquatic flowering plants during 70 years in Put-in-Bay harbor, Lake Erie, Ohio. *Ohio J. of Sci.* 72:321–42.

———. 1976. Aquatic vascular plants of Sandusky River Basin. In *Sandusky River Basin Symposium*, ed. D.B. Baker, W.B. Jackson and B.L. Prater. International Joint Commission. Windsor Ontario N9A 6T3. 475 pp.

Surveillance Subcommittee. 1976. Great Lakes Water Quality Fourth Report, Appendix B. 255 pp. International Joint Commission, Windsor, Ontario N9A 6T3.

Swain, W.R. 1981. Ecosystem monitoring in the Great Lakes: Research needs, public health implications. *Great Lakes Focus on Water Quality* 7:1–12.

Taft, C.E. 1975. Summary of workshop presentation of "History of *Cladophora* in the Great Lakes," in *Cladophora in the Great Lakes*. International Joint Commission, Windsor, Ontario N9A 6T3.

Taft, C.E., and Kishler, W.J. 1973. Cladophora as related to pollution and eutrophication in western Lake Erie. Water Resources Center, Ohio State Univ., 103 pp.

Task Group III. 1978. Report of Task Group III. A technical group to review phosphorus loadings. International Joint Commission, Windsor, Ontario N9A 6T3.

Thomas, R.L., and J.-M. Jaquet. 1976. Mercury in the surficial sediments of Lake Erie. *J. Fish. Res. Board Can.* 33:404–12.

Thomas, R.L., J.M. Jaquet, A.L.W. Kemp, and C.F.M. Lewis. 1976. Surficial sediments of Lake Erie. *J. Fish Res. Board Can.* 33:385–403.

Thomas, R.L., J.-M. Jaquet, and A. Mudroch. 1975. Sedimentation processes and associated changes in surface sediment trace metal concentrations in Lake St. Clair, 1970–1974. *Proc. Internat. Conf. on Heavy Metals in the Environment*, Toronto, Ontario (1975). Pp. 691–708.

Thomas, R.L., and A. Mudroch. 1979. Small Craft Harbours sediment survey Lakes Ontario, Erie and St. Clair. Report to Small Craft Harbours, Ontario Region from Great Lakes Biolimnology Laboratory, Canada Centre for Inland Waters, Burlington, Ont. L7R 4A6.

Thomas, N.A., A. Robertson, and W.C. Sonzogni. 1980. Review of control objectives: New target loads and input controls. In *Phosphorus Management Strategies for Lakes*, ed. by R.C. Loehr, C.S. Mortimer, and W. Rast. Ann Arbor, Mich.: Ann Arbor Sci.

Thorndale, T. 1898. *Sketches and Stories of the Lake Erie Islands*. Sandusky, Ohio: I.F. Mack and Brother. 379 pp. (Souvenir volume.)

Trautman, M.B. 1949. The invasion, present status and life history of the sea lamprey in the waters of the Great Lakes, especially the Ohio waters of Lake Erie. F.T. Stone Laboratory Manuscript Report.

———. 1957. *The Fishes of Ohio*. Columbus: Ohio State Univ. Press. 683 pp.

———. 1976. The fishes of the Sandusky River system, Ohio. In *Proc. of Sandusky River Symp.*, International Joint Commission, Windsor, Ont. N9A 6T3. 475 pp.

———. 1977. The Ohio country 1750 to 1977—A naturalists view. Ohio Biological Survey Biol. Note #10, 25 pp.

Upchurch, S.B. 1975. Impact of coastal dynamics on man in Lakes Erie and Ontario. *Proc. Conf. on Changes in Physical Aspects of Lakes Erie and Ontario. Bull. Buffalo Soc. Nat. Sci.* 25(3)1–37.

U.S. Army Corps of Engineers. 1979. Lake Erie Wastewater Management Study Methodology Report. Report by U.S. Army Corps of Engineers, Buffalo District. 1776 Niagara St., Buffalo, N.Y. 14207.

———. 1982. Lake Erie Wastewater Management Study Final Report. Report by U.S. Army Corps of Engineers, Buffalo District, 1776 Niagara St., Buffalo, N.Y. 14207.

U.S. Environmental Protection Agency. 1970. Algae-temperature-nutrient relationships and distribution in Lake Erie 1968. U.S. EPA Region V,—Cleveland, Ohio. 87 pp.

———. 1978. Report on the degree of pollution of bottom sediments, Cleveland, Ohio. U.S. EPA Region V, Chicago.

U.S. Federal Water Pollution Control Administration (FWPCA). 1968. Lake Erie Report—A plan for water pollution control. U.S. Dept. of Interior. 107 pp.

U.S. Federal Water Pollution Control Administration and Ohio Dept. of Health. 1970. Lake Erie Ohio intake water quality summary (1969). 310 pp.

U.S. Geological Survey. 1980. U.S.G.S. Water Data Report OH-80-2.

U.S. Weather Service Climatological Data, Michigan Annual Summary, 1914–present. National Weather Service, National Oceanographic and Atmospheric Admins., Dept. of Commerce, Washington, D.C.

Vallentyne J.R. 1974. *The Algal Bowl*. The Department of the Environment, Ottawa, Canada. 154 pp.

———. 1978. Presidential Address: Today is yesterday's tomorrow. Verh. Internat. Verin. Limnol. 20(1–12).

Verduin, J. 1969. Man's influence on Lake Erie. *Ohio J. of Sci.* 69(2):65–70.

Verhoff, F.H., S.M. Yasich, and D.A. Melfi. 1980. River nutrient and chemical transport estimation. *J. Environ. Env. Div.* (ASCE) 106 (EE3):591–608.

Vollenweider, R.A. 1968. Scientific fundamentals of the eutrophication of lakes and flowing waters, with particular reference to phosphorus and nitrogen as factors in eutrophication. OECD Tech. Rept. DAS/CS1/68.27. 159 pp.

———. 1975. Input-output models with special reference to the phosphorus loading concept in limnology. *Schwerz, Z. Hydrol.* 37:53–84.

———. 1977. Memorandum to members of Task Group on phosphorus loadings for the re-negotiation of the U.S.–Canada Agreement. July 7, 1977.

———. 1982. Energy, pollution and the disruption of environmental equilibria. *Proc. of Giornate Internazionali di Boiologia: Le Vie della Sopravviuenza.*

Vollenweider, R.A., W. Rast, and J. Kerekes. 1980. The phosphorus loading concept and Great Lakes eutrophication. In *Phosphorus Management Strategies for Lakes.*, ed. R.C. Loehr, C.S. Martin, and W. Rast. Ann Arbor, Mich: Ann Arbor Science.

Waldechuk, M. 1974. Some biological concerns in heavy metal pollution. In *Pollution and Physiology of Marine Organisms*. New York: Academic Press.

Watson, N.H.F. 1976. Seasonal distribution and abundance of crustacean zooplankton in Lake Erie, 1970. *J. Fish. Res. Board Can.* 33:612–21.

Watson, N.H.F., K.P.B. Thompson, and F.C. Elder. 1975. Sub-thermocline biomass concentration detected by transmissometer in Lake Superior. *Verh. Internat. Verein. Limnol.* 19:682–88.

Weatherley, H.H., P.S. Lake, and S.C. Rodgers. 1980. Zinc pollution and ecology of the freshwater environment. In *Zinc in the Environment— Part I*, ed. J.O. Nriagu. New York: Wiley-Interscience.

Webber, M.D. 1982. Land utilization of sewage sludge—a discussion paper. Wastewater Technology Centre, Environmental Protection Service, Burlington, Ontario L7R 4A6 (unpublished).

Weiler, R.R. 1978. The chemistry of Lake Superior. *J. Great Lakes Res.* 4:370–85.

Wetzel, R.G. 1975. *Limnology.* Toronto: W.B. Saunders Co. 660 pp.

Whillans, T.H. 1979a. Response of fish communities to stress: A historical study of Inner Bay, Long Point. *Contact* 11:1–18.

————. 1979b. Historic transformations of fish communities in three Great Lakes bays. *J. Great Lakes Res.* 5:195–215.

————. 1981. Remembering the blue walleye. *Seasons* 21:45–49.

Wianko, P.M. 1981. Environmental design and operation of Nanticoke Thermal Generating Station. *J. Great Lakes Res.* 7:96–104.

Williams, J.D.H., J.-M. Jaquet, and R.L. Thomas. 1976. Forms of phosphorus in the surficial sediments of Lake Erie. *J. Fish. Res. Board Can.* 33:413–29.

Williams, J.D.H., T. Mayer, and J.O. Nriagu. 1980. Extractability of phosphorus from phosphate minerals common in soils and sediments. *J. Soil Sci. Soc. Amer.* 44:462–65.

Williams, J.D.H., T.P. Murphy and T. Mayer. 1976. Rates of accumulation of phosphorus forms in Lake Erie sediments. *J. Fish. Res. Board Can.* 33:430–39.

Williams, J.D.H., H. Shear, and R.L. Thomas. 1980. Availability to *Scenedesmus quadricauda* of different forms of phosphorus in sedimentary materials from the Great Lakes. *Limnol. and Oceanogr.* 25:1–11.

Wilson, F.E., ed. 1935. *Journal of Capt. Daniel Bradley (an Epic of the Ohio Frontier, with Copious Comments).* Greenville, Ohio: F.H. Jobes and Son. Pp. 1–76.

Wong, P.T.S., Y.K. Chau, O. Kramer, and G.A. Bengert. 1981. Accumulation and depuration of tetramethyllead by rainbow trout. *Water Research* 15:621–25.

Wong, P.T.S., Y.K. Chau, and P.L. Luxon. 1978. Toxicity of a mixture of metals on freshwater algae. *J. Fish. Res. Board Can.* 35:479–81.

Wright, S. 1955. Limnological survey of western Lake Erie. U.S. Fish and Wildlife Service Special Scientific Report - Fisheries #139. 341 pp.

Zapotosky, J.E., and C.E. Herdendorf. 1980. Oxygen depletion and anoxia in the Central and Western Basins of Lake Erie, 1973–1975. In *Lake Erie Nutrient Control Program—An Assessment of Its Effectiveness in Controlling Lake Eutrophication* U.S. EPA Rept EPA - ·600/3-80-062.

Zapotosky, J.E., and W.S. White. 1980. A reconnaissance survey for lightweight and carbon tetrachloride extractable hydrocarbons in the Central and Eastern Basins of Lake Erie: September 1978. Argonne National Laboratory, Argonne, Ill., Rept. #ANL/ES-87.

Photo Credits

Barry, J.P., 353 Fairway Boulevard, Columbus, Ohio 43213

Booth, W., Canada Centre for Inland Waters, Burlington, Ontario L7R 4A6.

Britt, N.W., Ohio State University, Columbus, Ohio 43210.

Brown, J., 415 Parkside Drive, Toronto, Ontario M6R 2Z7.

Center for Archival Collections, Bowling Green State University, Bowling Green, Ohio 43403.

Chapman A., Waikato University, Hamilton, New Zealand.

CLEAR (Center for Lake Erie Area Research). Ohio State University, 484 W. 12th Av., Columbus, 43210.

Etheredge, K., Biology Department, University of Waikato, Hamilton, New Zealand.

Leach, J., Lake Erie Research Station, Wheatley, Canada.

Parks Canada, Point Pelee National Park, Leamington, Ontario.

Rukavina, N., Canada Centre for Inland Waters, Burlington, Canada L7R 4A6.

Index